Neurobiology of
Stress-Informed Counseling

Neurobiology of Stress-Informed Counseling

Healing and Prevention Practices
for the Helping Professions

Yoon Suh Moh

Thomas Jefferson University

SAN DIEGO

Bassim Hamadeh, CEO and Publisher
Amy Smith, Senior Project Editor
Celeste Paed, Associate Production Editor
Jess Estrella, Senior Graphic Designer
Kylie Bartolome, Licensing Coordinator
Ursina Kilburn, Interior Designer
Natalie Piccotti, Director of Marketing
Kassie Graves, Senior Vice President, Editorial
Jamie Giganti, Director of Academic Publishing

Cover image copyright © 2020 iStockphoto LP/Grafissimo.
Cover image copyright © 2017 iStockphoto LP/yodiyim.
Cover image copyright © 2021 iStockphoto LP/mycola.
Cover image copyright © 2006 iStockphoto LP/angelhell.

Printed in the United States of America.

3970 Sorrento Valley Blvd., Ste. 500, San Diego, CA 92121

Brief Contents

Preface   xiii
Acknowledgments   xv

Part I   Overview   1

Chapter 1   An Overview of the Neurobiology of Stress-Informed Counseling   3
Chapter 2   Perspectives and Frameworks   13

Part II   Neurobiology of Stress and the Human Microbiome   29

Chapter 3   Human Suffering   31
Chapter 4   Early Toxic Stress and Its Developmental Disruptions in Human Development   43
Chapter 5   Empathy-Based Stress in Helping Professionals   59
Chapter 6   The Human Gut, Brain, and Human Microbiome   65
Chapter 7   Heart, Immune System, and Human Microbiome   91

Part III   Healing and Prevention Actions and Practices for Helping Professions   105

Chapter 8   Healing and Prevention Actions and Practices at Microbial, Individual, and Relationship Levels   107
Chapter 9   Healing and Prevention Actions and Practices at Community and Society Levels   132
Chapter 10   Healing and Prevention Actions and Practices in Helping Professions   145

Glossary   165
Index   173

Detailed Contents

Preface   xiii
Acknowledgments   xv

PART I   Overview   1

CHAPTER 1   An Overview of the Neurobiology of Stress-Informed Counseling   3

Why Is the Neurobiology of Stress-Informed Counseling Important?   3
  Stress and Stress Responses   *4*
  A Biological Basis of Behavior   *5*
  The Neurobiology of Stress-Informed Counseling   *6*
  Helping Professionals as Readers   *6*
Informative Resources   7
Summary   8
Case Study   9
References   10

CHAPTER 2   Perspectives and Frameworks   13

Contemporary and Contextual Information   13
  Environmental Challenges   *13*
  The Impact of Climate Change on Mental Health   *14*
  Prolonged COVID-19 Pandemic   *15*
Human Development, Health, and Disease   16
  A Modified Ecobiodevelopmental Framework of Human Development and
  Human Diseases   *17*
Healing Justice Approaches in a Multicultural Frame   21
Prevention Approaches, Actions, and Practices   22
  The Social-Ecological Model for Prevention—Modified (SEMP-M)   *23*
Summary   26
Experiential Questions   26
References   27

PART II   Neurobiology of Stress and the Human Microbiome   29

CHAPTER 3   Human Suffering   31

The Global Burden of Diseases and Risk Factors   31
Human Health and the Global Burden of Diseases   33
Stress Taxonomy   35
Physiological Responses to Stress   35
A Conceptual Taxonomy of Stress Responses   36
Epigenetic Influences of Stress   37
The Orchid and Dandelion: Stress Reactivity and Susceptibility   38
Summary   40
Experiential Questions   41
References   41

CHAPTER 4   Early Toxic Stress and Its Developmental Disruptions
in Human Development   43

Conceptualizing Trauma   44
Cultural Trauma   45
Toxic Stress Early in Life and Developmental Trauma   46
Attachment Ruptures   48
Abandonment and Neglect in Childhood   49
Developmental Trauma Disorder   50
Proposed Developmental Trauma Disorder Diagnostic Criteria   51
Systemic Racism and Discrimination   52
Summary   54
Experiential Questions   55
Informative Resources   55
References   55

CHAPTER 5   Empathy-Based Stress in Helping Professionals   59

Empathy-Based Stress   60
Preventive Measures and Practices   62
Summary   62
Experiential Questions   63
References   63

CHAPTER 6   The Human Gut, Brain, and Human Microbiome   65

The Role of Stress in Human Gut and Gut Microbiota   65
Gut Microbiota as Helpers   66
Dysbiosis in the Gut Microbiota   67
Gut Microbiome and Its Dialogue with the Brain   67
Effects of Gut-Brain Bidirectional Dialogue on Brain Health   67
Gut Microbiome Development and Change over the Lifespan   68
Effects of Early Childhood Adversity or Toxic Stress on Gut Microbiome   69
Summary   70
Informative Resources   71
The Role of Stress in Brain Development and Function   71
The Brain Development   72
The Brain Function   72
The Role of Early Caregiving on Neurodevelopment and Its Functioning   73
The Role of Stress in Human Function: The Sense of Self   73
Neurobiology of the Sense of Self: The Default Mode Network   75
The Role of the DMN in the Hijacked Sense of Self   77
The Role of Stress in Human Function: Sensory Processing   79
Summary   85
Informative Resources   86
Experiential Questions   86
References   87
Sense of Self   87
Sensory Processing   88
General   88

CHAPTER 7   Heart, Immune System, and Human Microbiome   91

The Association Between Heart Health and Mental Illness   91
Summary   93
The Role of Stress in the Immune System   94
Immune System   95
Immune Signaling Between the Gut and Brain   96
The Interplay Between the Immune System and Human Microbiome   97
The Role of Chronic Stress and Microbiome-Gut-Brain Network   97
The Role of Dietary Inflammation in Human Disease   99
Summary   101
Experiential Questions   102
References   102
Heart   102
Immune System   103

PART III Healing and Prevention Actions and Practices for
Helping Professions   105

CHAPTER 8   Healing and Prevention Actions and Practices at Microbial,
Individual, and Relationship Levels   107

At the Microbial and Individual Levels   108
Biopsychosocial and Lifestyle Approaches   108
Clinical Interventions for Healing and Prevention   111
Screening and Assessment   113
Summary   115
Informative Resources   116
At the Relationship Level   116
Women During Perinatal Pregnancy and Their Children   117
Complicated Grief Prevention   120
Social Isolation and Loneliness Prevention   124
Summary   125
Informative Resources   126
Experiential Questions   127
References   127
At the Microbial and Individual Level   127
At the Relationship Level   130

CHAPTER 9   Healing and Prevention Actions and Practices at Community
and Society Levels   132

At the Community Level   132
Healing-Centered Engagement   133
At the Society Level   134
State-Level Trauma Prevention Initiatives   134
Policy Development, Implementation, and Evaluation   135
Summary   136
Experiential Questions   136
Informative Resources   144
References   144

CHAPTER 10   Healing and Prevention Actions and Practices in
Helping Professions   145

Healing and Prevention Practices in Clinical Education
and Training Programs   146
Trauma-Informed Educational Practices   *146*
Summary   148
Experiential Questions   149
References   163

Glossary   165
Index   173

Preface

Purpose of the Text

Humans are social animals. This means that socialization is integral to the human lifespan. When we are born, we, as humans, are hugely dependent on the adult caregiver for survival until we become independent. Additionally, from the time of birth to the time we take a last breath, many of us surround ourselves with other living beings to improve our quality of life. Similarly, human bodies are a complex ecosystem consisting of their own cells cohabiting with other microorganisms (e.g., bacteria, archaea, bacilli, and viruses) that are situated in a larger ecosystem.

In day-to-day life, people are constantly exposed to life stressors (e.g., a change in lifestyle due to the current pandemic) causing different levels of stress, and thus, it is inevitable that we experience the effects of life stress. Also, a number of different factors (e.g., genetic programming; the expression of genetic information; unjust systems, structures, and institutions; social environments; physical environments; microbial environments; climate change; etc.) can lead to life stress. Despite common views on the concept of stress that typically come with a negative connotation, this textbook introduces different ways of conceptualizing stress that are supported by anecdotal and empirical evidence. Although not all stress responses are deleterious, when such responses (e.g., a toxic stress response) disrupt a homeostasis in human function, they can lead to not only immediate but also long-lasting, concerning effects on human development and health. Thus, this textbook invites readers to explore such scenarios and calls for actions and practices that can help alleviate the harmful effects of stress on human health.

Furthermore, this text also emphasizes the significance of preventive actions and practices—particularly by helping professionals—that may prevent the sources of negative stress at varying levels. In this textbook, *helping professions* is used as an umbrella term to refer to professions that include, but are not limited to, counseling, counselor education and supervision, psychology, social work, psychiatry, and primary and secondary education. In a similar vein, **helping professionals** are those whose work involves helping other humans in need. Given that such professionals usually work in culturally diverse settings where a wide array of individuals and families with different social identities live and interact with one another, this textbook intentionally describes culturally responsive approaches to actions and practices for healing and prevention. Moreover, helping professionals are not immune to the effects of life stress as well as work stress. As a result, it is hoped that this textbook helps enhance their awareness about it and invites their healing and prevention actions and practices for their own wellness.

xiv | Neurobiology of Stress-Informed Counseling

Organization and Structure of the Text

The first two chapters of the textbook provide foundational frameworks for the later chapters; they organize information and resources regarding neurobiology of stress, and describe a variety of the effects of stress on human development, human health, and disease. Chapter 1 introduces a description of the neurobiology of a stress-informed approach to health-related actions and practices. Additionally, a case study provided at the end of Chapter 1 is intended to facilitate experiential questions pertaining to the content addressed in each of the later chapters (Chapters 2 through 10). Chapter 2 delineates a few frameworks and perspectives that influence the lens on human development across the lifespan and highlight the importance of healing from and prevention of human suffering.

Chapters 3 through 7 are mainly informative and focus on the enhancement of knowledge of human suffering and its complex, interrelated, developmental effects on human development, human health, and disease. Chapters 8 through 10 are focused on the application of the knowledge addressed in the earlier chapters and provide anecdotally and empirically supported implications for actions and practices tailored toward healing from human suffering and its prevention, particularly for helping professionals.

Each chapter starts with the few key points to be addressed, moves on to provide the main content, followed by a summary. The majority of these chapters provides a section titled "Informative Resources," in which readers of this text can find relevant resources to help increase their understanding of the content addressed in the accordant chapter. Moreover, in Chapters 2 through 10, the experiential questions pertaining to the case study provided in Chapter 1 are included at the end, as a guide to facilitate reflective exercises.

Acknowledgments

I would like to thank my family, especially my deceased mother. Her prolonged illness and its long-lasting effects on her whole being, as well as on the surrounding supports (myself included), helped me increase awareness on the importance of better understanding acute and chronic stress in the context of caregiving. A special thank you to Kevin Melanson, my beloved husband, for his tireless support and the time spent reading through this textbook in the editing process.

I would also like to thank the contributors, Christine Curtois, Jeanne Felter, and Janice Carello. Each of these incredible scholars' work in trauma in the disciplines of psychology, counseling and counselor education, and social work, respectively, have constantly motivated me to learn and continue learning more about stress and trauma.

In addition, I thank Allen E. Ivey for his encouragement and continued mentoring that has helped me write this monograph. Without his wisdom and insight, this textbook could not have come to fruition. Thank you to my neuroscience-informed counseling community for the inspiration and appreciation for taking a lifelong learning approach to incorporating neuroscience and neurobiology into counseling, counselor education, and counseling research. A special thank you to Thomas A. Field for his mentorship.

I would also like to thank Pamela Walter, Director at the Office for Professional Writing, Publishing, & Communication at Thomas Jefferson University (TJU) for her editorial support. Thank you to my Community and Trauma Counseling program colleagues at TJU for constantly inviting me to explore a variety of approaches to stress management and stress prevention that have been addressed in the textbook.

Finally, I thank Cognella staff, in particular, Amy Smith, Kassie Graves, and Celeste Paed for the immense guidance and support for writing and publishing the textbook.

PART I

Overview

CHAPTER ONE

An Overview of the Neurobiology of Stress-Informed Counseling

The key points addressed in this chapter are

- to address varied perspectives on stress, with focus given to a neurobiological view
- to define the neurobiology of stress-informed counseling and highlight the importance of its application
- to address helping professionals as readers of this textbook

---

Why Is the Neurobiology of Stress-Informed Counseling Important?

> "Stress involves two-way communication between the brain and the cardiovascular, immune, and other systems via neural and endocrine mechanisms."
>
> *McEwen (2007, p. 873)*

S tress is a part of our daily lives, and stress responses are fundamental to our functioning. This textbook will address stress specifically from a neurobiological perspective, and will examine its immediate and long-lasting effects on development across our life course. The following section will describe how stress and its responses are conceptualized in this textbook.

Stress and Stress Responses

If you are a clinician, ask your client to describe what comes to mind when they hear the word *stress*. Similarly, if you are an educator, ask the same and have your students describe their reaction to this word. You will quickly realize that many of them appear to have a disproportionate perception of stress because, in many cases, individuals report on negative stress responses more often than positive stress responses. Some individuals may not be able to perceive positive effects of stress on human functioning at all. Bruce S. McEwen, an American neuroendocrinologist, describes **stress** as "experiences that are challenging emotionally and physiologically" (2007, p. 874). In addition, good stress refers to "those experiences that are of limited duration and that a person can master and which leave a sense of exhilaration and accomplishment," whereas bad stress refers to "experiences where a sense of control and mastery is lacking and which are often prolonged or recurrent, irritating, emotionally draining, and physically exhausting or dangerous" (McEwen, 2007, p. 874).

In behavioral health, stress has been mostly conceptualized through a psychological lens. However, it is important that stress also be understood from a neurophysiological perspective. Physiological responses to stress in mammalian bodies recruit two distinct but interrelated systems—the sympathetic-adrenomedullary system (SAM; Frankenhaeuser, 1986) and the hypothalamic-pituitary-adrenocortical system (HPA; Stratakis & Chrousos, 1995). The SAM system involves a sympathetic division of the autonomic nervous system and releases stress mediators such as epinephrine (Gunnar & Quevedo, 2007). The SAM system may be seen as a broadcasting system in the body, and the increased epinephrine it triggers helps facilitate efficient mobilization of metabolic resources and accordingly coordinates adaptive responses (e.g., fight or flight responses; Gunnar & Quevedo, 2007). In contrast, the HPA system may be viewed as a localized response, and it releases steroid hormones such as glucocorticoids (Gunnar & Quevedo, 2007). Furthermore, the HPA system activation recruits a gradual response, as opposed to a rapid adaptive response (e.g., running away from a sea gull flying toward you on a boardwalk), because the production of glucocorticoids takes approximately 25 minutes to reach peak levels in the body (Gunnar & Quevedo, 2007).

As stress responsiveness is individualized, individuals differ in their stress vulnerability or resilience to life stressors (Gunnar & Quevedo, 2007). In addition, life events early in childhood as well as the constant interaction with the social and physical environment influence long-lasting patterns of emotionality and stress responsiveness (McEwen, 2007). These may alter the rate of brain and body aging, and include the human gut (Mayer, 2021; McEwen, 2007).

Functionally, stress responses are necessary for our survival. However, unnecessarily frequent or prolonged neurobiological stress responses increase the risk of both physical and mental health problems (Gunnar & Quevedo, 2007). Moreover, stress is not only involved with immediate effects but also can lead to developmental disruptions, particularly when experienced during periods of brain development. For instance, some regions in the human brain (e.g., the amygdala, hippocampus, and prefrontal cortex) undergo stress-induced structural remodeling that results in the alteration of behavioral and physiological responses (McEwen, 2007). The impact of physiological stress reactions on the rapidly developing nervous system may help explicate the importance of better understanding how adverse childhood experiences (ACEs) heighten the risk of behavioral and emotional problems in children and adolescents (Gunnar & Quevedo, 2007) and chronic health conditions (i.e., heart disease, metabolic diseases, or depression) or premature death in adulthood (Centers for Disease Control and Prevention [CDC], 2019; Felitti et al., 1998). Moreover, having a good understanding of all this is critical, considering that over 70% of individuals worldwide will experience a traumatic event at some point in their lives, with a potential likelihood of it having long-lasting negative effects on their health (Benjet et al., 2016).

A Biological Basis of Behavior

In human service fields in the United States, such as mental health, a biological basis of behavior competencies has been developed and has long influenced doctoral-level psychology training (D'Amato et al., 2021). In contrast, other mental health professionals (e.g., professional counselors) had no requirement to be trained in this area until the Advancement of Clinical Practice Committee (previously known as the Professional Standards Committee), within the American Mental Health Counselors Association (AMHCA), identified four areas of clinical practice standards (i.e., the biological basis of behavior, psychological trauma, substance abuse, and specialized assessment; Field et al., 2022). Thus, it does not come as a surprise that many professional counselors have substantial gaps in neuroscience training (Russo et al., 2021). Furthermore, the 2021 AMHCA standards included and expanded a set of robust clinical competencies pertaining to the integration of neuroscience into counseling practice for the first time in the field of professional counseling. The revised standards for the practice of clinical mental health counseling are still the only existing clinical practice standards in the field of professional counseling for clinicians, such as clinical mental health counselors, to promote the integration of neuroscience into counseling practice.

According to the 2021 core standards of biological bases of behavior provided by AMHCA, "the origins of human thought, feeling, and behavior, from the more adaptive to the less adaptive, are the result of complex interactions between biological, psychological, and social factors" (AMHCA, 2021, p. 11). Similarly, the 2016 standards of the Council for Accreditation of Counseling and Related Educational Programs (CACREP) submit that entry-level counselor education programs must cover content or foundational knowledge in the areas in the program curriculum that include human growth and development. In particular, among the standards included in this core knowledge area, one standard (i.e., II.F.3.e) particularly pertaining to this textbook addresses the importance of being knowledgeable about "biological, neurological, and physiological factors that affect human development, functioning, and behavior" (CACREP, 2015, II.F.3.e., p. 11).

In a similar vein, the 2016 standards of the Commission on Accreditation of Allied Health Education Programs (CAAHEP) advise that "art therapy program curricula must provide students with the opportunity to integrate stages of human growth and development in assessment and treatment of typical and atypical client and patient populations" (2016, p. 22). Particularly, the standard Appendix B, III.H.k.2. advocates for education to "examine theoretical and biopsychosocial roots of developmental crises, trauma, disabilities, addictions, and exceptionality on development across the lifespan." Also, standard III.J.k.4 recommends that it is important for art therapists to "understand neuroscience theory as applied to art therapy interventions."

To date, several academic textbooks have been published to help promote the integration of neuroscience into counseling practice: *Neurocounseling: Brain-Based Approaches* (Field et al., 2017), *Neuroscience-Informed Counseling with Children and Adolescents* (Field & Ghoston, 2020), *Neuroscience for Counselors and Therapists: Integrating the Sciences of the Mind and Brain* (Luke, 2019), and *The Neuroeducation Toolbox: Practical Translations of Neuroscience in Counseling and Psychotherapy* (Miller & Beeson [Eds.], 2020). Helping professionals, particularly mental health professionals such as professional counselors, and clinical training programs (e.g., counselor training programs) would benefit from these textbooks when developing and modifying their programmatic curricula by incorporating neuroscience into counseling practice.

The Neurobiology of Stress-Informed Counseling

In the field of counseling, the integration of neuroscience into counseling practice has multiple terms: *neurocounseling* (Beeson & Field, 2017; Russell-Chapin, 2016), *neuro-informed mental health counseling*, or *neuroscience-informed counseling* (Luke et al., 2019). Despite similarities to this integrative approach, *neurobiology of stress-informed counseling* (NSIC) is a developmental approach to counseling that specifically addresses immediate and long-lasting effects of stress on human development, functioning, and behavior from a neurobiological perspective. Although neuroscience and neurobiology have much in common, neurobiology is considered to be a subdiscipline of both biology and neuroscience.

Also, it is important to recognize that acknowledging the importance of integrating neurobiology and neuroscience into counseling practice neither negates the role of humanistic underpinnings of counseling in practice nor discourages helping professionals from embracing and promoting the inherent nature of relational work in professional human relationships. Similarly, Luke (2020) stated in his book that he hoped that readers would apply well-validated neuroscientific findings to clinical practice efficiently and effectively. This textbook aligns with his point of view, and my hope is that NSIC can be used among helping professionals as guidance on how to enhance the developmental approach to human development, functioning, human health, and health conditions that account for contextual and environmental factors affecting each of the areas mentioned above. Furthermore, NSIC will be guided by a framework in this textbook that has been adapted from the ecobiodevelopmental framework of human development (Shonkoff et al., 2012) and modified to be more comprehensive and holistic by incorporating mounting research derived from the field of human microbiome. The modified ecobiodevelopmental framework will be described in depth in Chapter 2 of this book.

Helping Professionals as Readers

Additionally, it is worth noting that NSIC must be practiced in a way that honors and respects a multicultural framework that actively embraces diversity and inclusion. As community members, we live, interact, and work in this multicultural context. Furthermore, this textbook was written broadly for helping professionals working in a human service field and collaborating with individuals, families, and groups. Some examples of such individuals include, but are not limited to, mental health professionals (e.g., creative art therapists, play therapists, professional counselors, psychiatrists, psychologists, social workers, etc.), trainees (e.g., counseling students in training), case workers, case managers, life coaches, domestic caregivers, nutritionists and dietitians, and medical providers and assistants. Additionally, others such as teachers and educators might also find this textbook useful because it addresses content areas in human development, human functioning, human health, and human health conditions, with focus given to the effects of stress in those areas. However, some content in this book pertaining to NSIC will be more applicable to professional counselors than non-counselor helping professionals because *counseling* is a direct service rendered by such individuals that is inherent to the work they do, in addition to other services (e.g., diagnosing, treatment planning, or clinical assessment) provided by them. Moreover, this textbook particularly emphasizes the importance of collaborative relationships between the helped and helper, and among helping professionals, given the inherently relational nature of work such individuals do. In such relationships, each individual is viewed as a micro-ecosystem with capacities, abilities, and the potential to adapt to and heal from life stressors, regardless of their magnitude and frequency, with timely and appropriate healing practices and actions at varying levels. Also, helping professionals are considered to be constantly interacting with one another in a dynamic, versatile, diverse environment.

Informative Resources

This section will address a selective list of accreditation standards for those who are classified as helping professionals in relation to the application of NSIC.

- Art therapy

  Commission on Accreditation of Allied Health Education Programs (CAAHEP):

  2016 Standards and Guidelines for the Accreditation of Educational Programs in Art Therapy

  https://caahep-public-site-5be3d9.webflow.io/program-directors/standards-and-guidelines

- Counseling

  The Council for Accreditation of Counseling and Related Educational Programs (CACREP):

  2016 CACREP Standards

  https://www.cacrep.org/for-programs/2016-cacrep-standards/

- Psychology

  American Psychological Association (APA)

  Commission for the Recognition of Specialties and Subspecialties in Professional Psychology (CRSSPP):

  - General

    https://www.apa.org/about/policy/approved-guidelines

  - Standards of Accreditation for Health Service Psychology approved in 2015

    https://www.apa.org/ed/accreditation/about/policies/standards-of-accreditation.pdf

  - Guidelines on Trauma Competencies for Education and Training approved in 2015

    https://www.apa.org/ed/resources/trauma-competencies-training.pdf

- Social work

  Council on Social Work Education (CSWE):

  2015 Educational Policy and Accreditation Standards for Baccalaureate and Master's Social Work Programs

  https://www.cswe.org/accreditation/standards/2015-epas/

Summary

This chapter was written to help orient readers of this textbook to the comprehensive perspective of stress and the impact of stress on human development and function. Furthermore, the chapter gave a description of the NSIC, particularly for helping professionals as readers, and emphasized the importance of the approach to counseling specifically and the human service fields broadly.

As noted earlier in the chapter, stress is viewed as a part of our daily lives. In addition, stress responses are essential to human functioning, including survival. In behavioral health, it is common that stress has been primarily conceptualized from a psychological perspective. In contrast, it is important that stress also be understood from a neurobiological lens. Specifically, physiological responses to stress in mammals (e.g., humans) involve two distinct but interrelated systems—the SAM (Frankenhaeuser, 1986) system and the HPA (Stratakis & Chrousos, 1995) system. The SAM may be seen as a broadcasting system in the body with an increase in signaling molecules (e.g., epinephrine) to help facilitate efficient mobilization of metabolic resources and subsequently coordinate adaptive response to an acute stress (Gunnar & Quevedo, 2007). In contrast, the HPA recruits the activation of a localized, gradual response involving the production of stress molecules such as glucocorticoids in response to the same stimulus (Gunnar & Quevedo, 2007).

Individuals vary in stress responsiveness, stress vulnerability, or resilience to life stressors (Gunnar & Quevedo, 2007). Moreover, life early in childhood alongside interactions with the social and physical environment constantly influence long-lasting patterns of emotionality and stress responsiveness (McEwen, 2007). Importantly, stress recruits an acute response, as noted earlier, and both immediate and prolonged effects of stress can also lead to developmental disruptions, particularly when experienced during periods of human development. Thus, it is imperative for helping professionals working in a human service field to better understand and practice a developmental approach to their work that specifically addresses immediate and long-lasting effects of stress on human development, functioning, and behavior from a neuro-biological perspective. This approach is termed the NSIC in the context of this textbook. This chapter gave a selective list of examples of the helping professionals as the desired audience that included mental health professionals (e.g., creative art therapists, play therapists, professional counselors, psychiatrists, psychologists, social workers, etc.), trainees (e.g., counseling students in training), case workers, case managers, life coaches, domestic caregivers, nutritionists and dietitians, and medical providers and assistants. In addition, it is emphasized that NSIC must be practiced in a way that honors and respects a multicultural framework that actively embraces diversity and inclusion.

Case Study

A is a 69-year-old Asian American living in the greater Philadelphia area. A currently resides with their daughter and son-in-law in their house. A was born in a rural area in South Korea during the Korean War to a poor family of six. They are the youngest daughter in the family, and they have three older sisters. Their father passed away when they were in childhood due to cancer and their mother was the breadwinner in the family. She passed away approximately 10 years ago due to Alzheimer's disease.

A recently moved to the United States as a permanent resident. While A is very interested in learning another language and has had a high level of continued interest in American history throughout the majority of their life, they are not yet fluent in the English language. Due to the lack of language proficiency in English, they are hugely relying on their daughter and son-in-law in varying domains of their daily life activities, from regular grocery shopping to doctors' appointments. In addition, A does not own a driver's license, lacks driving skills, and is not interested in getting a driver's license at this time. Additionally, A seems to be hesitant to try out new activities, such as going out to meet new people, which is unusual for them, given that they had always been known to be sociable. Although A lives in a suburban area where there is great access to almost everything, such as a shopping mall, restaurants to dine out, community centers, and a few major hospitals in the area, they are challenged by traveling alone from one place to another due to their inability to drive and limited communication in English.

A has a long history of health conditions experienced on and off throughout their life. In particular, A has always been sensitive in their gut, and thus, they throw up easily in response to their stressful life events. Also, since they were young, they have been susceptible to frequent urinary infections that were treated with immediate medical care. A also first experienced depressive moods and fleeting suicidal thoughts during their perinatal period in their early 30s. Although they were not formally diagnosed with a mental disorder or identified medical condition, they report that they experienced episodic anhedonia, extreme sadness, heightened sensitivity to social relationships, sleep disturbance, and bouts of constipation and diarrhea several times in their 20s. However, these episodes subsided without psychological or pharmacological treatment.

About 3 months ago, A started to experience the following: uncontrollable, seemingly endless blues at times, noticeably decreased appetite, difficulty in falling asleep with early wake-ups, the loss of pleasure in reading books and magazines that was one of their lifetime favorite activities prior to the current experience, and perturbed daily hygiene (e.g., a lack of brushing their teeth before bedtime due to feeling fatigued). Furthermore, A started to drink beer frequently to feel "better." The increased drinking seems to be getting more pronounced lately. One afternoon, A was found in their room seemingly unconscious. Later, A noted that they drank a massive amount of alcohol that morning with an antidepressant (i.e., Zoloft) that their primary doctor had prescribed for the treatment of the depressive symptoms. After this concerning event, A experienced episodic suicidal thoughts albeit they report that they naturally went away.

A used to be a bright, pleasant person to be around, and their friends and neighbors used to describe them as "fun to be around" or "funny." A was also seen as a big eater who always had an insatiable stomach and the joy of savoring a variety of foods. Moreover, A had always had interest in practicing a healthy lifestyle, including regular walks, a balanced diet, and socializing with their family, friends, and neighbors, until they developed the current concerning experience. A has a support system including their daughter and son-in-law as well as their oldest sister and her family, who live 3 hours away by car. However, because of the current state of their physical and mental health, they are reserved and reluctant to try new things. At times, they do not even feel like going on a walk in the neighborhood.

References

American Mental Health Counselors Association. (2021). *AMHCA standards for the practice of clinical mental health counseling.* https://www.amhca.org/HigherLogic/System/DownloadDocumentFile. ashx?DocumentFileKey=cea86111-9bdb-984a-c14f-8528a3b3d83f&forceDialog=0

Beeson, E. T., & Field, T. A. (2017). Neurocounseling: A new section of the *Journal of Mental Health Counseling. Journal of Mental Health Counseling, 39*(1), 71–83. https://doi.org/10.17744/mehc.39.1.06

Benjet, C., Bromet, E., Karam, E. G., Kessler, R. C., McLaughlin, K. A., Ruscio, A. M., Shahly, V., Stein, D. J., Petukhova, M., Hill, E., Alonso, J., Atwoli, L., Bunting, B., Bruffaerts, R., Caldas-de-Almeida, J. M., de Girolamo, G., Florescu, S., Gureje, O., Huang, Y., Lepine, J. P., ... Koenen, K. C. (2016). The epidemiology of traumatic event exposure worldwide: Results from the World Mental Health Survey Consortium. *Psychological Medicine, 46*, 327–343. http://dx.doi.org/10.1017/S0033291715001981

Centers for Disease Control and Prevention. (2019). *Preventing adverse childhood experiences.* https://www.cdc.gov/violenceprevention/pdf/preventingACES.pdf

Council for the Accreditation of Counseling and Related Educational Programs. (2015). *2016 CACREP standards.* http://www.cacrep.org/wp-content/uploads/2017/08/2016-Standards-with-citations.pdf

Commission on Accreditation of Allied Health Education Programs (2016). *2016 standards and guidelines for the Accreditation of Educational Programs in Art Therapy.* https://caahep-public-site-5be3d9. webflow.io/program-directors/standards-and-guidelines

D'Amato, R. C., Davis, A. S., Power, E. M., & Eusebio, E. C. (Eds.). (2021). *Understanding the biological basis of behavior.* Springer.

Felitti, V. J., Anda, R. F., Nordenberg, D., Williamson, D. F., Spitz, A. M., Edwards, V., Koss, M. P., & Marks, J. S. (1998). Relationship of childhood abuse and household dysfunction to many of the leading causes of death in adults: The Adverse Childhood Experiences (ACE) study. *American Journal of Preventive Medicine, 14*(4), 245–258. https://doi.org/10.1016/S0749-3797(98)00017-8

Field, T. A., & Ghoston, M. R. (2020). *Neuroscience-informed counseling with children and adolescents.* American Counseling Association.

Field, T. A., Jones, L. K., & Russell-Chapin, L. (2017). *Neurocounseling: Brain-based approaches.* Wiley.

Field, T. A., Moh, Y., Luke, C., Gracefire, P., Beeson, E. T., & Russo, G. M. (2022). A training model for the development of neuroscience-informed counseling competencies. *Journal of Mental Health Counseling, 44*(3), 266–281. https://doi.org/10.17744/mehc.44.3.05

Frankenhaeuser, M. (1986). A psychobiological framework for research on human stress and coping. In M. H. Appley & R. Trumbull (Eds.), *Dynamics of stress: Physiological, psychological, and social perspectives* (pp. 101–16). Plenum.

Gunnar, M., & Quevedo, K. (2007). The neurobiology of stress and development. *The Annual Review of Psychology, 58*, 145–173. https://doi.org/10.1146/annurev.psych.58.110405.085605

Luke, C. (2019). *Neuroscience for counselors and therapists: Integrating the sciences of the mind and brain.* Cognella Academic Publishing.

Luke, C., Miller, R., & McAuliffe, G. (2019). Neuro-informed mental health counseling: A person-first perspective. *Journal of Mental Health Counseling, 41*(1), 65–79. https://doi.org/10.17744/mehc.41.1.06

Mayer, E. (2021). *The Gut-immune connection: How understanding the connection between food and immunity can help us regain our health.* Harper Wave.

McEwen, B. S. (2007). Physiology and neurobiology of stress and adaptation: Central role of the brain. *Physiological Reviews, 87*, 873–904. https://doi.org/10.1152/physrev.00041.2006

Miller, R., & Beeson, E. T. (Eds.). (2020). *The neuroeducation toolbox: Practical translations of neuroscience in counseling and psychotherapy.* Cognella.

Russell-Chapin, L. A. (2016). Integrating neurocounseling into the counseling profession: An introduction. *Journal of Mental Health Counseling, 38*(2), 93–102. https://doi.org/10.17744/mehc.38.2.01

Russo, G. M., Schauss, E., Naik, S., Banerjee, R., Ghoston, M., Jones, L. K., Zalaquett, C. P., Beeson, E. T., & Field, T. A. (2021). Extent of counselor training in neuroscience-informed counseling competencies. *Journal of Mental Health Counseling, 43*(1), 75–93. https://doi.org/10.17744/mehc.43.1.05

Shonkoff, J., P., Garner, A. S., the Committee on Psychosocial Aspects of Child and Family Health, Committee on Early Childhood, Adoption, and Dependent Care, & Section on Developmental and Behavioral Pediatrics. (2012). The lifelong effects of early childhood adversity and toxic stress. *The American Academy of Pediatrics, 129*(1), e232–e246. https://doi.org/10.1542/peds.2011-2663

Stratakis, C. A., & Chrousos, G. P. (1995). Neuroendocrinology and pathophysiology of the stress system. In G. P. Chrousos, R. McCarty, K. Pacak, G. Cizza, E. Sternberg, P. W. Gold, & R. Kvetsnansky (Eds.), *Stress: Basic mechanisms and clinical implications* (pp. 1–18). NY Academic Science.

CHAPTER TWO

Perspectives and Frameworks

The key points addressed in this chapter are

- the contextual factors that affect stress levels and mental health

- the human developmental model that helps better conceptualize human health and disease across the lifespan

- healing justice approaches that promote individual and collective healing in relationships

- prevention approaches that help guide actions and practices from a social and ecological perspective

Contemporary and Contextual Information

Environmental Challenges

"Natural ecosystems provide useful services for humanity, such as regulating climate, preventing floods and filtering water."

The 2020 State of the World's Plants and Fungi Report (Royal Botanic Gardens, 2020, p. 11)

We are facing many environmental challenges contemporarily that impact our physical and mental health, but climate change is one of the biggest challenges of our time, with the greatest impact on our lives. The consequences of climate change not only affect vulnerable communities and societies directly exposed at a large scale, but also individual humans and other living beings sharing the ecological system with us. Furthermore, climate change is also a concern for the entire scientific community (Cianconi et al., 2020). Climate change–induced conditions, such as rising temperatures; an increased frequency of heat waves, floods, tornadoes, droughts, and wildfires; a loss of forest and glaciers; and the shrinkage of sources of water, can cause human suffering through a variety of states and conditions, including physical and mental health (Cianconi et al., 2020).

At the time that parts of this textbook were written, I was in South Korea for a family visit and happened to come across an environmental program on the television while I was staying in Seoul that featured the recently opened Baekdudaegan National Arboretum Seed Vault Center in Bonghwa, South Korea. This seed vault is one of only two facilities existing in the world and was built to preserve numerous different wild plant species through their seeds. One might ask, "What is this facility for?" Its purpose is to preserve and keep those wild seeds safe in case they are lost due to events caused by reasons such as climate change, or natural and manmade disasters. The other facility is located in Svalbard, an Arctic Norwegian archipelago, and stores samples of food crops. You may wonder why we must preserve those wild plant species. Food insecurity caused by varied reasons such as climate change is one concern in recent years. This food insecurity is associated with a number of deleterious events and conditions, such as wars and refugees, that have global scale in the contemporary era.

Research has suggested that it is important to preserve wild plants, some of which are the source of the crops that we consume today. Given the significance of biodiversity and its impact on our health, many crop species in the wild could play a vital role in promoting and sustaining this biodiversity and help in the long term with food security in our lives, as delineated in the 2020 State of the World's Plants and Fungi Report (Royal Botanic Gardens, 2020). Unfortunately, this report indicates that we are contemporarily facing a significant loss or even extinction of plants and fungi due to environmental challenges such as climate change and destruction of their habitats. This is problematic because plants and fungi are important members of ecosystems and have the potential to help us address environmental challenges. Also, wild plants have potential as fuel, future medicine, and food (Royal Botanic Gardens, 2020). As a result, it becomes important for us to better understand what is happening with such loss and extinction in some plants and fungi, how biodiversity is compromised, and how these relate to the health of ecosystems, including us as members of the systems.

The Impact of Climate Change on Mental Health

"Climate change and related disasters cause anxiety-related responses as well as chronic and severe mental health disorders."

The American Psychiatric Association (n.d.)

It was addressed in the previous section that both we and our ecosystems are facing environmental challenges. Climate change is not only leading to suffering such as food insecurity but is also associated with mental health states. For instance, it is evident that extreme weather events (e.g., droughts, wildfires, or flooding) are related to increasing aggressive behavior and domestic violence (U.S. Global Change Research Program, 2016). It is understandable that extreme weather events such as flooding and droughts, especially when prolonged, can be stressors to those affected directly and indirectly. Subsequently, they may lead to the manifestation of elevated levels of anxiety, depression, and stressor disorders (U.S. Global Change Research Program, 2016).

Climate change and its consequences affect all of us. However, they affect individuals, families, and communities differently and disproportionately, as some are more vulnerable than others to the impacts of climate change. The American Psychiatric Association (APA, n.d.) acknowledges that children, the elderly, people with cognitive impairments, people with a chronic health condition, women during the perinatal period, and people with mental illness are more vulnerable than others to extreme weather events and the potential impacts of such challenges. In particular, those with mental health conditions who take psychiatric medications are more vulnerable to such events because medications can interfere with their ability to regulate heat (APA, n.d.). Thus, their cognitive functions, such as their awareness, can be compromised so that they may not be fully aware of their body temperature rising. This is concerning because it is associated with injury and death (Climate Psychiatry Alliance, n.d.). Although further details of the impacts of climate change on mental health and human health at large are outside of the scope of this chapter, helpful resources for those who are interested in furthering their knowledge in these areas may be the U.S. Global Change Research Program (https://health2016.globalchange.gov/climate-change-and-human-health) or Mental Health and Our Changing Climate: Impacts, Implications, and Guidance by the American Psychological Association and ecoAmerica (https://www.apa.org/news/press/releases/2017/03/mental-health-climate.pdf).

Prolonged COVID-19 Pandemic

"Although large numbers of people throughout the world will show resilience to the profound loss, stress, and fear associated with COVID-19, the virus will likely exacerbate existing mental health disorders and contribute to the onset of new stress-related disorders for many."

Horesh and Brown (2020, p. 331)

Our contemporary lives and environments have been transformed drastically due to COVID-19 since the virus was identified in late 2019 and its transmission accelerated globally. Although our enormous malleability and regulatory and adaptive capacities have rallied to accept the new ways of living, we are certainly not free of the negative impacts of COVID-19, which affect every facet of society. In addition, at the time this chapter was written and subsequently revised, a recent resurgence of confirmed COVID-19 cases has been reported nationally. Specifically, according to the Centers for Disease Control and Prevention (CDC) COVID Data Tracker Weekly Review dated May 27, 2022 (https://covid.cdc.gov/covid-data-tracker-datatracker-home), the confirmed cases, hospitalizations, and deaths are increasing in many states of the United States, primarily influenced by the Omicron variant. Furthermore, the same report states that the total cases reported added up to 34,722,631, while the current 7-day moving average of daily new cases plunged to 64.1% compared with the previous 7-day data. In addition, Zhou et al. (2021) suggested that during a period between March and December 2020, many extra COVID-19 cases and deaths in California, Oregon, and Washington may be associated with the increase in air pollution caused by fine particulate matter (PM2.5) from wildfire smoke.

Thus, it is not difficult to propose that the impacts of the prolonged COVID-19 pandemic may have enduring effects that will take a psychological toll on all, particularly on individuals, families, communities of color, and at-risk populations. Among many, one example includes that among more than 3,900 individuals with prior COVID-19 illness who participated in a study between May 2020 and January 2021, 52.4% were vulnerable for moderate or greater symptoms of a major depressive disorder (Perlis et al., 2021). Not surprisingly, Horesh and Brown (2020) argue that the current pandemic and its long-lasting impacts should be viewed from the perspective of trauma. Indeed, it is likely that exposure to toxic/traumatic stress or chronic stress in both acute and chronic terms in the U.S. population will continue to increase. Moreover, the resurgence of outcry at long-standing systemic racism and racial inequities historically rooted in the nation may continuously add stress to the tension of the pandemic (Galea & Abdalla, 2020).

For these reasons, helping professionals, especially those who have the knowledge and skills in traumatic stress from both academia and practice, should be enlisted for individual and collective actions to provide critical support, and effective and culturally responsive care, during this time and thereafter (Horesh & Brown, 2020). Furthermore, the interprofessional collaboration and partnership among mental health researchers, practitioners, and academicians working in helping professions in which exposure to traumatic stress is ubiquitous must become increasingly vital, not only to care for the affected but also to help reduce the incidence of COVID-19-related traumatic stress (Horesh & Brown, 2020). In other words, the contemporary COVID-19 era and its future requires such individuals to invest more in the enhancement of prevention practices and actions in human service fields.

Human Development, Health, and Disease

"Complex brain disorders cannot be adequately explained by simple linear concepts, but rather require the more comprehensive lens of network science, which shows that chronic stress and anxiety combined with an unhealthy diet and lack of regular exercise exert a synergistic detrimental effect on gut health."

Emeran Mayer in The Gut-Immune Connection *(2021, p. 54)*

One of the previous mission statements of the American Counseling Association (ACA; n.d.) states that the association is "to enhance human development throughout the lifespan and to promote the counseling profession" (cited in Myers, 1992, p. 137). This explicitly supports the association's orientation toward a proactive position on human development. The Council for Accreditation of Counseling and Related Educational Programs (CACREP) standards for counselor preparation also reveal human development as one of eight core curricular areas for counselor preparation. Additionally, wellness is a philosophical cornerstone of the profession of counseling alongside development across the lifespan and prevention. As a paradigm, wellness can help promote counseling and development (Myers, 1992). Thus, the counseling profession has oriented development and developmental approaches as the means of achieving wellness that have brought about unique contributions to broader mental health (Myers, 1992).

Development is concerned with positive human change and is the goal of all counseling interventions (Ivey, 1991; Van Hesteren & Ivey, 1990). Thus, it is imperative and integral that we as helping professionals promote development. Furthermore, given the importance of development, counseling must embrace and be practiced using developmental approaches that promote wellness in people's lives. In addition, helping professionals have advanced individual and collective prevention practices. As one example, the counseling profession has evolved over time to embrace a professional philosophy oriented toward the future in terms of prevention practices. However, prevention is often challenged because prevention interventions may be considered non-third-party reimbursable services in the current U.S. mental health system. In the following section, a modified framework of human development will be described, as it will guide the conceptualization of human development and better understanding human health and disease over the course of the lifespan in the context of this textbook.

A Modified Ecobiodevelopmental Framework of Human Development and Human Diseases

"A recent technical report from the American Academy of Pediatrics reviewed 58 years of published studies and characterized racial and ethnic disparities in children's health to be extensive, pervasive, persistent, and in some cases, worsening."

Shonkoff et al. (2012, p. e233)

The *ecobiodevelopmental (EBD) framework* was developed to promote healthy development. This framework puts focus on the significance of early development in childhood and prevention of disease across the lifespan (Shonkoff et al., 2012). This framework can provide a perspective for helping professionals working in the human service field to help guide their practices and approaches, including case formulation, service delivery, treatment planning, and prevention.

It proposes a scientifically grounded view to promote the development and implementation of strategies to decrease toxic stress in early childhood. Using this framework, individual and collective endeavors are not only aimed at treatment of conditions, but also at preventing and reducing complex and perpetuating problems at the societal level, such as disparities in health (Shonkoff et al., 2012).

Furthermore, the EBD framework was intended to "better understand the complex relationships among adverse childhood circumstances, toxic stress, brain architecture, and poor physical and mental health well into adulthood" (Shonkoff et al., 2012, p. e233). In this innovative and integrated framework, development is perceived to be driven by "an ongoing, inextricable interaction between biology as defined by genetic predispositions and ecology as defined by the social and physical environment" (Shonkoff et al., 2012, p. e234). In particular, the framework is supported by an emerging multidisciplinary science of development that involves the actively evolving field of epigenetics. *Epigenetics* are described as "the molecular biological mechanisms such as DNA methylation and histone acetylation that affect gene expression without altering DNA sequence" (Shonkoff et al., 2012, p. e234). Investment in its research aims to understand both normal and pathological neuronal development and function, and developmental neuroscience (Shonkoff et al., 2012). Emerging research in the field of epigenetics suggests that human development goes beyond the influence of genetic predispositions. Rather, it supports the importance of ongoing dynamic interactions between genetic predispositions, and physical and social environment on development across the lifespan.

Additionally, the EBD framework encourages helping professionals to better understand both the factors that promote or compromise early human development and set a trajectory for later development and health in adulthood. Moreover, the framework is also supported by findings from longitudinal studies showing that long-lasting consequences of childhood adversity do not only involve direct biological mechanisms but also are associated with alterations in a developing child's ecology (social and physical environment) that can lead to noticeable effects on their developmental trajectory (Shonkoff et al., 2012). Some of these effects include health status and longevity (Flaherty et al., 2006).

Despite the integrative and developmental nature of the EBD framework, this framework can benefit from emerging research in microbiome science. In the following paragraph, readers will be invited to learn more about the burgeoning research in the field of human microbiome and how it intersects with the EBD framework to help promote a more holistic perspective on human development, health, and disease. In the context of this textbook, the EBD framework has been adapted, and subsequently a modified framework (Figure 2.1) will be employed to promote better understanding.

Additionally, biology, as one component of the modified EBD framework, goes beyond genetic dispositions that human bodies have. Rather, the interconnectedness of bodily systems is important, and this is recognized and studied in systems biology as an approach influenced by network science. *Network science* is a discipline that studies "the interplay among individual elements in complex networks using such methods as graph theory, statistical mechanics, and data mining to create predictive models" (Mayer, 2021, p. 18). Additionally, developed in the

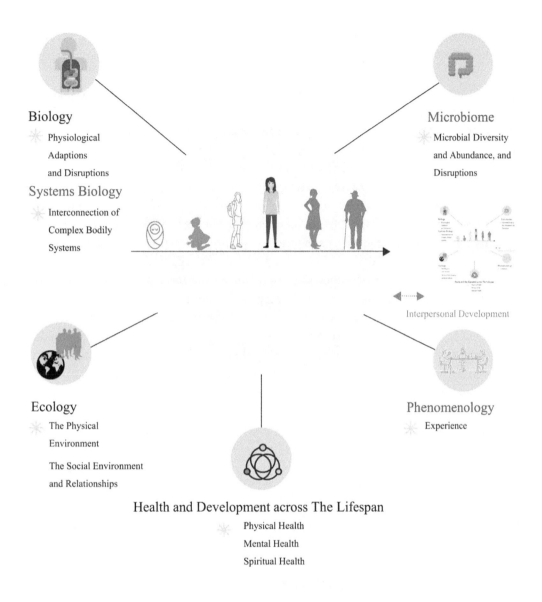

FIGURE 2.1   An Ecobiodevelopmental Framework—Modified (EBD-M)

1950s, systems biology has been a catalyst for the paradigm shift within science to emphasize the importance of interconnection while transitioning away from specialization (Mayer, 2021). In this approach, each of the domains is referred to using the suffixes *-ome* and *-omics* (Mayer, 2021). For example, epigen*omics* is a field of study accounting for the environmental influences on all genes in the body that modify their expression (Mayer, 2021). In contrast, epigenetics studies the environmental effects on specific genes in the body (Mayer, 2021). Each of the domains in systems biology intricately interacts with and modifies the other players, and thus, these relationships are responsible for a "huge interdependent, multiscale network" in our bodies (Mayer, 2021, p. 20). Needless to say, the interconnected systems in our bodies play a significant role in our health.

Now, let's take a close look at the human body in this section. It is documented that the human body consists of its host cells, which range from 10^{12} to 10^{14} cells (Sender et al., 2017). Yet when the influence of genetic dispositions on human development and health is addressed, it is not always inclusive of the influence on the host body's development and health of microorganisms (e.g., bacteria, viruses, archaea, and fungi) that reside on and inside our bodies, their genetic programming, and their metabolic substances.

Rather than viewing the human body as an individual organism, it can be conceptualized as a complex ecosystem, particularly from a cellular point of view, where the host cells and micro-organisms cohabit in dialogue with each other constantly in an intricate manner. Alongside the numerous host cells that make up the human body, microorganisms cohabit on the surface of the skin, inside the mouth, in the eyelashes, in the nose, and mostly in the gastrointestinal (GI) system or the human gut. These little guys vary in type and composition (Mayer, 2018). They are collectively called *microbiota*. Given the current contemporary state we call the COVID-19 pandemic, it would not be surprising that some readers of this textbook might hold a biased view on microorganisms or microbes regarding their roles. However, Hill and Round (2021) encourage us to think that indeed these little guys can play both roles of being pathogenic or harmful, and commensal or helpful. Furthermore, the lines between the good and bad guys among microbes do not appear to be clear cut.

In recent years, mounting research indicates that microorganisms residing particularly in the human gut influence the development and function of almost all systems of human bodies (Hill & Round, 2021). For example, commensal microorganisms play imperative roles in homeostatic development of many organs and systems, such as the brain and gut. In the brain, microbes can regulate the development of specific cells, such as microglia, and in the intestine, they can act similarly in the development of intestinal epithelial cells (Hill & Round, 2021).

Functionally, the gut microbiota are like helpers for several areas in the human function. However, evidence also shows that they can be affected by adversity early in life and have a prolonged impact on our health. As an example, early childhood adversity is responsible for altered microbial patterns in developing youths, while the altered bacteria-brain associations are seen in functional reactivity in brain regions, such as prefrontal cortex and posterior cingulate cortex, known to be implicated in emotional functioning (Callaghan et al., 2019).

The ecobiodevelopmental framework has been modified in the context of this textbook to help better understand multifaceted factors and the interconnection of such factors affecting human development across the lifespan, health, and disease. The factors highlighted in red in Figure 2.1 are added into the framework to describe the complexity of development in humans.

Healing Justice Approaches in a Multicultural Frame

Healing from adversity (e.g., neglect, abuse, systemic racism, poverty, food insecurity, negative consequences of COVID-19, etc.) is a path to help optimize wellness in a society and its members. Healing also helps restore optimal quality of life and is a critical part of human experience to repair harm and injustice. Furthermore, healing can occur at varying levels, ranging from individuals to relationships to collective healing in social situations. National organizations (e.g., the American Counseling Organization [ACA] or the American Psychological Association [APA]) in human service fields, such as professional counseling and psychology, promote the wellness of society and of individuals, families, and communities that compose the society. To help increase healing from adversity in individuals, families, and communities in need, as well as in the general public, helping professionals play a vital role.

Both individually and collectively, helping professionals employ a variety of relevant professional practices and actions, including advocacy for social justice. Approaches to social justice have led to community change, but their outward focus rarely prepares individuals in need of healing to turn inward in order to focus on their own health and wellness (Ginwright, 2016). Furthermore, social justice organizing movements with an outward focus (e.g., counteracting against systemic changes to remove barriers) are not fully suitable to deal with human suffering (Social Justice Leadership, 2010, cited in Ginwright, 2016). Ginwright describes *suffering* as "the result of the psycho-spiritual injury resulting from oppression" (2016, p. 28). Therefore, helping professionals can function at the convergence of organizing advocacy for social justice and healing from human suffering.

Moreover, it is important to seek approaches and strategies that both speak to and act on oppression (e.g., racism, sexism, Asian hate, poverty) and commensurate suffering (e.g., toxic stress). As one example, Ginwright (2016) suggests in his book, titled *Hope and Healing in Urban Education*, that a healing justice framework is designed to promote and sustain social change by "shifting how individuals, organizations, and communities relate to one another as they envision a new way of creating collective hope" (p. 28). Specifically, the healing justice framework emphasizes the significance of healing, and fully acknowledges and maximizes the power of healing, inherent resources, and strengths existing within the communities of color contextualized in the historically marginalizing and interlocking, oppressive systems in the United States (Ginwright, 2016). In addition, although it is important for society members, including helping professionals, to exert individual and collective advocacy efforts to counteract the pathological, oppressive, White-glamorizing U.S. systems, the healing justice framework highlights the significance of giving community members the insight to shift how they relate to others (Ginwright, 2016).

There are varying perspectives on healing and different approaches to healing justice. *Transformative organizing* is one approach alongside restorative justice, healing circles, and mindful practices (Ginwright, 2016). This approach can be useful in guiding implications for practices and actions of helping professionals who are working with individuals, families, and communities, particularly those living in the White-dominant society and facing accordant biased societal norms in everyday life, or throughout generations. Due to the space limit of this textbook, among these practices and actions, only transformative organizing will be described in depth in this section. Therefore, readers who are interested in learning about the full scope of the healing justice framework are encouraged to refer to Ginwright's book. Transformative organizing is a term used to "convey the idea that social change is the result of individual and collective transformation of how we treat ourselves and relate to one another" (Ginwright, 2016, p. 29). He eloquently notes that the goal of transformative organizing, broadly speaking, is to "reimagine ways to restructure our economic, political, and judicial systems in ways that create justice, democracy, and equality" (Ginwright, 2016, p. 29). Transformative organizing will not be a new concept to many helping professionals, because their practices are inherently deeply rooted in relationships with clients, other peers, or supervisors, to list a few.

Prevention Approaches, Actions, and Practices

> "Prevention requires a new focus away from diagnosis and treatment of pathology."
>
> *Myers (1992)*

Poor health is expensive, so efforts to prevent it and improve health have many benefits. From 1996 to 2016, total health care spending in the United States increased from an estimated $1.4 trillion to $3.1 trillion (Dieleman et al., 2020). Nonetheless, while over the past 75 years the population has been living longer lives, many individuals have suffered from a variety of serious chronic illnesses, such as cardiovascular diseases, diabetes, cancer, and neurodevelopmental and neurodegenerative disorders (Mayer, 2021). Related to this, the prevalence of these illnesses has been steadily increasing at shocking rates, as have the medical costs (Mayer, 2021). Mayer eloquently describes this condition as "America's silent public health crisis" (p. 1).

In addition, U.S. health care spending was estimated to account for 18% of the U.S. economy over that same period (Dieleman et al., 2020). Among the 154 conditions reported on, metabolic diseases such as diabetes and hypertension were responsible for a higher stake in health care dollars spent in 2016. For instance, diabetes accounted for the third highest amount of health care spending, estimated at $111.2 billion, while an estimated $79 billion was spent caring for those with hypertension (Dieleman et al., 2020). In recent years, it is estimated that there was an increase in U.S. health care expenditure to $4.1 trillion, or $12,530 per person in the calendar year of 2020 (Centers for Medicare and Medicaid Services, n.d.).

To put this in perspective using visualization, readers are encouraged to consider utilizing the following source through Information is Beautiful to help them better understand what the estimated health care spending means relative to other sources of spending at national and global levels: https://informationisbeautiful.net/visualizations/trillions-what-is-a-trillion-dollars/.

Among the health care expenditures in 2019, an estimate of nearly 51% was spent on hospital care and physician and clinical services, whereas an estimated 3% was spent on public health activities (Centers for Medicare and Medicaid Services, n.d.).

In addition, the U.S. federal government spent an estimated $1.2 trillion on health care in fiscal year 2019, according to Tax Policy Center at Urban Institute and Brookings Institution (https://www.taxpolicycenter.org/briefing-book/how-much-does-federal-government-spend-health-care). In past years, more than 75% of federal funding in health care was spent caring for persons with chronic illnesses (e.g., heart disease, stroke, and cancer). These increasing health care expenditures do not appear to be an effective approach to health promotion, given the steadily increasing rates of chronic illnesses in the U.S. general public (Mayer, 2021).

When considering the persistent relationships existing among adversity-causing toxic stress early in life, poor health outcomes in adulthood, and unhealthy adult lifestyles, it becomes important to seek other avenues. As the costs of chronic illnesses may have their roots early in life (Shonkoff et al., 2012), this presents an opportunity for society members, including helping professionals, to create more effective approaches and strategies to help promote and enhance lifelong improved outcomes in health and optimal quality of life. As one example, "interventions that strengthen the capacities of families and communities to protect young children from the disruptive effects of toxic stress are likely to promote healthier brain development and enhanced physical and mental well-being" (Shonkoff et al., 2012, p. e239). Increased investment in lifelong health promotion and prevention of adversity, particularly early in childhood, is needed in this new era where the overwhelming levels of stress are affecting us constantly at individual, community, national, and global levels. Furthermore, contemporary stressors are associated with the consequences of the prolonged pandemic, climate change, and global conflicts, in addition to the existing, perhaps deepening stressors (e.g., systemic injustices, poverty, violence, unequal access to resources).

To enable helping professionals to guide their prevention actions and practices, a prevention model will be presented in the following section. In relation to this, the prevention model used by the CDC (n.d.) has been adapted and subsequently modified in the context of this textbook to address varying factors that intricately interact with each other and affect the complexity of human health and the pathology of health conditions.

The Social-Ecological Model for Prevention—Modified (SEMP-M)

The CDC has employed the Social-Ecological Model (SEM) particularly for violence prevention in order to gain a better understanding of adversity, such as violence, and inform prevention strategies and practices accordingly (CDC, n.d.). This four-level model is concerned with the complex interplay among individual, relationship, community, and societal factors (CDC, n.d.). Although this model is employed to prevent violence, it can be relevant and applicable to prevent other types of adversity, such as toxic stress, because of the generic structure of the model and relationships among the individual levels reflective of our social contexts. In this textbook, the SEM has been adapted to help guide suggestions and recommendations for prevention actions and practices among helping professionals. However, a new level of microbial factors has been added to the model (Figure 2.2) to address the influences of microorganisms on development,

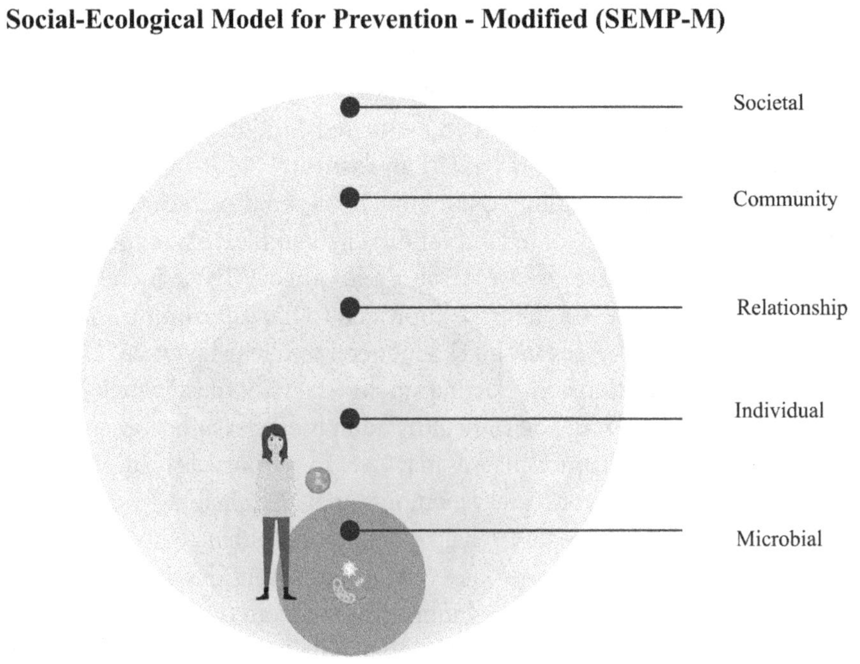

Social-Ecological Model for Prevention - Modified (SEMP-M)

FIGURE 2.2   A Social-Ecological Model for Prevention—Modified (SEMP-M)

health, and pathology in humans. And this modified model—consisting of five levels as opposed to the four levels—is called the Social-Ecological Model for Prevention—Modified (SEMP-M) in this textbook.

Microbial

The first level looks at microbial factors that increase the likelihood of putting people at risk for negative effects of toxic stress. These factors include the microbial composition, diversity, and magnitude in our gastrointestinal system; antibiotic use; inappropriate use of medication; pathogenic microbial infection; and microbial genetic information. Prevention strategies at this level may include learning to increase relevant knowledge, conscious awareness, clinical education programs that incorporate content about human microbiome, and a sustainable, healthy lifestyle, including healthy diet.

Individual

The second level identifies biological (e.g., genetic predispositions), personal-history-related factors, and individual health behaviors that are identified as increasing the vulnerability to effects of toxic stress. Some of these factors include genetic predispositions, a history of adversity, uncontrolled substance use or abuse, education, income, or employment. Prevention strategies at this level promote self-awareness, relevant knowledge, attitudes, beliefs, and active and sustained behaviors that prevent toxic or chronic stress. Additionally, some approaches may involve access and availability to information and resources, learning about stress management, healthy lifestyle programs, and healing-relationship skill programs.

Relationship

The third level identifies surrounding relationships that may increase the risk of being exposed to and experiencing toxic stress. A person's social-circle peers, parents, partners, family members, loved ones, educator-student relationships, co-workers, and close professionals working in human service fields influence their cognition, emotion, and behavior. They are also influential on the person's experience in different settings (e.g., home, work, or school). Prevention strategies at this level may include parent-child stress-prevention programs, peer support and mentoring programs, healing-centered professional and client relationship programs, and interdisciplinary collaboration in human service fields. These strategies are to promote and strengthen relational communication, healing in relationships, and nonjudgmental perspective-taking.

Community

The fourth level examines settings such as neighborhoods, schools, workplaces, and community centers in which social relationships are formed and maintained. This level intentionally and proactively seeks to identify the characteristics and conditions of these settings to reduce and prevent risk factors associated with toxic stress while acknowledging and honoring the existing strengths, resources, and practices in such settings. Prevention strategies at this level focus on improving the physical and social environment in these settings through collective and communal efforts, actions, and practices to create places where all community members live, learn, work, interact, and play with psychological, physical, and emotional safety.

Societal

The fifth level involves a broad scope of societal factors that generate and perpetuate a culture in which toxic stress is encouraged. These factors include cultural and social norms, systems, structures, and collective practices that support toxic or chronic stress and further sustain them without appropriate interventions. Other important societal factors are educational, health-related, economic, social, judicial, and corrective policies that help deepen and perpetuate inequalities between groups in society. Prevention strategies at this level may include collective and communal efforts that critique existing societal norms carefully and promote societal norms and collective practices that prevent risk factors leading to toxic or chronic stress.

The SEMP-M framework gives helping professionals the opportunity to address at the five levels factors that make people vulnerable to negative effects of toxic stress and that protect them from being exposed to or experiencing adversity. However, not all strategies, illustrated in depth in Chapter 9 of this textbook at each of the five levels, are necessarily fully evidence based, although many of those strategies involve scientific support from the research community.

Summary

This chapter addressed the contextual factors that affect levels of stress and mental health in the contemporary era. Among environmental challenges we are facing, one of the biggest challenges of our time includes climate change, which has a significant impact on our lives. As a consequence, many individuals, families, and communities are directly and indirectly affected. Furthermore, climate change also affects other living beings (e.g., animals and insects) or plants sharing the ecological system with us. Climate-change-induced conditions (e.g., rising temperatures, tornadoes, loss of forest and glaciers, etc.) can cause human suffering through varied states and conditions, including physical and mental health (Cianconi et al., 2020).

In addition, our contemporary lives and environments have substantially been transformed due to the COVID-19 pandemic, despite our enormous adaptability and regulatory capacities. For instance, of individuals who participated in a study between May 2020 and January 2021, 52.4% were vulnerable for moderate or greater symptoms of a major depressive disorder (Perlis et al., 2021). Some scholars argue that the current pandemic and its long-lasting impacts should be seen from the perspective of trauma (Horesh & Brown, 2020).

For these reasons, helping professionals, particularly those who have the knowledge and skills in trauma from both academia and practice, should be enlisted for individual and collective actions to provide critical support as well as effective and culturally responsive professional care during this time and thereafter (Horesh & Brown, 2020). In doing so, comprehensive and developmental perspectives to help guide such endeavors will be helpful. As one example, the chapter examined the EBD framework (Shonkoff et al., 2012) that was designed to help promote healthy development with focus given to the importance of early development in childhood and prevention of disease across the lifespan. However, in the context of this textbook, the EBD has been adapted and modified to assist helping professionals in better understanding multifaceted factors and the interconnection of such factors affecting human development, health, and disease. This modified framework, named the EBD-modified (EBD-M), includes microorganisms residing on and in us affecting our development and function of all systems (Hill & Round, 2021).

Furthermore, healing justice approaches in a multicultural frame was addressed. Healing is an essential part of human experience to repair harm and injustice, and it can occur at varying levels, ranging from individuals to relationships to collective healing in social situations. Among different approaches to healing justice is transformative organizing, a term used to emphasize social change that is gained through individual and collective transformation (Ginwright, 2016). In addition, to enable helping professionals to guide their prevention actions and practices, the social-ecological model (SEM; Centers for Disease Control and Prevention, n.d.) and its modified version as a prevention model was presented.

Experiential Questions

1. What factors informed by the modified ecobiodevelopmental framework addressed in the chapter do you think might have influenced A's development across their lifespan?

2. How do healing justice approaches help tailor your professional practice based on your primary professional role to help alleviate A's current experience in their health state?

3. Based on your primary professional role, what actions and practices can be exercised at each level of the social-ecological model for prevention—modified to help prevent A from facing the worsening of their current experience pertaining to their mental health?

References

American Counseling Association. (n.d.). *Our vision and mission: ACA's strategic plan.* https://www.counseling.org/about-us/about-aca/our-mission

The American Psychiatric Association. (n.d.). *How extreme weather events affect mental health.* https://www.psychiatry.org/patients-families/climate-change-and-mental-health-connections/affects-on-mental-health

Callaghan, B. L., Fields, A., Gee, D. G., Gabard-Durnam, L., Caldera, C., Humphreys, K. L., Goff, B., Flannery, J., Telzer, E. H., Shapiro, M., & Tottenham, N. (2019). *Mind and gut: Associations between mood and gastrointestinal distress in children exposed to adversity. Development and Psychopathology, 32*(1), 309–328. https://doi.org/10.1017/s0954579419000087

Centers for Disease Control and Prevention. (2021). *Don't run down the shot clock.* COVID Data Tracker Weekly Review. Retrieved August 1, 2021, from https://www.cdc.gov/coronavirus/2019-ncov/covid-data/covidview/index.html

Centers for Disease Control and Prevention. (n.d.). The social-ecological model: A framework for prevention. https://www.cdc.gov/violenceprevention/about/social-ecologicalmodel.html

Centers for Medicare and Medicaid Services. (n.d.). *The nation's health dollar ($4.1 trillion), calendar year 2020: Where it went.* https://www.cms.gov/files/document/nations-health-dollar-where-it-came-where-it-went.pdf

Cianconi, P., Betro, S., & Janiri, L. (2020). The impact of climate change on mental health: A systematic descriptive review. *Frontiers in Psychiatry, 11*(74). https://doi.org/10.3389/fpsyt.2020.00074

Climate Psychiatry Alliance. (n.d.). *Coping with extreme heat.* Retrieved August 1, 2021, from https://www.climatepsychiatry.org/coping-with-extreme-heat-english?_ga=2.25891645.161946042.1627653228-978074735.1627653228

Crimmins, A., Balbus, J., Gamble, J. L., Beard, C. B., Bell, J. E., Dodgen, D., Eisen, R. J, Fann, N., Hawkins, M. D., Herring, S. C., Jantarasami, L., Mills, D. M., Saha, S., Sarofim, M. C., Trtanj, J., & Ziska, L. (Eds.). *The impacts of climate change on human health in the United States: A scientific assessment.* U.S. Global Change Research Program 2016. http://dx.doi.org/10.7930/J0R49NQX

Dieleman, J. L., Cao, J., Chapin, A., Chen, C., Li, Z., Liu, A., Horst, C., Kaldjian, A., Matyasz, T., Woody Scott, K., Bui, A. L., Campbell, M., Duber, H. C., Dunn, A. C., Flaxman, A. D., Fitzmaurice, C., Naghavi, M., Sadat, N., Shieh, P., Squires, E. ... Murray, C. J. L. (2020). US health care spending by payer and health condition, 1996–2016. *JAMA, 323*(9), 863–884. https://doi.org/10.1001/jama.2020.0734

Flaherty, E. G., Thompson, R., Litrownik, A. J., Theodore, A., English, D. J., Black, M. M., Wike, T., Whimper, L., Runyan, D. K., & Dubowitz, H. (2006). Effect of early childhood adversity on child health. *Archives of Pediatrics and Adolescent Medicine, 160*(12), 1232–1238. https://doi.org/10.1001/archpedi.160.12.1232

Galea, S., & Abdalla, S. M. (2020). COVID-19 pandemic, unemployment, and civil unrest: Underlying deep racial and socioeconomic divides. *JAMA, 324*(3), 227–228. https://doi.org/10.1001/jama.2020.11132

Ginwright, S. (2016). *Hope and healing in urban education: How urban activists and teachers are reclaiming matters of the heart.* Routledge/Taylor & Francis Group.

Hill, J. H., & Round, J. L. (2021). SnapShot: Microbiota effects on host physiology. *Cell, 184*(10), 2796–2796. e1. https://doi.org/10.1016/j.cell.2021.04.026

Horesh, D., & Brown, A. D. (2020). Traumatic stress in the age of COVID-19: A call to close critical gaps and adapt to new realities. *Psychological Trauma: Theory, Research, Practice, and Policy, 12*(4), 331–335. http://dx.doi.org/10.1037/tra0000592

Ivey, A. E. (1991). *Developmental strategies for helpers: Individual, family, and network interventions.* Books/Cole.

Mayer, E. (2018). *The mind-gut connection: How the hidden conversation within our bodies impacts our mood, our choices, and our overall health.* Harper Wave.

Mayer, E. (2021). *The Gut-immune connection: How understanding the connection between food and immunity can help us regain our health.* Harper Wave.

Myers, J. (1992). Wellness, prevention, development: The cornerstone of the profession. *Journal of Counseling and Development, 71*(2), 136–139. https://doi.org/10.1002/j.1556-6676.1992.tb02188.x

Perlis, R. H., Ognyanova, K., Santillana, M., Baum, M. A., Lazer, D., Druckman, J., & Volpe, J. D. (2021). Association of acute symptoms of COVID-19 and symptoms of depression in Adults. *JAMA Network Open, 4*(3), e213223. https://doi.org/10.1001/jamanetworkopen.2021.3223

Royal Botanic Gardens Kew. (2020). *State of the world's plants and fungi.* Retrieved July 30, 2021, from https://www.kew.org/science/state-of-the-worlds-plants-and-fungi

Shonkoff, J., P., Garner, A. S., the Committee on Psychosocial Aspects of Child and Family Health, Committee on Early Childhood, Adoption, and Dependent Care, & Section on Developmental and Behavioral Pediatrics. (2012). The lifelong effects of early childhood adversity and toxic stress. *The American Academy of Pediatrics, 129*(1), e232–e246. https://doi.org/10.1542/peds.2011-2663

Sender, R., Fuchs, S., & Milo, R. (2017). Revised estimates for the number of human and bacterial cells in the body. *bioRxiv.* https://doi.org/10.1371/journal.pbio.1002533

U.S. Global Change Research Program (2016). The impacts of climate change on human health in the Unied States: A scientific assessment. https://health2016.globalchange.gov/

Van Hesteren, F., & Ivey, A. E. (1990). Counseling and development: Toward a new identity for a profession in transition. *Journal of Counseling and Development, 68*(5), 524–528.

Zhou, X., Josey, K., Kamareddine, L., Caine, M. C., Liu, T., Mickley, L. J., Cooper, M., & Dominici, F. (2021). Excess of COVID-19 cases and deaths due to fine particulate matter exposure during the 2020 wildfires in the United States. *Sciences Advances, 7*(33), 1–11. https://doi.org/10.1126/sciadv.abi8789

Figure Credits

Fig. 2.1: 1) Generated with Visme. Copyright © by Easy WebContent, Inc. 2) Adapted from Jack P. Shonkoff and Andrew S. Garner, "The Lifelong Effects of Early Childhood Adversity and Toxic Stress," *The American Academy of Pediatrics*, vol. 129, no. 1. Copyright © 2012 by American Academy of Pediatrics.

Fig. 2.2: 1) Generated with Visme. Copyright © by Easy WebContent, Inc. 2) Adapted from Source: https://www.cdc.gov/violenceprevention/about/social-ecologicalmodel.html.

PART II

Neurobiology of Stress and the Human Microbiome

CHAPTER THREE

Human Suffering

The key points addressed in this chapter are

- the diseases, injuries, and risk factors at a global scale

- three distinct stress responses

- the effects of stress related to epigenetic programming from a developmental perspective

- stress reactivity and sensitivity to context

The Global Burden of Diseases and Risk Factors

Have you heard about the Global Burden of Diseases, Injuries, and Risk Factors Study (GBD)? The GBD study is assessing global health by systematically conducting a scientific assessment of data on incidence, prevalence, and mortality for a mutually exclusive and collectively exhaustive list of diseases, injuries, and risk factors globally. In this context, *incidence of diseases and injuries* signifies the occurrence of such diseases and injuries at a global scale. *Prevalence* is information regarding the proportion of a global population who has a disease or injury in a given time period. Finally, *mortality* in the context of the study refers to death due to the diseases or injuries of investigation. The assessment data are pulled from numerous sources: censuses, household surveys, civil registration and vital statistics, disease registries, health service use, air pollution monitors, satellite imaging, disease notifications, and other sources (GBD 2019 Diseases and Injuries Collaborator, 2020). Excluding the COVID-19 pandemic, the GBD 2019 provides assessment of epidemiological data on the list of diseases and injuries for 204 countries and territories from 1990 to 2019. Therefore, this assessment is indicative of information on the global trends of major causality of burden at a global level, as well as regionally, and by country or territory, for the aforementioned period of time.

According to the GBD 2019 study, the health of the global population is steadily improving (GBD 2019 Diseases and Injuries Collaborator, 2020). As an example, life expectancy at birth globally increased to 73.5 years in 2019 from 67.2 years in 2000. Despite this increasing global health, the GBD also reminds us that health depends not only on health systems but also on varying factors, such as social determinants: average income per capita, education attainment, access to resources (e.g., health insurance), and total fertility rates (GBD 2019 Diseases and Injuries Collaborator, 2020). Furthermore, one may question if the current COVID-19 pandemic may have reinforced the divide between those who have access to health care and those who do not, albeit the most recent GBD study had been conducted prior to the pandemic.

Relevant to the GBD study, it is critical to address our experience related to the burden of diseases. Therefore, readers should consider the following question: What is human suffering? Before we explore the topic of human suffering in depth, let's take a moment to think about human health and well-being, and how human suffering relates to these areas. The World Health Organization (WHO, 2004) conceptualizes *human health* as states of absence and presence. Albeit it is frequently used to mean "the absence of disease or disability" it is also used to describe "a state of fitness and ability" (WHO, 2004, p. 16). Consistent with this, mental health does not imply an absence of illness. The WHO (2004) defines *mental health* as "a state of well-being in which the individual realizes his or her own abilities, can cope with the normal stresses of life, can work productively and fruitfully, and is able to make a contribution to his or her community" (p. 12). Similarly, *well-being* is regarded as a positive concept in a 2018 report (Patel et al., 2018) from *The Lancet* commission on global mental health and sustainable development that incorporates subjective satisfaction with life and positive affect or mood, and meaningful functioning and human development. In contrast, the same source defines *mental disorders* as "disturbances of thought, emotion, behavior, and relationships with others that lead to substantial suffering and functional impairment in one or more life activities" (Patel et al., 2018, p. 1562). As you see in this definition, many individuals with a mental disorder suffer from the mental state associated with the disorder and its related consequences and conditions at varying levels. Next, it becomes critical to address the relationship between mental health and mental illness, known to refer to a collective term of mental disorders.

A course on Food and Mood offered in 2020 by Deakin University in Australia stated that mental health and mental illness exist on a continuum, ranging from normal functioning of being and active participation in life, to severe distress and disability involving a functional impairment in life. It is critical to understand that a relationship between the two must not be seen as linear. Rather, it is a dynamic process constantly influenced by numerous factors, such as social interactions and relationships; physical health; lifestyle factors; stress levels; individual, collective, and intergenerational determinants; cultural resources; personal traits; physical environmental factors; microbial ecosystems in and outside the human body; climate change, and so on. As these two states of mental illness and mental health are positioned on a continuum through this dynamic process, a client with symptoms of a mental disorder (e.g., somatic manifestations of anxiety or sleep disturbance) can still enjoy a certain degree of their mental state in line with their expectations of being content with some domains of their life and achieving their potential to be a productive community member.

Human Health and the Global Burden of Diseases

Although the GBD revealed a pattern of stable or gradually changing rates of mortality and disability in most diseases from 1990 through 2009, some noticeable exceptions to these trends are noteworthy. As an example, rates of death due to substance use disorders have increased sharply over the past decade (GBD 2019 Diseases and Injuries Collaborator, 2020). Furthermore, the increase of metabolic risks seems concerning, in particular high fasting plasma glucose (FPG) and high body mass index (BMI; GBD 2019 Diseases and Injuries Collaborator, 2020). Metabolic disorders stem from varying reasons, including malnutrition, or from excesses, deficiencies, or imbalances in specific nutrients (Nobs et al., 2020). Closely related disorders, metabolic syndrome, or cardiometabolic disease are a group of disorders including the following: obesity, glucose intolerance, adult-onset diabetes mellitus, hypercholesterolemia, non-alcoholic fatty liver disease, and hypertension (Nobs et al., 2020). Figure 3.1 shows global attributable deaths for females and males in 2019 for the 20 risk factors in hierarchy (GBD 2019 Risk Factors Collaborators, 2020).

Specifically, for females, the highest five risks for attributable deaths included high systolic blood pressure (SBP; 5.25 million deaths or 20.3% of all female deaths in 2019), dietary risks (3.48 million deaths or 13.5% of all female deaths in 2019), high FPG (3.09 million deaths or 11.9% of all female deaths in 2019), air pollution (2.92 million deaths or 11.3% of all female deaths in 2019), and high BMI (2.54 million deaths or 9.8% of all female deaths in 2019). By contrast, for males, the top five risk factors were tobacco (smoked, second-hand, and chewing; 6.56 million deaths or 21.4% of all male deaths in 2019), high SBP (5.6 million deaths or 18.2% of all male deaths in 2019), dietary risks (4.47 million deaths or 14.6% of all male deaths in 2019), air pollution (3.75 million deaths or 12.2% of all male deaths in 2019), and high FPG (3.14 million deaths or 11.1% of all male deaths in 2019).

In addition, there has been a noticeable shift towards a larger proportion of burden due to years lived with disability (YLDs) from non-communicable diseases (NCDs) and injuries (GBD 2019 Diseases and Injuries Collaborator, 2020), including cardiometabolic disease, allergic diseases, and mental disorders. In the following section, major topic areas of how some of lifestyle factors (e.g., diet) relate to human health and disease will be covered in detail. It will be effective for helping professionals to understand these areas to help enhance their clinical competencies, with focus given to holistic approaches to counseling, and prevention actions and practices.

Firth and colleagues (2019) suggested that lifestyle factors, such as use of substances, diet, physical activity, stress, and sleep, can affect the development and persistence of numerous states of mental health across socio-ecological and cultural settings. Similarly, findings from the GBD Study 2017 demand our increased attention. For example, risk factors related to diet, such as high sodium intake, low intake of whole grains, and low intake of fruits, contributed to 11 million deaths at a global scale. Moreover, it is important to highlight that those dietary risks affected people regardless of age, gender, and their place of residence.

The United States is also subject to this global health issue. For instance, dietary risk factors were identified as the third-leading factor facilitating the most deaths and disabilities combined in the United States in 2017, followed by only high BMI and tobacco use (GBD 2017 Collaborators, 2019). Additionally, according to the 2020–2025 Dietary Guidelines for Americans (DGA; U.S. Department of Agriculture and U.S. Department of Health and Human Services, 2020), approximately 74% of adults living in the United States are overweight or have obesity.

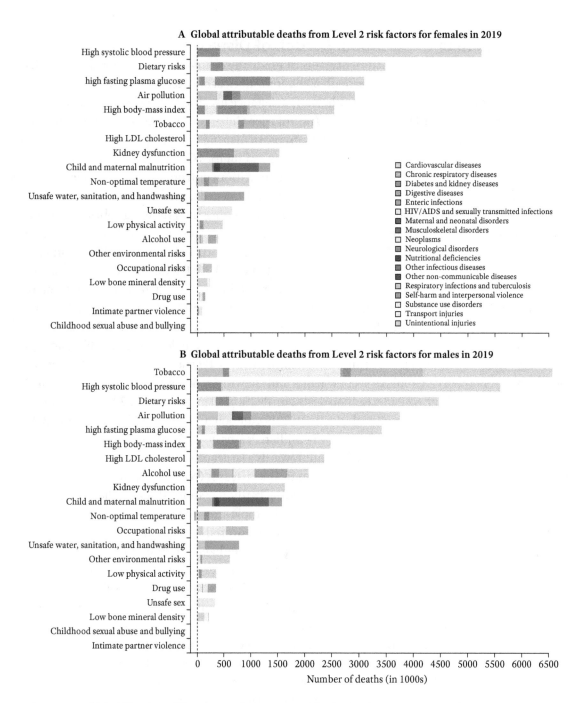

FIGURE 3.1   Global Number of Deaths and Percentage of DALYs Attributable to Level 2 Risk Factors, by Cause and Sex, 2019

Note. DALYs = disability-adjusted life-years.

In a similar vein, about 40% of children and adolescents are either overweight or have obesity. However, it is imperative for helping professionals to consider a variety of potential avenues for this increasing national epidemic from a public health rather than an individual heath viewpoint.

Stress Taxonomy

"Early experiences and environmental influences can leave a lasting signature on the genetic predispositions that affect emerging brain architecture and long-term health."

Shonkoff et al. (2012, p. e232)

"Exposure to stress during neurodevelopment has an effect on the quality of physical and mental health."

Murgatroyd et al. (2009, p. 1559)

The neurobiology of stress was addressed in Chapter 1 of this textbook. It is imperative for helping professionals to deepen their understanding of stress, because its immediate and long-lasting effects are inevitable when we address our development across the lifespan. Varying influential factors play a role in stress reactivity, including genetic variability, experiences early in life, physical and social environment, and introspective sensitivity (Barrientos et al., 2020; Shonkoff et al., 2012). One way to describe *stress reactivity* in the context of this book is one's capacity to respond to life stressors.

In addition, fetal exposure to maternal stress during the prenatal period can influence later stress responsiveness (Shonkoff et al., 2012). For instance, in an animal study, research has demonstrated that this effect on stress responsiveness in the offspring of the studied pregnancy is likely related to epigenetic modifications of DNA.

Physiological Responses to Stress

As addressed in Chapter 1 of this book, the stress response in the human body involves several systems collaborating with one another. Among those systems, activation of the HPA axis and the SAM system has been studied extensively. In a brief review, this activation leads to increased levels of stress mediators, such as neuroendocrine chemicals (i.e., corticotropin-releasing hormone [CRH], cortisol, norepinephrine, and epinephrine).

These physiological changes happen concurrently with the activation of other systems, such as the immune system, the gastrointestinal barrier, and the parasympathetic nervous system (PNS), which counterbalances both inflammation responses and sympathetic activation (Shonkoff et al., 2012). Functionally, an acute stress response to a stimulus (e.g., change in a work setting) is necessary for human survival. Thus, a stress response itself is protective and essential for healthy human functioning. However, excessively high levels of stress hormones at a given time or chronic exposure to stressors can be detrimental because they can result in not only immediate but also long-lasting troublesome consequences, including developmental disruptions. Thus, the dysregulation of stress response systems can cause a chronic wear and tear effect on numerous tissues, organs, and organ systems in the human body, and this can lead to a variety of attributable health conditions (Shonkoff et al., 2012).

Similarly, *allostasis* is the term used to refer to "the adaptive processes that maintain homeostasis through the production of mediators such as adrenalin, cortisol, and other chemical messengers" (McEwen, 2005, p. 315). In the article entitled "Stressed or Stressed Out: What Is the Difference?" Bruce McEwen addresses a conceptual framework that helps us better understand the wisdom of the human body related to the stress response. This term, in particular, attempts to clarify the ambiguity of stress. The work of stress mediators in the human body is critical because it helps the human body make an efficient adaptation to challenges in life. Through the adaptive processes, the human body responds efficiently to such challenges, also called stressors, that cause acute stress. Not surprisingly, these adaptive processes employ a systemic approach coordinating varying organs and organ systems to promote homeostasis in human functioning (McEwen, 2005). Such processes for coping and returning to homeostasis have been described using the term *allostatic load* (McEwen, 2005).

A Conceptual Taxonomy of Stress Responses

The National Scientific Council on the Developing Child at Harvard University has proposed a conceptual taxonomy of stress responses (see Figure 3.2) with focus given particularly to young children. This comprises three distinct types of stress responses in contrast to the actual stressors themselves that involve positive, tolerable, and toxic responses. These distinct types are centered around "the basis of postulated differences in their potential to cause enduring physiological disruptions as a result of the intensity and duration of the response" (Shonkoff et al., 2012, p. e235).

In detail, a *positive stress response* results from an experience that leads to activation of stress response systems and is a physiological state that is brief, and mild-to-moderate in magnitude. Importantly, in this case, an adult who provides a protective effect can help a child cope with the transient stressor and return efficiently to baseline in a homeostatic state. An example of the positive stress response includes a child who is getting a COVID-19 vaccination in the presence of their supportive caregiver. In contrast, a *tolerable stress response* results from an unusual experience, such as the death of a family member. This can lead to a greater intensity of activation of the stress response systems. However, the child can cope with such stress if a caring, protective adult who can help mediate the effect of the stress is available. In contrast, *toxic stress* results from the greatest magnitude of activation of stress response systems, either frequently, or in a chronic manner, or both, in the absence of the counterbalancing protection of a supportive adult. Examples may include child neglect or maltreatment.

Similarly, adversity causing toxic stress responses can result in developmental disruption in the formation and function of networks of nerve cells and other metabolic systems during sensitive developmental periods (Shonkoff et al., 2012). Such disruption may result in anatomical changes and/or physiological dysregulations. These changes typically precede later impairments

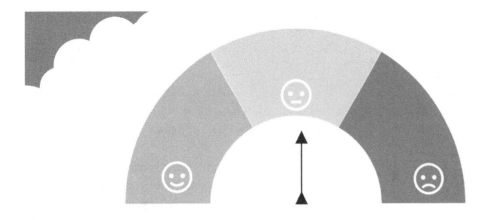

Positive Stress	- A physiological state that is brief and mild to moderate in magnitude - A caring, responsive adult is available who helps the child cope with stressors and provides a protective effect that facilitates the return to baseline state	
Tolerable Stress	- Exposure to non-normative experiences that present a greater magnitude of adversity or threat	
Toxic Stress	- Strong, frequent, or prolonged activation of the body's stress response systems in the absence of the buffering protection of a supportive, adult relationship	

FIGURE 3.2   Conceptual Taxonomy of Stress Responses

in learning and behavior (Shonkoff et al., 2012). Furthermore, children with such developmental disruptions are vulnerable for chronic, stress-related, physical and mental illness later in adulthood (Shonkoff et al., 2012).

Epigenetic Influences of Stress

"DNA methylation is one of the most intensely studied epigenetic mechanisms, and recent work has suggested that this form of gene regulation may determine risk for psychiatric disorders."

Murgatroyd et al. (2009, p. 1559)

Early experiences in adversity after birth can affect future stress reactivity. For instance, in animal studies, stress induced by infant-mother separation during early postnatal life in rodents has resulted in persistent hyperactivity of the HPA axis (Murgatroyd et al., 2009). Similarly, in another animal study, Tania Roth and colleagues demonstrated that maternal maltreatment early in life has an enduring signature on the DNA methylation of brain-derived neurotrophic factor (BDNF) in rodents that caused altered BDNF gene expression throughout the lifespan to adulthood (Roth et al., 2009). This effect has led to reduced BDNF gene expression in the adult prefrontal cortex (Roth et al., 2009).

In this study, the researchers created a maternal maltreatment by exposing rat pups to either an abusive mother with distress or a nurturing mother for 30 minutes daily during the first 7 weeks after birth. The condition of abusive mother rats was created by limiting resources for nesting in an unfamiliar environment. Cruelly, rat pups within the maternal maltreatment condition received a great deal of abusive maternal behaviors, such as being frequently stepped on, dropped during transportation, being dragged, actively rejected, and coercively handled. In contrast, nurturing mother rats were provided with ample nesting resources in a family environment. The counterpart rat pups to rat pups with maltreatment were exposed to those nurturing mothers 30 minutes daily during the same period of time.

In addition, these researchers explored the endurance of maternal abusive behavior and stress-induced DNA methylation across a generation. The rats that experienced maternal abuse growing up mistreated their own rat pups. In addition, their offspring also had noticeable DNA methylation. In summary, it is suggested that the stress-induced sustainable changes in BDNF DNA methylation early in life can perpetuate within the individual across its lifespan, and that the altered DNA methylation can pass from one generation to the next (Roth et al., 2009). Alongside previous studies, findings from this study suggest that adverse experiences in early life can lead to persistent epigenetic programming on specific genes, and this may result in later susceptibility to dysfunction in behavior (Murgatroyd et al., 2009).

The Orchid and Dandelion: Stress Reactivity and Susceptibility

> "Certain children are usually susceptible to the nature of their social, interpersonal environment."
>
> *Boyce (2019, p. 60)*

The previous section described that in response to a stressor, young children have different stress responses. These responses involve the activation of a coordinated network of stress response systems in the body. The neuroendocrine chemicals are orchestrated depending on the magnitude, frequency, and duration of a stressor. Here you may raise a question: Do children react to a stressor the same way as do their peers? Or are there individual biological differences in stress reactivity to a stressor? Let's imagine two 12-year-old children receiving a vaccine for COVID-19. The two might have drastically different reactions to this seemingly stressful experience. But why?

In his book, titled *The Orchid and the Dandelion: Why Some Children Struggle and How All Can Thrive*, W. Thomas Boyce, a pediatrician, addresses individual differences in *stress sensitivity* and *stress susceptibility* to context in children (Boyce, 2019). Specifically, he and his colleagues conducted an experimental, longitudinal study that involved more than 450 4-to-8-year-old children from four separate projects in four different cities; two samples of children from his own laboratory recruited in San Francisco and Berkeley, one sample from the long-term study of child development led by Marily Essex at the University of Wisconsin for the Wisconsin Study of Families and Work, and a sample studied by Jerome Kagan at Harvard University. In order for the researchers to assess stress reactivity to a specific regimen set and its associated manifestations, eardrum temperatures in the children were recorded repeatedly in both ears using infrared thermometers. In addition, brainwaves were also measured using electroencephalogram (EEG) in the children. All of these studies provided a way of differentiating children who show biological and behavioral patterns suggestive of the phenotype of sensitivity to environmental, conditional, and social-relational cues in the context.

As a result, differences in temperature between the left and right eardrums were recorded and distributed in a bell-shaped curve, implying that these individual differences were normally distributed (Boyce, 2019). Additionally, some children in the experiment who had warmer left eardrums were associated with the characteristics of being more risk-taking and sociable, as compared to those with warmer right eardrums, who were associated with the observation of seemingly emotionally negative behaviors. The findings from this study suggested that children with warmer right eardrums tended to be sensitive to the social environment, had a tendency to negative emotion, and showed vulnerability to depression. By contrast, children with warmer left eardrums were, to some degree, less sensitive to the surrounding social world, were prone to positive emotion, and manifested relative resistance to depression.

Furthermore, children with warmer right ears were associated with the increased activation in the right brain. W. Thomas Boyce (2019, p. 66) notes, "The right prefrontal cortex is more attuned than the left to emotion regulation, to understanding the importance of contextual and relational aspects of experience." It is known that the autonomic system in the body controls blood flow to the brain for healthy functioning. He explains in his book that when blood flow to one side of the brain is increased, flow to other parts of the brain on the same side is proportionally decreased. Relatively, activation of the right prefrontal cortex involves diminishing flow to the skin, and therefore, it results in a cooling of the same arteries that supply the eardrum. Consequently, this means that a rise in blood flow to the right prefrontal cortex results in a parallel enhancement in flow to the right eardrum. In summary, right prefrontal activation leads to an increase in right ear temperatures, and a parallel decrease in the skin temperature of the same side of the head.

These individual differences in stress reactivity in children to contextual, environmental, and social cues can indicate that stress reactivity is not a unitary process, and it involves individual differences, as also described earlier in this chapter. However, the effects of high stress reactivity on psychological outcomes are known to be multifaceted from a phenotypic perspective. In a similar vein, increased stress reactivity may be reflective of an increased biological sensitivity to context (Boyce, 2019). This may involve potential negative effects in health under certain conditions, such as adversity in life, resulting in toxic stress responses, particularly early in childhood

(Boyce, 2019). Similarly, individual differences in stress reactivity are known to have an impact on the executive functions, such as attention control, decision making, and introspective systems in our bodies (Barrientos et al., 2020). *Introspection*, described as the necessary ability to "access and report one's own mental content" (Barrientos et al., 2020, p. 1), and its sensitivity are related to stress reactivity. Therefore, individuals differ in their abilities to monitor their own mental processes, and this is closely associated with individual differences in stress reactivity.

By contrast, this may also be associated with potential positive effects under certain conditions, such as predictable, consistent, timely support and protection (Boyce, 2019). Also, stress reactivity related to health may suggest that children with highly reactive phenotypes may have heightened biological sensitivity to context (Boyce, 2019). Extensive research has documented that *developmental trauma* (adversity causing developmental disruptions in development) experienced early in life has a potential to predispose an individual toward biological reactivity. Similarly, in recent years, it has been suggested in the research community that the association between adversity early in life and stress reactivity is curvilinear in character, meaning that both highly stressful and highly protective social and physical environments are likely to lead to disproportionate numbers of highly reactive children (Ellis et al., 2011). From the findings of these research studies, it is imperative for helping professionals to address the significance of "good enough" physical and social environments in development and how they align with individual biological differences in stress susceptibility.

Summary

The GBD study has been conducted using a systematic process to assess incidence, prevalence, and mortality for diseases, injuries, and risk factors at a global level. Particularly, the GBD 2019 study (GBD 2019 Diseases and Injuries Collaborator, 2020) provides the most recent assessment of epidemiological data on the aforementioned areas for 204 countries and territories from 1990 to 2019. The results of this study remind us that health depends on a variety of factors, such as social determinants. Despite the increasing global health, including an increase in life expectancy at birth to 73.5 years in 2019 from 67.2 years in 2000, some discernible exceptions to the trends of a pattern of stable or slowly changing rates of death and disability were recorded (GBD 2019 Diseases and Injuries Collaborator, 2020). Some examples include the increase of substance use disorders and increasing metabolic risks (GBD 2019 Diseases and Injuries Collaborator, 2020).

In a similar vein, there have been global changes in lifestyle factors, such as use of substances, diet, physical activity, stress, and sleep (Firth et al., 2019). Specifically, dietary risk factors (e.g., high sodium intake, low whole grains intake, etc.) have been associated with 11 million deaths at a global scale. The United States is not immune to this global health issue. Furthermore, as stress is one lifestyle factor, it is important for helping professionals to deepen their understanding of the effects of stress on our development, health, and disease. One strategy can be to increase an understanding of conceptualizing stress responses using a scientifically supported framework, such as the taxonomy of stress responses proposed by the National Scientific Council on the Developing

Child at Harvard University. This framework addresses the three distinct types of stress responses in response to an acute stress—positive, tolerable, and toxic responses (Shonkoff et al., 2012).

As opposed to both the positive and tolerable stress responses, a toxic stress response can result in developmental disruptions that lead to an altered developmental trajectory. Such disruptions may result in anatomical changes in brain development, physiological dysregulations, and subsequently, later impairments in learning and behavior (Shonkoff et al., 2013). As a result, children with these developmental disruptions are vulnerable to stress-related physical and mental illness later in adulthood (Shonkoff et al., 2012).

Similarly, early experiences in trauma after birth can affect future stress reactivity through persistent hyperactivity of the HPA axis (Murgatroyd et al., 2009). In addition, stress-induced sustainable changes in BDNF DNA methylation early in life can persist within the individual across its lifespan, and this epigenetic programming may pass from one generation to the next (Roth et al., 2009).

However, extensive research has unraveled that stress reactivity in children to contextual, environmental, and social signals is not a unitary process, and individuals differ in stress reactivity influenced by varying factors (Boyce, 2019). Also, these individual differences in stress reactivity are known to have an impact on the executive functions (e.g., attention control, decision making, and introspection; Barrientos et al., 2020).

Experiential Questions

1. Using the concept of the stress taxonomy addressed in the chapter, what stressors may cause different stress responses by A?

2. Considering epigenetic influences of stress addressed in the chapter, what in A's social environment could potentially change to help prevent the negative consequences of toxic stress they might be facing?

3. Given the information regarding A and their family history from the case study, how would you describe the level of their reactivity and susceptibility to life stressors in general?

References

Barrientos, M., Tapia, L., Silva, J. R., & Reyes, G. (2020). Biological stress reactivity and introspective sensitivity: An exploratory study. *Frontiers in Psychology, 11*(543), 1–8. https://doi.org/10.3389/fpsyg.2020.00543

Boyce, W. T. (2019). *The orchid and the dandelion: Why some children struggle and how all can thrive.* Knopf.

Ellis, B., Shirtcliff, E., Boyce, W., Deardorff, J., & Essex, M. (2011). Quality of early family relationships and the timing and tempo of puberty: Effects depend on biological sensitivity to context. *Development and Psychopathology, 23*(1), 85–99. https://doi.org/10.1017/S0954579410000660

Firth, J., Ward, P. B., & Stubbs, B. (2019). Editorial: Lifestyle psychiatry. *Psychiatry, 10*, 597. https://doi.org/10.3389/fpsyt.2019.00597

GBD 2017 Collaborators. (2019). Health effects of dietary risks in 195 countries, 1990–2017: A systematic analysis for the Global Burden of Disease Study. *The Lancet, 393,* 1958–1972. http://dx.doi.org/10.1016/S0140-6736(19)30041-8

GBD 2019 Risk Factors Collaborators. (2020). Global burden of 87 risk factors in 204 countries and territories, 1990–2019: A systematic analysis for the Global Burden of Disease Study 2019. *The Lancet, 396*(10258), 1223–1249. https://doi.org/10.1016/S0140-6736(20)30752-2

GBD 2019 Risk Factors Collaborators (2019). Global burden of 369 diseases and injuries in 204 countries and territories, 1990–2019: A systematic analysis for the Global Burden of Disease Study 2019. *The Lancet, 396*(10258), 1204–1222. https://doi.org/10.1016/S0140-6736(20)30925-9

McEwen, B. S. (2005). Stressed or stressed out: What is the difference? *Journal of Psychiatry Neuroscience, 30*(5), 315–318.

Murgatroyd, C., Patchev, A. V., Wu, Y., Micale, V., Bockmühl, Y., Fischer, D., Holsboer, F., Wotjak, C. T., Almeida, O. F. X., & Spengler, D. (2009). Dynamic DNA methylation programs persistent adverse effects of early-life stress. *Nature Neuroscience, 12*(12), 1559–1566. https://doi.org/10.1038/nn.2436

Nobs, S. P., Zmora, N., & Elinav, E. (2020). Nutrition regulates innate immunity in health and disease. *Annual Review of Nutrition, 40,* 189–219. https://doi.org/10.1146/annurev-nutr-120919-094440

Patel, V., Saxena, S., Lund, C., Thornicroft, G., Baingana, F., Bolton, P., Chisholm, D., Collins, P. Y., Cooper, J. L., Eaton, J., Herrman, H., Herzallah, M. M., Huang, Y., Jordans, M. J. D., Kleinman, A., Medina-Mora, M. E., Morgan, E., Niaz, U., Omigbodun, O., Prince, M., … UnÜtzer, J. (2018). The *Lancet* Commission on global mental health and sustainable development. *The Lancet, 392*(10157), 1553–1598. https://doi.org/10.1016/S0140-6736(18)31612-X

Reichelt, A. C., & Rank, M. M. (2017). The impact of junk foods on the adolescence brain. *Birth Defects Research, 109*(20), 1649–1658. https://doi.org/10.1002/bdr2.1173

Roth, T. L, Lubin, F. D., Funk, A. J., & Sweatt. J. D. (2009). Lasting epigenetic influence of early-life adversity on the *BDNF* gene. *Biological Psychiatry, 65*(9), 760–769. https://doi.org/10.1016/j.biopsych.2008.11.028

Shonkoff, J., P., Garner, A. S., the Committee on Psychosocial Aspects of Child and Family Health, Committee on Early Childhood, Adoption, and Dependent Care, & Section on Developmental and Behavioral Pediatrics. (2012). The lifelong effects of early childhood adversity and toxic stress. *The American Academy of Pediatrics, 129*(1), e232–e246. https://doi.org/10.1542/peds.2011-2663

U.S. Department of Agriculture & U.S. Department of Health and Human Services. (2020). *Dietary guidelines for Americans, 2020–2025* (9th ed.). https://www.dietaryguidelines.gov/resources/2020-2025-dietary-guidelines-online-materials

World Health Organization. (2004). *Promoting mental health: Concepts, emerging evidence, and practice.* https://apps.who.int/iris/bitstream/handle/10665/42940/9241591595.pdf

Figure Credits

CHAPTER FOUR

Early Toxic Stress and Its Developmental Disruptions in Human Development

---

The key points addressed in this chapter are

- to better conceptualize trauma and understand its immediate and long-lasting effects on human development
- to address the impact of developmental trauma on varied domains of human development
- to note the likely synergistic effects of individual trauma, interpersonal trauma, and cultural trauma

---

Prior to the COVID-19 pandemic, trauma was identified as a public health problem in the United States that was widespread, prevalent, and costly related to mortality and morbidity (Substance Abuse and Mental Health Services Administration [SAMHSA], 2014). Trauma is a universal experience, as research suggests that over 70% of individuals globally experience a traumatic event at some point in their lives (Benjet et al., 2016). However, it is important to note that individuals, families, and communities that are minoritized and marginalized are at higher risk for exposure to trauma and socioeconomic constraints at a global level (Allwood et al., 2021).

In the United States, the general population experiences adversity in early childhood at an alarming rate (CDC, 2019; Felitti et al., 1998; Flaherty et al., 2009). It is also widespread specifically in people with health conditions, including mental health and substance use disorders. Furthermore, the impact of prolonged COVID-19 may have long-lasting effects that will result in a mental toll on individuals, families, minoritized communities, and at-risk populations. Given the chronic pandemic and its negative consequences (e.g., deepened health disparities and collective grief and loss), exposure to toxic stress or chronic stress in the U.S. population likely will continue to increase if appropriate and timely interventions are unavailable and inaccessible. When considering the synergistic impact of all these conditions, it is critical for helping professionals to approach trauma as an important component of effective human service delivery. Addressing trauma should also be a prerequisite for entry-level clinical training for such individuals, rather than a specialized training added to entry-level graduate clinical programs (Moh & Sperandio, 2022). Similarly, continuing education in trauma content and trauma training should also be available and accessible for helping professionals to continuously increase their competencies.

Trauma occurs as a result of numerous factors, such as social (e.g., violence, abuse, maltreatment, neglect, traumatic loss, attachment disruptions) and economic factors (e.g., financial disadvantages and a lack of health insurance coverage), environmental factors (e.g., natural and manmade disaster, food insecurity), and other emotionally or psychologically harmful experiences (e.g., systemic racism, antisemitism, homophobia, or xenophobia). In the initial landmark public health study known as the Adverse Childhood Experiences (ACE) study, 17,337 adults responded to a questionnaire designed to examine ACEs (i.e., childhood abuse, neglect, and home dysfunction) prior to the age of 18 (Felitti et al., 1998). ACEs are detrimental in human development because they cause the toxic stress that was introduced in detail in Chapter 3 of this book.

According to the findings from the ACE study, approximately 10.8% of the participants reported physical abuse, 22% sexual abuse, and 11% emotional abuse. Since this landmark study was conducted, subsequent mounting evidence has supported that the immediate and long-lasting effects of adversity experienced in childhood lead to an increase in the risks of injury, sexually transmitted infections, maternal and child health problems, teen pregnancy, involvement in sex trafficking, and a wide range of chronic diseases and leading risks for premature death, such as metabolic syndrome (e.g., cancer, diabetes, and cardiovascular disease) and suicide in later adulthood (CDC, 2019; Felitti et al., 1998; Shonkoff et al., 2012).

Tackling and preventing trauma should probably not be an individual issue, because it requires a multidisciplinary public health approach inclusive of public education, with accessible and available resources and awareness (SAMHSA, 2014). Furthermore, prevention at varying levels, early detection, and effective trauma-specific assessment and treatment are critical components of service delivery (SAMHSA, 2014). Moreover, it does not seem to be conducive to healing that the consequences and complications of trauma experience are seen from a deficit-oriented, pathological lens. Rather, trauma should require a perspective that promotes a healing-centered recovery as a process that is optimized in the community context. These efforts will certainly seek an interprofessional and collaborative interplay whose processes embrace trauma-informed, healing-centered, culturally responsive, relational practices and actions.

Conceptualizing Trauma

Trauma has been conceptualized in varying ways, and this concept has evolved over time through decades of work in multiple disciplines. The concept of traumatic stress emerged in the field of mental health five decades ago (SAMHSA, 2014). This concept is similar in conceptualization to the toxic stress presented in the previous chapter of this book. In the process of defining trauma in mental health, the American Psychiatric Association (APA) also contributed to it to some degree, although it does not seem to fully address the complexity of effects of social and systemic factors or the synergistic effects of such factors at play when conceptualizing trauma. The definition of trauma itself and diagnostic criteria for stress-related and traumatic stress-related disorders have undergone several iterations for the *Diagnostic and Statistical Manual of Mental Disorders* (DSM; SAMHSA, 2014).

Concurrently, as neuroscience has advanced, a biopsychosocial and lifestyle approach to traumatic experiences has initiated to delineate the dynamic mechanisms in which neurobiological, psychological, neurophysiological, and neuro-immunological processes interact with social factors (e.g., social attachment) and contribute to mental and substance use disorders across the lifespan (SAMHSA, 2014). In recent years, with the advances of the human microbiome, the bidirectional dialogue between the gut and the brain has contributed to a more comprehensive perspective on traumatic experiences and their impact on human health and human disease. Additionally, an increased trauma survivor movement has also provided another perspective to promote a deeper understanding of experiences in trauma (SAMHSA, 2014).

According to SAMHSA (2014, p. 7), the concept of *trauma* is that "individual trauma results from an event, series of events, or set of circumstances that is experienced by an individual as physically or emotionally harmful or life threatening and that has lasting adverse effects on the individual's functioning and mental, physical, social, emotional, or spiritual well-being." One example to apply to this conceptualization of trauma is an event of the loss of normalcy in our contemporary lifestyles influenced by the current COVID-19 pandemic. As of May 27, 2022, the World Health Organization (https://covid19.who.int/) reported that 6,285,171 lives were lost globally due to the coronavirus, while there have been about 525 million confirmed cases of COVID-19.

In the midst of this global pandemic, a 14-day, mandatory self-quarantine was taking place in Seoul, Korea, at the time this chapter was first written. At the moment, I am halfway through, and the majority of my time has been spent in a tiny hotel room in the city where I am not allowed to leave the room for any reason except for a COVID-19 test required by the Korean government. My location is being monitored by a government officer through an app that has been downloaded on my personal cell phone. Additionally, the self-quarantine has meant I have lost precious time that could have been spent visiting my sick mother in a nursing facility in the city. This is despite my being a fully vaccinated individual. Whether or not these events are perceived as traumatic depends on how they are experienced. Furthermore, the immediate and potentially enduring effects of these experienced events may lead me to different ways of assigning meaning. Although I do not see the experience of these events as traumatic at this time, it is stressful. However, this experience might be a traumatic experience for others depending on the different aspects, circumstances, and internal and external stimuli that can synergically affect the experience.

Cultural Trauma

"Culture represents an unrecognized flexible resource for health that is foundational to human survival."

Subica and Link (2021, p. 3)

In contrast, *cultural trauma* is defined as "an overwhelming and often ongoing physical or psychological assault or stressor perpetuated by an oppressive dominant group on the culture of a group of people sharing a specific shared identity or affiliation (e.g., race/ethnicity, nationality, religion)" (Subica & Link, 2021, p. 2). This conceptualization of cultural trauma encompasses many collective and historical traumas in the way it defines these two concepts. In conceptualizing *collective trauma*, for instance, it addresses the psychological or emotional responses to a trauma event experienced and shared by a social group of individuals that becomes persistent in the group's collective traumatic memories (Hirschberger, 2018; Subica & Link, 2021). In a similar vein, *historical trauma* is conceptualized as the psychological, emotional, and social responses to a traumatic event inflicted on a group of people who share a social identity or affiliation that has been experienced collectively and passed down from one generation to another over time (Evans-Campbell, 2008; Subica & Link, 2021). However, the most recent conceptualization of cultural trauma is differentiated from the aforementioned conceptualizations of collective trauma and historical trauma in that it centers the focus on the impact of the traumatic event on a culture or cultural resources of a group, as opposed to their psychological or physical well-being (Subica & Link, 2021).

Toxic Stress Early in Life and Developmental Trauma

Toxic stress early in life and ACEs (e.g., child maltreatment and neglect) lead to varied consequences. Neurobiologically, it produces a cascade of events that have the potential to cause long-lasting, pervasive changes in neurocognitive development (Teicher et al., 2003). These changes take place on multiple levels, from neuroendocrine (e.g., HPA axis) to structural and functional to immunological to microbial levels. For instance, structurally, the major consequences of early toxic stress lead to a reduced size of the mid-portions of the corpus callosum and attenuated development of the left neocortex, hippocampus, and amygdala (Teicher et al., 2003).

Toxic stress experienced in childhood constitutes a public health crisis from a developmental perspective (Magruder et al., 2016; van der Kolk, 2005). Toxic stress occurring during the first months of life may be particularly influential for neurodevelopment (Hambrick et al., 2019). This is because the stress is experienced at a time when systems or networks in the brain are rapidly developing and organizing. The impact of the stress experienced during sensitive periods leads a child's genetic programming to interact substantially with the physical and social environment to begin determining the most adaptive phenotypic expression (epigenetic programming; Hunter, 2012; Yehuda & Lehrner, 2018). Specifically, the primary nature of a dynamic system is that human development occurs dynamically in response to its environment (Tronick & Hunter, 2016). Functionally, the pronounced consequences of early life stress include increased electrical activity in limbic structures and decreased functional activity of the cerebellar vermis, leading to alterations in the function of the stress response systems (Teicher et al., 2003).

However, the effects of toxic stress are not only detrimental in early childhood. They are also influential during fetal development in the womb. One example includes pioneering research supporting evidence that unborn babies can suffer trauma to their developing body when they are in the womb (Lyons et al., 2020). Also, it is acknowledged that trauma experienced in the parents can influence the function of the unborn baby's genetic programming through epigenetic mechanisms (Yehuda & Lehrner, 2018). As a review, the potentially heritable changes in the genetic programming described as epigenetics that are induced by environmental events can be transmissible from one generation to another. The transmission of the effects of parental trauma to their child is explicated in the concept of *intergenerational trauma*, which is "exposure to extremely adverse events that have the ability to impact individuals to a high degree so that their children find themselves dealing with their parents' post-traumatic state" (Yehuda & Lehrner, 2018, p. 243). Conceptually, intergenerational trauma is similar to historical trauma, although the former addresses individual-level effects of trauma while the latter places focus on a traumatic event inflicted on a group of people who share a social identity or affiliation.

In addition, postnatally, the impact of toxic stress early in childhood may vary depending on the timing and type of stress experiences on neurodevelopmental outcomes (e.g., multisensory integration, self-regulation, relational functioning, cognitive functioning, or emotional functioning (Hambrick et al., 2019). Research has suggested that toxic stress stemming from a lack of positive relational experiences (e.g., caregiver neglect or lack of caregiver attunement) during the first two months of life is associated with the multisensory integration and self-regulation (Hambrick et al., 2019).

As noted earlier in this chapter, trauma leads to disruptions in human development. Those developmental disruptions inflicted by trauma are conceptualized in the term developmental trauma. *Developmental trauma* is the term used to refer to "the impact of early, repeated trauma and loss which happens within the child's important relationships, and usually early in life" (Lyons et al., 2020, p. 5). However, it is important to note that the experience of developmental trauma does not alone definitely hijack a child's future (Hambrick et al., 2019). Other influential experiences (e.g., the presence of safety and support by available adults in the face of trauma or the developmental age at the time of traumatic experience) can help buffer the impact of the traumatic experience (Lyons et al., 2020). Bessel van der Kolk, a pioneer in the field of trauma, and his colleagues have conducted extensive research that shows us that trauma imprints on the child's development over time. Consequently, such children are at high risk for developing a variety of unhealthy coping strategies (Lyons et al., 2020). Equally important, the experience of trauma early in life can prevent the appropriate development of the essential executive functions (e.g., emotion regulation, behavioral regulation, cognitive development, decision making, impulse control, or social engagement) in children. Such individuals may not fully employ curiosity to explore potential in their lives. As a result, developmental trauma experienced can lead to a variety of long-lasting, developmental disruptions in numerous areas of our lives. Beacon House in the United Kingdom organized developmental trauma into the following seven areas: sensory development, dissociation, attachment development, emotion regulation, behavioral regulation, cognition, and the development of the sense of the self and identity development (Lyons et al., 2020). In the following section, a few selective areas will be delineated in detail in the interest of limited space in this textbook.

Attachment Ruptures

Mounting evidence has acknowledged that children learn to regulate their emotions and behaviors in repeated interactions and relationships with their caregiver by anticipating their caregivers' responses to them (van der Kolk, 2005). From extensive research by Patricia Crittenden, an American psychologist, it is known that the effects of early attachment patterns play a significant role in the quality of information processing throughout the lifespan (Crittenden, 1990; 1992). Similarly, research by Judith Schore and Allan Schore, a clinical social worker and an American neuropsychologist, respectively, indicates that a secure attachment of emotional communication between the infant and the primary caregiver is essential, particularly during the first year of life. This is because this attachment relationship is fundamental and functions as a mediator to the dyadic regulation of emotion wherein the primary caregiver co-regulates the infant's developing central nervous system and autonomic nervous system (Schore & Schore, 2008).

Specifically, if a child is feeling distressed and overwhelmed, the child is disadvantaged in ability to modulate their physiological state (e.g., arousal). This can disrupt their capacity to effectively process and subsequently integrate with other contextual information (e.g., what is occurring in their surrounding environment) at the cortex level (van der Kolk, 2005). If the distress is persistent or if help by the caregiver is unavailable to alleviate the immediate effect of the distress, the process in associating the relevant sensations, affects, and cognitions is disrupted in that child. Thus, this can potentially lead to dissociation into sensory fragmentation (van der Kolk & Fisler, 1995). When these processes are in place, the child is disadvantaged in comprehending what is happening and may be prevented from making appropriate plans of action in response to the demands in the surrounding environment.

In addition, pioneering research strongly supports the importance of quality of caregiver-child interaction in infancy and middle childhood (Lyons-Ruth et al., 2013). In this longitudinal study, 56 low-income families participated and were first observed when the offspring were in infancy to 18 months. Among those children, by age 18 months, 14% were being followed by state protective services for poor quality care. By adolescence, 48% reported by self-report that they had experienced sexual or physical abuse, while 7% reported experience of severe verbal abuse. Findings from this study suggest that developmental trauma (the severity of child abuse in this study) was highly associated with the degree of borderline symptoms (Lyons-Ruth et al., 2013). In addition, maternal withdrawal in infancy was also a significant predictor of borderline symptoms in adolescence. However, security of the infant's attachment did not suggest a significant relationship to predict borderline symptoms in adolescence. Specifically, maternal withdrawal to the infant's attachment cues of emotional communication was significantly related and had a predictive value of later outcomes in adolescence (Lyons-Ruth et al., 2013).

These findings provide us with important clinical implications that the quality of maternal caregiving in infancy may hold the key as compared to the assessment of infant behavior alone when predicting mental health in their children later in adolescence. Additionally, in the mediation model (Figure 4.1; Lyons-Ruth et al., 2013) in which maternal withdrawal was the independent variable while borderline symptoms in adolescence was the dependent variable, severity of abuse served as a mediator. Results suggested that experienced child abuse could not account for the independent effect of maternal withdrawal on borderline symptoms later in adolescence (Lyons-Ruth et al., 2013).

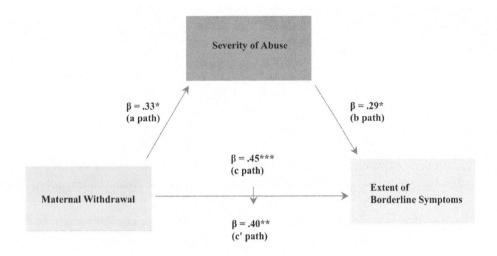

FIGURE 4.1   Severity of Abuse Does Not Mediate the Effect of Early Maternal Withdrawal on Later Borderline Symptoms

The results from the study strongly suggest the lack of quality child-caregiver interaction or attachment ruptures can result in significant consequences in the child from a developmental perspective. Specifically, maternal withdrawal is critical and can predict mental health problems in progeny, more so than child abuse itself.

Abandonment and Neglect in Childhood

> "Childhood trauma, including abuse and neglect, is probably the single most important public health challenge in the US, a challenge that has the potential to be largely resolved by appropriate prevention and intervention."
>
> *van der Kolk (2005, p. 401)*

According to the Child Maltreatment 2019 report, for the federal fiscal year 2019, a national estimate of 1,840 children died from abuse and neglect, or 2.50 per 100,000 children in the U.S. general population. In a similar vein, the national rounded number of children who received a child protective service investigation response or alternative response was estimated to be 3,476,000 for the same period of time. In the context of the report, an alternative response is the term used to refer to "the provision of a response other than an investigation that determines if a child or family needs services" (U.S. Department of Health & Human Services, Administration for Children and Families, Administration on Children, Youth and Families, Children's Bureau, 2021, p. 17). As mentioned earlier in this chapter, developmental trauma results from varied experiences, yet most trauma begins in close relationships or at home (van der Kolk, 2005). For instance, numerous children are exposed to *complex trauma*, described as "the experience of multiple, chronic and prolonged, developmental adverse traumatic events, most often of an interpersonal nature and early-life onset" (van der Kolk, 2005, p. 401). Complex trauma experience, such as chronic maltreatment in familiar relationships, has severe, long-lasting, developmental effects on the development of children who are exposed that negatively affect many different domains (e.g., social development, emotional development, cognitive development, or identity development) of their developmental trajectories.

In addition, complex trauma negatively affects neurobiological and neurophysiological development in children. Furthermore, developmental trauma lays the foundation for unfocused responses to subsequent stress responses (Hambrick et al., 2019). Thus, the impact of developmental trauma or complex trauma leads such developing children to dramatically increased use of medical, correctional, social, behavioral, and mental health services (Drossman et al., 1990). Moreover, physical and sexual assault experienced in childhood is associated with a variety of psychiatric diagnoses in adolescence and adulthood. Some examples include personality disorders (e.g., borderline and antisocial personality disorders); eating and feeding-related disorders; and cardiovascular, metabolic, and immunological disorders (van der Kolk, 2003).

Developmental Trauma Disorder

The impact of trauma experienced early in life is pervasive and developmental, affecting a broad range of domains of development and function, such as cognitive, language, motor, social, sensory, emotional, microbial, and immune development. The diagnosis of posttraumatic stress disorder (PTSD) does not adequately describe this impact on the developing child due to a lack of representation of developmental disruptions in development and functioning (van der Kolk, 2005; Perry, 2017). However, the current diagnostic classification systems (e.g., *DSM*) do not describe adequately these effects of trauma on child development. Consequently, many children who have undergone repeated trauma in childhood over time are given a range of comorbid diagnoses (Ford et al., 2018; van der Kolk, 2005; van der Kolk et al., 2019).

To resolve these identified concerns, the Complex Trauma Taskforce of the National Child Traumatic Stress Network has made efforts over time to more clearly and adequately delineate the developmental trauma experience and its long-lasing profiles (van der Kolk, 2005). These efforts guided developmentally adequate therapeutic approaches and helped to conceptualize a clinical framework called *developmental trauma disorder* (DTD) for the sequelae of complex trauma exposure (van der Kolk, 2005; Spinazzola et al., 2018). Also, DTD has been proposed as "an integrative framework for assessing and treating children's emotional, biological, cognitive, behavioral, interpersonal, and self/identity dysregulation in the wake of traumatic victimization and disrupted attachment" (Spinazzola et al., 2018, p. 631).

Specifically, the findings of a study were consistent with those of previous studies that the combination of interpersonal trauma and attachment adversity has a synergistic, enduring effect on child development across varying domains of psychosocial development (Spinazzola et al., 2018). In the context of this study, examples of *interpersonal trauma* included physical abuse or assault, sexual abuse or assault, family violence, and community violence. In addition, *attachment adversity* included "traumatic loss due to death of or prolonged separation from primary care-giver(s) or other primary support relationships, primary caregiver(s) impaired by behavioral health problems, emotional abuse, and severe neglect" (Spinazzola et al., 2018, p. 633). In the study, 236 children aged 7 to 18 years from varied ethnocultural backgrounds (50.4% White non-Hispanic, 29.3% Black, 16.9% Latino/Hispanic, and 3.4% Asian American) were recruited at sites in four geographic regions (i.e., Northeast, Mid-Atlantic, South, and Midwest) in the United States. The findings of the study suggest that DTD may be uniquely associated with pervasive exposure to violent environments and impaired caregiving, and that exposure to both interpersonal trauma and attachment adversity are associated mostly with DTD symptom presentation (Spinazzola et al., 2018). In the following section, a summary of the proposed DTD criteria will be addressed.

Proposed Developmental Trauma Disorder Diagnostic Criteria

Criterion A: Lifetime contemporaneous exposure to both types of developmental trauma
  A1: Traumatic interpersonal victimization
  A2: Traumatic disruption in attachment with primary caregiver(s)

Criterion B: Current emotion or somatic dysregulation (4 items; 3 required for DTD)
  B1: Emotion dysregulation
  B2: Somatic dysregulation
  B3: Impaired access to emotion or somatic feelings
  B4: Impaired verbal mediation of emotion or somatic feelings

Criterion C: Current attentional or behavioral dysregulation (5 items; 2 required for DTD)
  C1: Attention bias toward or away from threat
  C2: Impaired self-protection
  C3: Maladaptive self-soothing
  C4: Non-suicidal self-injury
  C5: Impaired ability to initiate or sustain goal-directed behavior
Criterion D: Current relational or self-dysregulation (6 items; 2 required for DTD)
  D1: Self-loathing or self-viewed as irreparably damaged and defective
  D2: Attachment insecurity and disorganization
  D3: Betrayal-based relational schemas
  D4: Reactive verbal or physical aggression
  D5: Impaired psychological boundaries
  D6: Impaired interpersonal empathy

Source. The DTD diagnostic criteria (Spinazzola et al., 2021, p. 712)

Notably, the manifestation of the impact of trauma tends to be multifaceted, particularly from a developmental perspective. In addition to the above profiles, children who undergo developmental trauma are at risk for developing mental and physical illnesses, and a variety of impulsive and self-harming thoughts and behaviors (van der Kolk, 2005). These risks may be worsened if those children do not receive intervention during a sensitive period in development. Moreover, such children are likely to adopt unhealthy lifestyles (e.g., early use of alcohol and other substances, unbalanced diet, or lack of regular physical exercise), which may increase vulnerability for developing negative health conditions later in adulthood.

Systemic Racism and Discrimination

> "From a clinical perspective, children with early life stress are challenging to treat because we often notice their impairments long after the impaired systems have moved past a time of dynamic change."
>
> *Hambrick et al. (2019, p. 2)*

The Global Burden of Disease Study 2019 provides evidence that social and economic development is substantially associated with health outcomes. Related to this, mounting evidence has proven that the prolonged activation of the stress response systems at high levels in children can result in an adverse wear-and-tear effect on their neurodevelopment, and will influence other biological systems (Forde et al., 2019). It may also hijack the intimate two-way communication among microorganisms in and on their bodies.

Emergent research connects the concept of chronic wear-and-tear to racism (Geronimus et al., 2006; McEwen, 1998). This research suggests that constant coping with systemic racism and daily discrimination potently activates the stress response (The Center on the Developing Child, n.d.). In a similar vein, Blacks or African Americans had 40% higher death rates than Whites for all-cause mortality in all ages under 65 years (Cunningham et al., 2017). Figure 4.2 shows the comparison of death rates for selected leading causes of death among Blacks and Whites, by all ages. This may help us understand the early origins of racial disparities in chronic illness across the lifespan (Subica & Link, 2021; The Center on the Developing Child, n.d.).

Similarly, racial disparities in health conditions are explicated extensively in the proposed weathering hypothesis, in which *weathering* is "the result of chronic exposure to social and economic disadvantage that leads to the acceleration of normal aging and earlier onset of unfavorable physical health conditions among disadvantaged persons of similar age" (Forde et al., 2019, p. 1). It is concerning that academic literature and news media frequently portray racial disparities in health conditions (e.g., obesity) among minoritized groups in the United States as resulting from poor social control and unhealthy behaviors (Das, 2013). However, recent studies on stress-physiological associations have indicated one key biological mechanism of weathering is low-grade

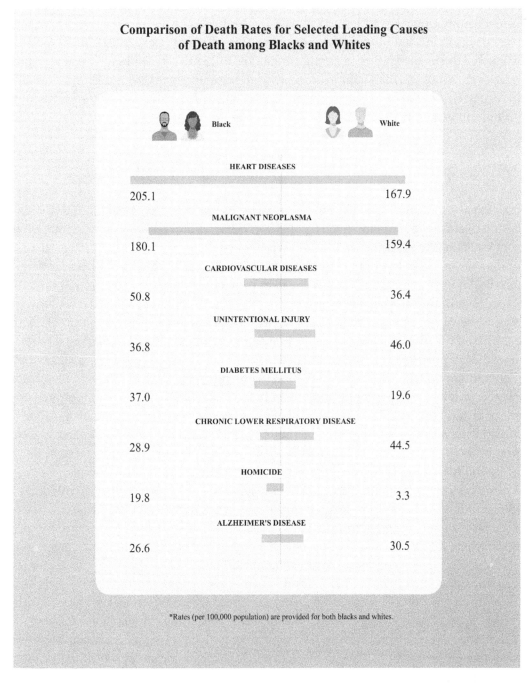

FIGURE 4.2   Comparison of Death Rates for Selected Leading Causes of Death Among Blacks and Whites, by All Ages, United States, 2015

chronic inflammation induced by cumulative and multi-dimensional stress experienced for a prolonged period in adult black men living in the United States (Das, 2013). Further, research has suggested the linkage between chronic low-grade inflammation and cardiovascular disease (Danesh et al., 2000) and metabolic syndrome (McDade & Hayward, 2009). The findings of this study suggest that it is necessary to focus attention on broader stress-inducing social inequities and to reduce such individuals' racial disparities in health (Das, 2013).

Summary

Trauma exposure is a universal experience in many individuals at a global level. Research has suggested that over 70% of individuals globally experience at least one traumatic life event at some point in their lives (Benjet et al., 2016). The United States is not an exception to this global phenomenon. Specifically, prior to the current COVID-19 pandemic, trauma was recognized as a public health issue in the United States due to its prevalence and persistence as well as its costly relevance to mortality and morbidity in the general public (SAMHSA, 2014). Particularly, it has been extensively documented that ACEs, such as exposure to abuse in the parental relationship, are associated with numerous health conditions, including physical and mental problems, uncontrolled or misused substances, and premature death in adulthood (CDC, 2019; Felitti et al., 1998). Moreover, the prolonged COVID-19 pandemic may involve potentially long-lasting effects that will lead to a psychological toll on individuals, families, communities, and at-risk populations, although its full breadth and depth of consequences are yet unknown. When considering the likely synergistic impact of all these conditions, helping professionals have a critical responsibility to address trauma as a requisite component of effective human service delivery available and accessible, ideally at a reasonable cost for all.

Trauma typically results from varied factors (e.g., violence, neglect, maltreatment, abuse, attachment ruptures, insufficient health insurance coverage, natural and manmade disasters, and other emotionally or psychologically harmful experiences). Similarly, the conceptualization of trauma has been diverse over decades of collective endeavors by numerous helping professionals, researchers, and governmental and national organizations.

In addition, trauma is associated with developmental disruptions leading to an unlikely healthy developmental trajectory in many individuals, associated with or worsened by the unhealthy or risky lifestyle (e.g., excessive or uncontrolled drinking). Mounting research has suggested that the experience of toxic stress early in life can lead to varied consequences, including chronic illnesses (e.g., depression) in adulthood. Neurobiologically, toxic stress precipitates a cascade of events that have the potential to cause long-lasting changes in neurocognitive development (Teicher et al., 2003). In addition, toxic stress experienced particularly during the first months of life may be influential for neurodevelopment because it is a sensitive time when systems or networks in the nervous system are developing and organizing at a rapid rate (Hambrick et al.,

2019). However, the effects of toxic stress are not only detrimental in early childhood, but they are also influential during the fetal development in the womb.

Furthermore, trauma cannot be perceived from an individual arena. For instance, research has suggested that constant coping with systemic or environmental demands (e.g., systemic racism, and daily discrimination and oppression) recruits the chronic activation or overactivation of the stress response system (e.g., the HPA axis and autonomic nervous system). Mounting evidence has proven that this excessive activation of the stress response programming in children at higher levels can result in an adverse wear-and-tear effect on their neurodevelopment and also influences other biological systems (Forde et al., 2019).

Experiential Questions

1. What potential adverse childhood experiences A might have experienced do you think would have an impact on their current mental health–related experience?

2. What additional information do you think would be helpful for you to know to better understand the potential A has for effects of developmental trauma they might have experienced?

3. What do you think would be the potential impact of a type of cultural trauma A might have experienced on their current family members (e.g., A's daughter and their son-in-law)?

Informative Resources

• The Center on the Developing Child (n.d.). How Racism Can Affect Child Development. https://developingchild.harvard.edu/resources/racism-and-ecd/

• Image or information courtesy of Beacon House Therapeutic Services & Trauma Team (2021). Resources. https://beaconhouse.org.uk/resources/

References

Allwood, M. A., Ford, J. D., & Levendosky, A. (2021). Introduction to the special issue: Disproportionate trauma, stress, and adversities as a pathway to health disparities among disenfranchised groups globally. *Journal of Traumatic Stress, 34*(5), 899–904. https://doi.org/10.1002/jts.22743

Benjet, C., Bromet, E., Karam, E. G., Kessler, R. C., McLaughlin, K. A., Ruscio, A. M., Shahly, V., Stein, D. J., Petukhova, M., Hill, E., Alonso, J., Atwoli, L., Bunting, B., Bruffaerts, R., Caldas-de-Almeida, J. M., de Girolamo, G., Florescu, S., Gureje, O., Huang, Y., Lepine, J. P., ... Koenen, K. C. (2016). The epidemiology of traumatic event exposure worldwide: Results from the World Mental Health Survey Consortium. *Psychological Medicine, 46*, 327–343. http://dx.doi.org/10.1017/S0033291715001981

Centers for Disease Control and Prevention. (2019, November 5). *Preventing Adverse Childhood Experiences (ACEs) to improve U.S. health.* https://www.cdc.gov/media/releases/2019/p1105-prevent-aces.html

The Center on the Developing Child (n.d.). How racism can affect child development. https://developingchild.harvard.edu/resources/racism-and-ecd/

Crittenden, P. M. (1990). Internal representational models of attachment relationships. *Infant Mental Health Journal, 11*(3), 250–277. https://doi.org/10.1002/1097-0355(199023)11:3<259::AID-IMHJ2280110308>3.0.CO;2-J

Crittenden, P. M. (1992). Treatment of anxious attachment in infancy and early childhood. *Development and Psychopathology, 4*(4), 575–602. https://doi.org/10.1017/S0954579400004880

Cunningham, T. J., Croft, J. B., Liu, Y., Lu, H., Eke P. I., & Giles, W. H. (2017). Vital signs: Racial disparities in age-specific mortality among Blacks or African Americans—United States, 1999–2015. *MMWR Morbidity and Mortality Weekly Report, 66*, 444–456. http://dx.doi.org/10.15585/mmwr.mm6617e1

Danesh, J., Whincup, P., Walker, M., Lennon, L., Thomson, A., Appleby, P., & Gallimore, J. R. (2000). Low grade inflammation and coronary heart disease: Prospective study and updated meta-analyses. *BMJ, 321*, 199–204. https://doi.org/10.1136/bmj.321.7255.199

Das, A. (2013). How does race get "under the skin"?: Inflammation, weathering, and metabolic problems in late life. *Social Science & Medicine, 77*, 75–83. https://doi.org/10.1016/j.socscimed.2012.11.007

Drossman, D. A., Leserman, J., Nachman, G., Li, Z., Cluck, H., Toomey, T. C., & Mitchell, C. M. (1990). Sexual and physical abuse in women with functional or organic gastrointestinal disorders. *Annual of Internal Medicine, 113*(11), 828–833. https://doi.org/10.7326/0003-4819-113-11-828

Evans-Campbell, T. (2008). Historical trauma in American Indian/Native Alaska communities: A multilevel framework for exploring impacts on individuals, families, and communities. *Journal of Interpersonal Violence, 23*(3), 316–338. https://doi.org/10.1177/0886260507312290

Felitti, V. J., Anda, R. F., Nordenberg, D., Williamson, D. F., Spitz, A. M., Edwards, V., Koss, M. P., & Marks, J. S. (1998). Relationship of childhood abuse and household dysfunction to many of the leading causes of death in adults: The Adverse Childhood Experiences (ACE) Study. *American Journal of Preventive Medicine, 14*(4), 245–258. https://doi.org/10.1016/S0749-3797(98)00017-8

Flaherty, E. G., Thompson, R., Litrownik, A. J., Zolotor, A. J., Dubowitz, H., Runyan, D. K., English, D. J., & Everson, M. D. (2009). Adverse childhood exposures and reported child health at age 12. *Academic Pediatrics, 9*(3), 150–156. https://doi.org/10.1016/j.acap.2008.11.003

Forde, A. T., Crookes, D. M., Suglia, S. F., & Demmer, R. T. (2019). The weathering hypothesis as an explanation for racial disparities in health: A systematic review. *Annals of Epidemiology, 33,* 1–18.e3.

Ford, J. D., Spinazzola, J., van der Kolk, B., & Grasso, D. J. (2018). Toward an empirically based Developmental Trauma Disorder diagnosis for children: Factor structure, item characteristics, reliability, and validity of the developmental trauma disorder semi-structured interview (DTD-SI). *Journal of Clinical Psychiatry, 79*(5), 17m11675. https://doi.org/10.4088/JCP.17m11675

Geronimus, A. T., Hicken, M., Keene, D., & Bound, J. (2006). "Weathering" and age patterns of allostatic load scores among blacks and whites in the United States. *American Journal of Public Health, 96*(5), 826–833.

Hambrick, E. P., Brawner, T. W., & Perry, B. D. (2019). Timing of early life stress and the development of brain-related capacities. *Frontiers of Behavioral Neuroscience, 13*, 183. https://doi.org/10.3389/fnbeh.2019.00183

Hirschberger, G. (2018). Collective trauma and the social construction of meaning. *Frontiers in Psychology*, *9*, 1444. https://doi.org/10.3389/fpsyg.2018.01441

Hunter, R. G. (2012). Epigenetic effects of stress and corticosteroids in the brain. *Frontiers in Cellular Neuroscience*, *6*, 18. https://doi.org/10.3389/fncel.2012.00018

Lyons-Ruth, K., Bureau, J.-F., Holmes, B., Easterbrooks, A., & Brooks, N. H. (2013). Borderline symptoms and suicidality/self-injury in late adolescence: Prospectively observed relationship correlates in infancy and childhood. *Psychiatry Research*, *206*(2–3), 273–281. https://doi.org/10.1016/j.psychres.2012.09.030

Lyons, S., Whyte, K., Stephens, R., & Townsend, H. (2020). Developmental trauma close up. https://beaconhouse.org.uk/wp-content/uploads/2020/02/Developmental-Trauma-Close-Up-Revised-Jan-2020.pdf

Magruder, K. M., Kassam-Adams, N., Thoresen, S., & Olff, M. (2016). Prevention and public health approaches to trauma and traumatic stress: A rationale and a call to action. *European Journal of Psychotraumatology*, *7*(1), 29715. https://doi.org/10.3402/ejpt.v7.29715

McDade, T. W., & Hayward, M. D. (2009). Rationale and methodological options for assessing infectious disease and related measures in social science surveys. *Biodemography and Social Biology*, *55*(2), 159–177. https://doi.org/10.1080/19485560903382478

McEwen, B. S. (1998). Protective and damaging effects of stress mediators. *New England Journal of Medicine, 338*(3), 171–179. https://doi.org/10.1056/NEJM199801153380307

Moh, Y., & Sperandio, K. (2022). The need to consider requiring trauma training in entry-level academic training programs in clinical mental health counseling. *Journal of Mental Health Counseling*, *44*(1), 18–31. https://doi.org/10.17744/mehc.44.1.03

Perry, B. D. (2017). Trauma- and stressor-related disorders in infants, children and adolescents. In T. P. Beauchaine & S. P. Hinshaw (Eds.), *Child and adolescent psychopathology* (3rd ed., pp. 683–705). Wiley.

Teplin, L. A., Abram, K. M., McClelland, G. M., Dulcan, M. K., & Mericle, A. A. (2009). Psychiatric disorders in youth in juvenile detention. *Archives of General Psychiatry*, *59*(12), 1133–1143. https://doi.org/10.1001/archpsyc.59.12.1133

Tronick, E., & Hunter, R. G. (2016). Waddington, dynamic systems, and epigenetics. *Frontiers in Behavioral Neuroscience*, *10*, 107. https://doi.org/10.3389/fnbeh.2016.00107

Shonkoff, J. P., Garner, A. S., the Committee on Psychosocial Aspects of Child and Family Health, Committee on Early Childhood, Adoption, and Dependent Care, & Section on Developmental and Behavioral Pediatrics. (2012). The lifelong effects of early childhood adversity and toxic stress. *The American Academy of Pediatrics*, *129*(1), e232–e246. https://doi.org/10.1542/peds.2011-2663

Schore, J. R., & Schore, A. N. (2008). Modern attachment theory: The central role of affect regulation in development and treatment. *Clinical Social Work Journal*, *36*(1), 9–20. https://doi.org/10.1007/s10615-007-0111-7

Spinazzola, J., van der Kolk, B., & Ford, J. (2018). When nowhere is safe: Interpersonal trauma and attachment adversity as antecedents of posttraumatic stress disorder and developmental trauma disorder. *Journal of Traumatic Stress*, *31*(5), 631–642. https://doi.org/10.1002/jts.22320

Spinazzola, J., van der Kolk, B., & Ford, J. (2021). Developmental trauma disorder: A legacy of attachment trauma in victimized children. *Journal of Traumatic Stress*, *34*(4), 711–720. https://doi.org/10.1002/jts.22697

Subica, A. M., & Link, B. G. (2021). Cultural trauma as a fundamental cause of health disparities. *Social Science & Medicine*, *292*(114574). https://doi.org/10.1016/j.socscimed.2021.114574

Substance Abuse and Mental Health Services Administration. (2014). TIP 57: Trauma-informed care in behavioral health services. https://store.samhsa.gov/product/TIP-57-Trauma-Informed-Care-in-Behavioral-Health-Services/SMA14-4816

Teicher, M. H., Andersen, S. L., Polcari, A., Anderson, C. M., Navalta, C. P., & Kim, D. M. (2003). The neurobiological consequences of early stress and childhood maltreatment. *Neuroscience & Biobehavioral Reviews*, *27*(1–2), 33–44. https://doi.org/10.1016/S0149-7634(03)00007-1

U.S. Department of Health & Human Services, Administration for Children and Families, Administration on Children, Youth and Families, Children's Bureau. (2021). *Child maltreatment 2019*. Retrieved July 7, 2021, from https://www.acf.hhs.gov/sites/default/files/documents/cb/cm2019.pdf

van der Kolk, B. A. (2003). The neurobiology of childhood trauma and abuse. *Child and Adolescent Psychiatric Clinics of North America*, *12*(2), 293–317. https://doi.org/10.1016/S1056-4993(03)00003-8

van der Kolk, B. A. (2005). Developmental Trauma Disorder: Toward a rational diagnosis for children with complex trauma histories. *Psychiatric Annals*, *35*(5), 401–408. https://doi.org/10.3928/00485713-20050501-06

van der Kolk, B. A., & Fisler, R. (1995). Dissociation and the fragmentary nature of traumatic memories: Overview and exploratory study. *Journal of Traumatic Stress*, *8*(4), 505–525. https://doi.org/10.1002/jts.2490080402

van der Kolk, B., Ford, J. D., & Spinazzola, J. (2019). Comorbidity of developmental trauma disorder (DTD) and post-traumatic stress disorder: Findings from the DTD field trial. *European Journal of Psychotraumatology*, *10*(1), 1562841. https://doi.org/10.1080/20008198.2018.1562841

World Health Organization. (2021). *WHO coronavirus (COVID-19) dashboard*. Retrieved July 9, 2021, from https://covid19.who.int/

Yehuda, R., & Lehrner, A. (2018). Intergenerational transmission of trauma effects: Putative role of epigenetic mechanisms. *World Psychiatry*, *17*(3), 243–257. https://doi.org/10.1002/wps.20568

Figure Credits

CHAPTER FIVE

Empathy-Based Stress in Helping Professionals

The key points addressed in this chapter are

- individual and synergistic effects of work-related stress
- empathy-based stress and its attributes among helping professionals
- the importance of preventive measures and practices for work-related stress among helping professionals

---

High prevalence of trauma exposure and experience in the United States in the general public was alarming prior to the current COVID-19 pandemic, which only increased trauma. Inevitably, we contemporarily live with the daily consequences of global challenges, such as the current prolonged pandemic and the effects of climate change. Alongside the public health issue of high trauma exposure in general, chronic stress associated with the prolonged pandemic, its attributes (e.g., deepened health disparities among minoritized individuals), and complications (e.g., heightened climate in racial injustice and discrimination, and gun violence) will take a mental toll on individuals, families, communities of color, and at-risk populations unequivocally.

Helping professionals, such as mental health professionals (e.g., professional counselors, psychologists, social workers, and psychiatrists), are not personally immune to the effects of chronic stress related to the pandemic itself and its attributes addressed previously. Particularly, mental health work may trigger burnout related to chronic work-related stress, resulting in negative consequences (e.g., emotional exhaustion) because mental health professionals are exposed to psychological and social stressors throughout their career (Rokach & Boulazreg, 2020).

Additionally, particularly for trainees in clinical training or clinical students (e.g., counseling students, clinical and counseling psychology students, and social work students), clinical training can be stressful at times in a unique way. The stress in clinical training is, among a variety of stressors, partially associated with the amount of demands of both clinical coursework and fieldwork (Collins et al., 2010). Also, trainees may be exposed to additional stressors, such as performance anxiety pertaining to academic demands, professional perceived self-doubt, peer competition, financial constraints, time and other resource constraints, and clinical role-related demands (Butler et al., 2017; Pakenham & Stafford-Brown, 2012). All these factors may produce a synergistic effect and unintentionally strengthen the experience in feeling clinical training-related stress (Butler et al., 2017).

Furthermore, it is evident that a history of personal traumatic experience among helping professionals is associated with an increase in the likelihood of compassion fatigue (Adams et al., 2006). When considering the potential dynamic interplay between the effects of these factors, in addition to such trainees' own trauma histories and vicarious experience in working with mental health clients who are exposed to widespread adversity, it is absolutely critical that there is increased awareness of the synergistic effects of all these stressors. Thus, stress prevention and management should be universally practiced throughout clinical training and education.

Empathy-Based Stress

Specifically, mental health professionals are vulnerable to effects of *empathy-based stress*, which is described as "a process of trauma exposure (i.e., a stressor) combined with the experience of empathy that results in empathy-based strain, adverse occupational health reactions, and other work-related outcomes" (Rauvola et al., 2019, p. 298). Briefly addressed earlier in this chapter, compassion fatigue, burnout, secondary traumatic stress, and vicarious traumatization as examples of empathy-based stress have been extensively documented in the literature (Rauvola et al., 2019). *Compassion fatigue* is a term used to describe an emotional experience in helping professionals who work with caregivers exposed to traumatic events, in which caregivers' stress reactions parallel those of the original caregivers or trauma survivors (Figley, 1995).

Mental health professionals who experience compassion fatigue may encounter decreased capacity for empathy toward clients resulting from the repeated or prolonged exposure to the trauma of such clients. This can be problematic because it not only affects professionals but also the clients they serve. Relevantly, *empathy* is considered to be "an inherently interpersonal ability that gradually develops as a result of interwoven biological processes involving the detection of distress cues, emotional sharing, emotional regulation, and mental state understanding, that are continuously interacting between a child and social environment" (Decety & Holvoet, 2021, p. 14). It is critical for helping professionals to better understand the functional components of empathy, and how the development of these components is molded by a variety of factors (e.g., genetic programming and the social environment), before empathy-based stress is further addressed (Decety & Holvoet, 2021).

Neuroscience research has revealed that infants are, from birth, sensitive to emotional cues that signify the internal affective states of others, as evidenced by studies reflecting activities in the insula and orbitofrontal cortex (Addabbo et al., 2020; Decety & Holvoet, 2021). Furthermore, empathetic concern, described as "the motivation to care for the well-being of others" (Decety & Holvoet, 202, p. 14), appears to emerge substantially in the second year of life and is also influenced by a combination of genetics as well as the social environment and social learning (Decety & Holvoet, 2021). In addition, the cognitive components of empathy that are associated with the ability to put ourselves in another's perspective are functionally related to executive functioning and theory of mind (Decety, & Holvoet, 2021). Developmentally, these components seem to emerge at the age of 3 years, before they are fully materialized by the age of 6 to 7 years (Decety & Holvoet, 2021).

Regarding empathy-based stress followed by compassion fatigue, Stamm (2010) furthered this construct and organized it in two distinct dimensions: *burnout* and *secondary traumatic stress*. *Burnout* involves a gradual process of negative effects (e.g., exhaustion, frustration, anger, and depression) as a result of working with clients who are exposed to adversity, while *secondary traumatic stress* concerns an acute negative reaction or feeling driven by fear and work-related trauma. Secondary traumatic stress is described as "natural and consequential behaviors and emotions resulting from knowing about a traumatizing event experienced by a significant other or client and the stress resulting from helping or wanting to help a traumatized or suffering person" (Figley, 1995, p. 7). Secondary traumatic stress may manifest in a way that resembles symptoms included in PTSD, including those related to avoidance behaviors, intrusive symptoms, and physiological activation (e.g., hyperarousal; Bride et al., 2007). However, there are varied perspectives in the literature on viewing burnout and secondary traumatic stress as two distinct concepts. In contrast, *vicarious traumatization* is defined as "the transformation that occurs within the therapist or other trauma worker as a result of empathic engagement with clients' trauma experiences and their sequelae" (Pearlman, & Mac Ian, 1995, p. 558; Pearlman & Saakvitne, 1995).

Moreover, although mental health professionals are trained in self-care, stress management, and work-life balance, research suggests that they might tend to overextend themselves with work (Luther et al., 2017). Due to the increasing mental health needs related to the pandemic in the U.S. general population, alongside the work-related stress inherent in the nature of mental health work, it is pivotal that resources for mental health professionals become available at varying levels and at varied times, from the pre-service training to regular mental health work. These may be used as preventive measures and practices to counteract against the effects of such stressors during and after the COVID-19 era.

Furthermore, educators who work in a clinical training program, such as counselor education programs, or whose roles include education and clinical mental health work, may also be exposed to the effects of empathy-based stress and other social stressors, given the nature of their professional roles, such as mental health practice, clinical supervision, clinical education and training, research and scholarship in human service fields, and leadership and advocacy in similar fields. For instance, while teaching in an urban area in a master's counselor education program that intentionally infuses trauma content across its program curriculum through trauma-related content in coursework and field placements, I (the author of this textbook) realized that many counseling students bring their own trauma histories into the counselor education process and that these intersect with those of others, whether they are their peers in the counselor education classroom or in their fieldwork. However, this does not come as a surprise, given the high prevalence of ACEs in the U.S. general population, which includes mental health professionals.

Preventive Measures and Practices

Even prior to the current pandemic, many students enrolled in clinical education or clinical training programs such as counselor education programs frequently reported trauma histories (Butler et al., 2017). Despite coping resources and coping strategies such students inherently have, these trauma histories can manifest in the counselor education classroom or in the field placements. Despite the urgent necessity of evidence-based resources and practices for stress prevention in this population, the current clinical education and training may not be fully invested in an intentional implementation of preventive measures and practices, especially during the pre-service training. Among varied strategies and tools for stress prevention and management, *self-care* can be an effective tool at an individual level. Defined as "the deliberate and self-initiated attempt to take care of oneself" (Rokach & Boulazreg, 2020, p. 1), self-care can be effective in promoting the wellness of clinicians (Butler et al., 2017). In a similar vein, in a study of 195 students enrolled in a social work program, reduced self-care effort was associated with the higher appraisal of training-related stress and higher levels of burnout and secondary traumatic stress (Butler et al., 2017).

Additionally, other factors—such as mindfulness practices or compassion satisfaction resulting from the perceived meaningful experience of being able to help others in need—may be protective against work-related and empathy-based stress and its effects. For instance, in a study of 41 volunteers and professionals at an agency serving survivors of traumatic bereavement, it was found that there was a significant positive association between attention awareness as a component of mindfulness and compassion satisfaction, and significant negative relationships between mindfulness and secondary traumatic stress, and mindfulness and burnout (Thieleman & Cacciatore, 2014).

Summary

Like others, helping professionals, such as mental health professionals, are exposed to the effects of chronic stress related to the prolonged pandemic itself, and its attributes and complications, addressed in this chapter of the textbook. Additionally, mental health work may precipitate additional effects of work-related stress, resulting in negative consequences (e.g., emotional exhaustion) due to the inherent nature of the work that exposes such individuals to psychological and social stressors throughout their career (Rokach & Boulazreg, 2020).

Particularly trainees in clinical training or clinical students can experience varied stressors at times in a distinct way during their training period. For instance, such individuals are exposed to stress related in part to the time and performance demands of both their academic coursework and clinical placements (Collins et al., 2010). Also, trainees may experience high levels of stress pertaining to performance anxiety, professional self-doubt due to a lack of perceived clinical competencies, peer competition, financial constraints, time pressures, and other resource constraints to coping meaningfully with their clinical, role-specific demands (Butler et al., 2017; Pakenham & Stafford-Brown, 2012). Moreover, many students enrolled in clinical education or clinical training programs frequently report trauma histories (Butler et al., 2017). In addition to an acute effect of these stressors individually, they may lead to a synergistic effect and negatively augment the experience in feeling clinical-training-related stress (Butler et al., 2017).

In addition, it is known that mental health professionals particularly are vulnerable to the effects of empathy-based stress described in this chapter, such as compassion fatigue, burnout, secondary traumatic stress, and vicarious traumatization (Rauvola et al., 2019). Also, research has suggested that a history of personal traumatic experience among helping professionals is associated with an increased likelihood of compassion fatigue (Adams et al., 2006). From birth, we humans are sensitive to emotional cues that signify the internal affective states of other humans, and this is supported by neuroscience studies (Addabbo et al., 2020; Decety & Holvoet, 2021).

Although helping professionals are equipped in self-care, stress management, and work-life balance, they must increase awareness of the potential dynamic and synergistic effects of all these stressors—empathy-based stress, other work-related stress, their own trauma histories or traumatic experiences, and vicarious experience in working with clients with trauma exposure. Therefore, it is critical that stress prevention and management are universally practiced throughout clinical training and education while stress coping resources become available and accessible for all in need.

Experiential Questions

1. Based on your primary professional role, what potential effects of work-related stress would there be if you worked with A for a human health service?

2. Based on your primary professional role, what type of potential empathy-based stress might you experience if you worked with A for a human health service?

3. What preventive actions and/or practices could you take to help reduce the effects on your wellness of the empathy-based stress you think of in response to question 2?

References

Adams, R. E., Boscarino, J. A., & Figley, C. R. (2006). Compassion fatigue and psychological distress among social workers: A validation study. *American Journal of Orthopsychiatry, 76*(1), 103–108. https://doi.org/10.1037/0002-9432.76.1.103

Addabbo, M., Bolognini, N., & Turati, C. (2020). Neural time course of pain observation in infancy. *Developmental Science, 24*(4), e13074. https://doi.org/10.1111/desc.13074

Bride, B. E., Radey, M., & Figley, C. R. (2007). Measuring compassion fatigue. *Clinical Social Work Journal, 35,* 155–163. https://doi.org/10.1007/s10615-007-0091-7

Butler, L. D., Carello, J., & Maguin, E. (2017). Trauma, stress, and self-care in clinical training: Predictors of burnout, decline in health status, secondary traumatic stress symptoms, and compassion satisfaction. *Psychological Trauma, 9*(4), 416–424. https://doi.org/10.1037/tra0000187

Collins, S., Coffey, M., & Morris, L. (2010). Social work students: Stress, support and well-being. *British Journal of Social Work, 40*(3), 963–982. http://dx.doi.org/10.1093/bjsw/bcn148

Decety, J., & Holvoet, C. (2021). The emergence of empathy: A developmental neuroscience perspective. *Developmental Review, 62,* 100999. https://doi.org/10.1016/j.dr.2021.100999

Figley, C. R. (1995). Compassion fatigue: Toward a new understanding of the costs of caring. In B. H. Stamm (Ed.), *Secondary traumatic stress: Self-care issues for clinicians, researchers, and educators* (pp. 3–28). The Sidran Press.

Luther, L., Gearhart, T., Fukui, S., Morse, G., Rollins, A. L., & Salyers, M. P. (2017). Working overtime in community mental health: Associations with clinician burnout and perceived quality of care. *Psychiatric Rehabilitation Journal, 40*(2), 252–259. https://doi.org/10.1037/prj0000234

Pakenham, K. I., & Stafford-Brown, J. (2012). Stress in clinical psychology trainees: A review of current research and future directions. *Australian Psychologist, 47,* 147–155. http://dx.doi.org/10.1111/j.1742-9544.2012.00070.x

Pearlman, L. A., & Mac Ian, P. S. (1995). Vicarious traumatization: An empirical study of the effects of trauma work on trauma therapists. *Professional Psychology: Research and Practice, 26*(6), 558–565.

Pearlman, L. A., & Saakvitne, K. (1995). *Trauma and the therapist: Countertransference and vicarious traumatization in psychotherapy with incest survivors.* W.W. Norton.

Rauvola, R., Vega, D., & Lavigne, K. (2019). Compassion fatigue, secondary traumatic stress, and vicarious traumatization: A qualitative review and research agenda. *Occupational Health Science, 3*(3), 297–336. https://doi.org/10.1007/s41542-019-00045-1

Rokach, A., & Boulazreg, S. (2020). The COVID-19 era: How therapists can diminish burnout symptoms through self-care. *Current Psychology: A Journal for Diverse Perspectives on Diverse Psychological Issues.* Advance online publication. https://doi.org/10.1007/s12144-020-01149-6

Stamm, B. H. (2010). *The concise ProQOL manual* (2nd ed.). ProQOL. Retrieved July 12, 2021, from https://img1.wsimg.com/blobby/go/dfc1e1a0-a1db-4456-9391-18746725179b/downloads/ProQOL%20Manual.pdf?ver=1622839353725

Thieleman, K., & Cacciatore, J. (2014). Witness to suffering: Mindfulness and compassion fatigue among traumatic bereavement volunteers and professionals. *Social Work, 59*(1), 34–41. https://doi.org/10.1093/sw/swt044

CHAPTER SIX

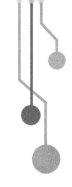

The Human Gut, Brain, and Human Microbiome

The key points addressed in this chapter are

- the effects of stress in human gut health
- the bidirectional dialogue between the brain and gut
- the effects of stress in brain development and function

The Role of Stress in Human Gut and Gut Microbiota

"Adversity early in life is associated with altered microbial patterns in developing youth, and that bacteria-brain associations are observable in functional reactivity in brain regions (PFC and PCC) well known to be implicated in emotional functioning."

Callaghan et al. (2019, p. 323)

"Time-limited exposure to caregiving adversities during the infancy-early childhood stages of life may be important for development of the brain-gut-microbiome axis in humans."

Callaghan et al. (2019, p. 325)

The human body consists of its host cells, with the number of these cells ranging from 10^{12} to 10^{14} (Sender et al., 2017). Those cells are the smallest functional unit in the body and are organized in an intricate manner. Alongside these host cells, we humans have numerous *microorganisms* or *microbes* that cohabit on and in our bodies—on the surface of the skin, in the mouth, in the eyelashes, in the nose, and in the gastrointestinal (GI) system. Logan and colleagues (2016) report that microbes are the most ancient, diverse, and perhaps the most successful form of life on Earth, as they contribute to the evolution and function of all more complex multicellular organisms, like mammalians. From this cellular point of view, the human body can be viewed as a complex ecosystem where the host cells live with those miniscule microorganisms. You may easily wonder which are good guys and bad guys among those cohabiting within us that affect our health. However, Hill and Round (2021) encourage us to think that microbes can play both roles that are pathogenic and commensal, and these lines between good and bad can be gray areas. As the detailed description and accordant information regarding the complexity of host-microbial interactions and relevant outcomes for human health are outside of the scope of this book, readers are encouraged to look into Hill and Round's amazing infographic illustrating the information at the following link, if they are interested: https://www.cell.com/cell/pdf/S0092-8674(21)00506-7.pdf?_returnURL=https%3A%2F%2Flinkinghub.elsevier.com%2Fretrieve%2Fpii%2FS0092867421005067%3Fshowall=true-relatedArticles

Gut Microbiota as Helpers

These little guys residing inside the gut, such as the archaea, bacteria, fungi, and viruses, are collectively called *gut microbiota* (Mayer, 2018). The largest collection of microorganisms, with the greatest diversity and abundance, is found in our gut, more precisely known as the gut ecosystem (Bastiaanssen et al., 2020). Particularly, the majority of commensal bacteria in the human body is found in the large intestine (Bastiaanssen et al., 2020; Mayer, 2018). Thus, the large intestine is the primary contributor to the total bacterial population in our bodies, while there are also bacteria existing in the stomach and small intestine. The recently updated ratio of bacteria to human cells in the body is estimated to be 1.3 to 1, despite the existence of a wide range of different estimates in ratio (Sender et al., 2017). At the time of writing this book, we were still in the midst of the prolonged COVID-19 pandemic, and thus, readers might have a strong, biased view on the impact of these little guys on our human lives.

In recent years, it has been well documented that the *microbiota*, a collective term used to refer to microorganisms as described earlier, influences the development and function of almost all systems of the mammalian body (e.g., human bodies; Hill & Round, 2021). Specifically, healthful microorganisms play imperative roles in homeostatic development of many organs and systems, such as the brain and gut. In the brain, microbes can regulate the development of specific cells, such as microglia, while they can act similarly in the development of intestinal epithelial cells in the gut (Hill & Round, 2021). Functionally, the gut microbiota are like *helpers* for several areas in the human function. *Did you hear me saying gut microbes—well, some of them—are helpers like us helping professionals*? Some studied benefits of these helpers include, but are not limited to, the following (Mayer, 2018, p. 95):

- metabolizing digestive compounds (e.g., bile acids produced by the liver)

- detoxifying foreign chemicals that our bodies have not experienced

- digesting dietary fiber and complex sugar molecules that the human digestive system cannot break down or absorb on its own

- educating and regulating our bodies' immune system

- receiving varied information transmitted by hormones, gut peptides, nerve impulses, and other chemical signaling, and using this to monitor the human emotional states and stress levels in the host

Dysbiosis in the Gut Microbiota

In contrast, disturbance in the microbiota in our bodies can perturb homeostatic processes (Hill & Round, 2021). If this condition persists without appropriate or timely intervention, it can lead to negative consequences, such as organ-specific diseases. This condition can be described as dysbiosis in the human gut. *Dysbiosis* is defined as "any change to the composition of resident commensal communities relative to the community found in healthy individuals" (Petersen & Round, 2014, p. 1024). In brief, microorganisms have the ability to produce molecules used as messengers that have a direct impact on the development and function of cells (e.g., immune cells within the bone marrow and thymus, nerve cells, and cells of the gut; Hill & Round, 2021).

Gut Microbiome and Its Dialogue with the Brain

Did you know that the adult gut microbiome consists of more genes than its human host? When we reference the role of human genes in human development or human health, the microbial genome is not included in this notion, but nonetheless affects our development across the lifespan. In addition, the gut is an amazing organ because it contains the largest number of nerve cells after the brain (Bastiaanssen et al., 2020). Now you might come to better understand why the gut is called "the second brain" (Gershon, 1999). In recent years, research has unraveled that the gut microbiome is in bidirectional interplay with the brain via a variety of mechanisms, including the microbiome-gut-brain axis (Bastiaanssen et al., 2020).

Effects of Gut-Brain Bidirectional Dialogue on Brain Health

The routes of communication between the microbiota and brain have emerged in recent years. This communication is known to be influenced by varying factors, such as bacterial metabolites (e.g., short chain fatty acids), the HPA axis, the vagus nerve, the signaling of gut hormones, the immune system, and tryptophan metabolism (Foster et al., 2017; Garcia-Cabrerizo et al.,

2021). Specifically, commensal microorganisms residing inside and on our bodies—good guys—promote neurodevelopment indirectly via neurogenesis, myelination, and synaptogenesis; the increase in the number of microglia cells; and serotonin production. For instance, it is evident that commensal bacteria (e.g., *Bifidobacterium infantis*) have the ability to help modulate the metabolism of molecules such as tryptophan (Desbonnet et al., 2010). Tryptophan is a building block or precursor for neurotransmitters such as serotonin, a messenger that nerve cells use for chemical communication with each other for varying functions. The significance of the gut microbiota cannot be emphasized enough, as it influences the early life developmental stages and their effects of neurodevelopment and further mental health. In addition, research has suggested that the microbiota-gut-brain axis may play a key role in managing reward processes in the brain in both animals and humans (Garcia-Cabrerizo et al., 2021).

Gut Microbiome Development and Change over the Lifespan

A vast number of factors can influence the development of the gut microbiome. The diversity and abundance of gut microbiota are critical across the lifespan because they are highly related to human health. Emeran Mayer, a gastroenterologist and author of *The Mind-Gut Connection* (2018), reported in his book that gut microbiota is low during the first three years of life, when the stability in the gut microbiome is being established, ideally without disturbance or unhealthy alterations. This low diversity during the early period of life puts infants at high risk for developing neurodevelopmental disorders (e.g., autism spectrum disorder). The microbial diversity steadily reaches its maximum level during adult life unless it is hijacked by internal and external adverse cues. Again, low diversity in the microbial composition is seen in humans during the late period of older adulthood. Thus, it does not come as a surprise that this period of life coincides with a greater risk of the emergence of neurodegenerative diseases (e.g., dementias). Lifestyle changes (e.g., the overuse of antibiotics or an unhealthy diet) related to industrialization would likely increase the risk for the onset of neurodegenerative conditions alongside the natural decline in microbial diversity in us during older adulthood (Mayer, 2018). Figure 6.1, adapted from Mayer (2018), illustrates the development of the gut microbiota across the lifespan.

In addition, a mixture of varying factors can influence the composition of the human gut microbiome that range from stage of life to physical activity to stress levels and diet (Bastiaanssen et al., 2020; Mayer, 2018). Additionally, a number of factors are known to influence the development of microbiota during infancy. For instance, beginning during the gestational period, the composition of gut microbes is influenced by varying factors, including the gestational age, mode of delivery (e.g., natural delivery or Cesarean delivery), and mode of feeding (e.g., breastfeeding; Desbonnet et al., 2010). Furthermore, maternal conditions (e.g., dietary practices, unhealthy lifestyles, maternal body weight) during gestation and lactation, as well as other factors (e.g., genetics, maternal microorganisms in the vagina or on the surface of the skin) play a pivotal role in the development of the microbial composition (Desbonnet et al., 2010).

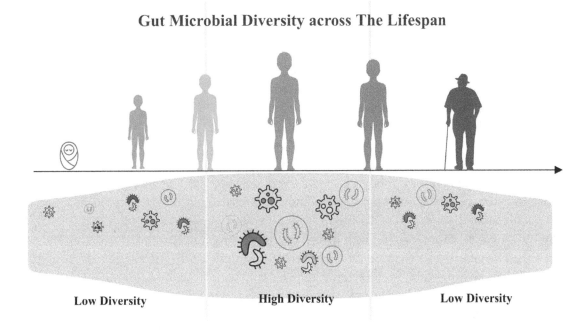

FIGURE 6.1   Gut Microbial Diversity

Effects of Early Childhood Adversity or Toxic Stress on Gut Microbiome

Previous studies have suggested associations between neural phenotypes and the microbiome in adults and children without a history of trauma (Carson et al., 2018). However, research has suggested consistently that exposure to trauma early in life is a potential risk factor for both the development of gastrointestinal (GI) distress or disorders (e.g., irritable bowel syndrome), and mental disorders (e.g., depressive and anxiety disorders) (Agrawal et al., 2021; Cowan et al., 2019; Park et al., 2016). Moreover, emerging research suggests that there is an association between GI distress (e.g., abdominal pain, constipation, nausea, or diarrhea), and mental disorders or negative mental health states (Callaghan et al., 2019). Additionally, the timing of exposure to early stressful experiences, such as abusive or neglectful caregiving, coincides with the sensitive period of the maturation of both the GI system and nervous system (Callaghan et al., 2019). Similarly, effects of stress can be another factor in the development of the gut and brain (Callaghan et al., 2019). As one example, Callaghan and colleagues explored in their study associations among trauma early in life, GI health, and anxiety symptoms using data from 344 youths with an age range of 3 to 18 years old. The participants consisted of those who were raised with their biological parents or who were counterparts exposed to trauma early in life related to negative caregiving experiences (i.e., caregiving inconsistency through institutional or foster care after international adoption).

Summary

Our bodies consist of numerous host cells, whose number ranges from 10^{12} to 10^{14} (Sender et al., 2017). Those cells are organized in a complex, intricate way. Furthermore, our bodies are considered a complex ecosystem that contains not only their own cells but also a number of microorganisms living inside and on the surface of the skin. Some of the microorganisms cohabiting with us include archaea, bacteria, fungi, and viruses. These little organisms are collectively called *microbiota* (Mayer, 2018). Despite divergent views of a variety of different estimates in ratio of bacteria cohabiting with us to human cells in the body, the recently updated estimate in ratio reports 1.3 to 1 (Sender et al., 2017). These microorganisms or microbes have genetic programming like our body's host cells, and the impact of the delicate dance between nature and nurture on their development and functioning are closely related to the host body's development and the function of almost all systems of our body (Hill & Round, 2021).

Specifically, microorganisms play both roles, the pathogenic (harmful) and commensal (healthful), depending on a variety of factors (Hill & Round, 2021). Although addressing the complexity of host-microbial interactions and relevant health outcomes in the human body goes beyond the scope of this textbook, this chapter illuminated the human gut and gut micro-biome in relation to human development across the lifespan, and health and diseases in the human body. As an example, healthful microorganisms are responsible for the homeostatic development of numerous organs and organ systems in the body. In a similar vein, some types of nerve cells, such as microglia, are particularly sensitive to the work of microorganisms in the context of their development. Moreover, mounting evidence has suggested that gut microorganisms are particularly beneficial in varied ways, such as helping with the digestion of food ingested that our bodies cannot manage alone, regulating metabolism in our bodies, influencing metabolizing medications taken, detoxifying harmful or unhealthy chemicals that invade the gut with the food ingested, educating and regulating our bodies' immune systems, and preventing potential invasion or unnecessary growth or overgrowth of pathogenic micro-organisms (Mayer, 2018).

Additionally, a number of factors can influence the development and health of the human gut microbiome. Particularly, the composition of the human gut microbiome is influenced by stage of life, physical activity, stress, and diet (Bastiaanssen et al., 2020). In addition, beginning during the gestational period, many factors influence the gut microbial composition that include the maternal gestational age, mode of delivery (e.g., natural delivery or Cesarean delivery), mode of feeding, maternal health conditions, maternal lifestyles during gestation and lactation, and other influences, such as maternal genetic programming (Desbonnet et al., 2010).

Also, the diversity and magnitude of gut microorganisms are important across the lifespan, given their intimate relationships to human health. Emeran Mayer (2018), a prominent scholar and researcher, describes a natural tendency across the lifespan that gut microorganisms are low in number during the first three years of life, and this low diversity is associated with high risks in infancy in the context of developing neurodevelopmental disorders (e.g., autism spectrum disorder). Although the diversity in microorganisms residing inside and on the surface of our bodies steadily peaks during adult life, it again declines in diversity and composition during the late period of older adulthood. It is well documented in the literature that this period of life coincides with a greater risk of developing neurodegenerative diseases (e.g., dementia). Furthermore, lifestyle changes due to heavy industrialization or environmental changes (e.g., air pollution or natural or manmade disasters) would fuel the risk of onset of such conditions alongside the naturally occurring decline in microbial diversity in our bodies during older adulthood (Mayer, 2018). Additionally, research has consistently suggested that exposure to trauma in early childhood is a potential risk factor for both the development of GI distress or disorders (e.g., IBS), and mental disorders (e.g., anxiety disorders). Furthermore, emerging research has identified an association between GI distress and negative mental health states (Callaghan et al., 2019). Importantly, the timing of exposure to early experiences of trauma seems to coincide with the sensitive period of the development and maturation of both the GI system and nervous system, implying the significant effects of developmental disruptions brought by early adverse experiences (Callaghan et al., 2019).

Informative Resources

- TED Ed on *How the Food You Eat Affects Your Gut*: https://ed.ted.com/lessons/how-the-food-you-eat-affects-your-gut-shilpa-ravella

- TED Ed on *How the Food You Eat Affects Your Brain* by Mia Nacamulli: https://ed.ted.com/lessons/how-the-food-you-eat-affects-your-brain-mia-nacamulli#review

- The microbes that live with us from cradle to grave by *Nature*: https://youtu.be/c_ZRZkU-FEw

- Ted Talk by Dr. Rob Knight 2014, *How our microbes make us who we are*: https://www.ted.com/talks/rob_knight_how_our_microbes_make_us_who_we_are?language=en

- TED Talk by Dr. Diego Bohorquez 2017, gut and brain: https://www.youtube.com/watch?v=utFG8GEvmfg

- TED ED on *How does the immune system work*? by Emma Bryce: https://www.ted.com/talks/emma_bryce_how_does_the_immune_system_work/transcript?language=en#t-308109

- A video clip on *The Link between Stress and Memory*: https://www.youtube.com/watch?v=hyg7lcU4g8E&list=PLWFnDuNhflZ0PGTcUnvqlpfqAYGfupzIC&index=4

- TED Ed on *How stress affects your body*: https://www.ted.com/talks/sharon_horesh_bergquist_how_stress_affects_your_body

The Role of Stress in Brain Development and Function

"Understanding the human brain in health and disease is a societal imperative."

Raichle (2011, p. 3)

The Brain Development

Why is it critical for helping professionals to understand the human brain in relation to human health? It is because brain health is integral to the overall health in us, humans. Furthermore, it is important to note that the first few years of life hold significance in the development of the healthy brain. For the same reason, a period prior to birth plays a pivotal role. In addition, during the postnatal period, the functional development of the mammalian brain (e.g., the human brain) is susceptible to a variety of factors, including internal and external environmental signals, such as attachment, caregiving experiences, or safety of surroundings (Malan-Muller et al., 2018).

The Brain Function

Now, let's look at functional aspects of the human brain in this section. In recent years, research has suggested that the human brain is innately organized into different functional networks that promote and support a number of different functions. Findings from those studies in functional connectivity at a resting state have suggested that there are at least three distinct networks, as follows (Sridharan et al., 2008, p. 12569):

- the central executive network (CEN)
- the default mode network (DMN)
- the salience network (SN)

Perhaps readers of this textbook may consider these networks to be different railroad systems in an urban area in the United States, such as the Philadelphia area. Each of those systems would take readers to different destinations of interest. However, the systems would have to coordinate with one another consistently and closely for effective, efficient communication, while also managing or preventing potential communication errors that might arise among the relationships of the systems. Now, let's look at major structural components of each of the functional networks, according to Sridharan and colleagues (2008, p. 12569).

First, the CEN involves key hubs of the dorsolateral prefrontal cortex (dlPFC) and posterior parietal cortex (PPC). In contrast, the DMN includes the ventromedial prefrontal cortex (vmPFC), posterior cingulate cortex (PCC), and the precuneus. In addition, the SN involves anterior insula, the anterior cingulate cortex (ACC), and the ventrolateral prefrontal cortex (vlPFC). In the SN, the vlPFC and anterior insula jointly form the fronto-insular cortex (FIC), functionally speaking. In particular, Sridharan and colleagues (2008) suggest that the right fronto-insular cortex (rFIC) specifically plays a critical role in partnership with the ACC in the context of switching between the CEN and DMN, by responding to the degree of subjective salience in the context of cognitive, homeostatic, and emotional salient signals. Among relevant previous studies, readers are encouraged to review Sridharan et al. (2008) for details of the functional connectivity experiments. Table 6.1 summarizes the aforementioned networks in the brain and their accordant functions.

TABLE 6.1   Three Distinct Functional Networks in the Human Brain

	Structure	Function
The central executive network (CEN)	• The dorsolateral prefrontal cortex (dlPFC) • The posterior parietal cortex (PPC)	• The active maintenance and manipulation of information in working memory • Judgement and decision making in the context of goal-directed behavior
The default mode network (DMN)	• The ventromedial prefrontal cortex (vmPFC) • The posterior cingulate cortex (PCC) • The precuneus	• Autobiographical memory • Self-reflection • Experience of having an embodied sense of self existing in space • Perceiving the perspectives of others/social interaction • Continued experience of self across and into the future
The salience network (SN)	• The ventrolateral prefrontal cortex (vlPFC) • Anterior insula • The anterior cingulate cortex (ACC)	• Responding to the degree of subjective salience • Activation and deactivation in the CEN and DMN • Integration of information from several brain regions

Source. The information included in the above table is adapted from Sridharan et al. (2008).

Note. The ventrolateral prefrontal cortex and anterior insula are referred to collectively as the fronto-insular cortex (FIC).

The Role of Early Caregiving on Neurodevelopment and Its Functioning

In animal studies, particularly in rodents, interpersonal trauma (e.g., adverse caregiving) early in life perturbs certain regions of the brain and their connectivity with one another, influencing amygdala, hippocampal, and prefrontal development (Roceri et al., 2004). Such experience is also known to be associated with increased visceral pain responses and augmented activation of the prefrontal cortex (PFC) and amygdala when experiencing the pain (Felice et al., 2013).

Similarly, research has indicated that the gut microbiome is reshaped by early adverse caregiving experiences while such microbial variation is related to brain reactivity within emotional networks (i.e., the PFC, PCC, and precuneus) in the brain (Callaghan et al., 2019).

The Role of Stress in Human Function: The Sense of Self

Lanius (2020) describes that the origin of the sense of self derives from the attachment relationship with a parental figure. Therefore, the development of secure attachment is foundational for the development and persistence of the social engagement system, addressed in Stephen Porges's polyvagal system (Porges, 2011). In his theory, the social engagement system is the primary defense in the hierarchical mechanism of human survival in the context of distress. In the face of trauma, the secure base of attachment is a primary survival mechanism. Thus, not having a secure base in the relationship with a primary parental figure early in life can profoundly affect varying domains of human functions, including developing a foundation for the sense of self and maturing it over time. Furthermore, the development and consistent maintenance of the sense of self is integral to the development of self-awareness and self-regulation (e.g., emotion regulation).

As addressed earlier in this chapter, trauma early in life can lead to both immediate and long-lasting effects. Specifically, trauma can have an immense effect on the sense of self and leave a signature on the cognitive and somatic domains of one's sense of self (Lanius, 2020). Ruth Lanius and her colleagues at University of Western Ontario refer to this phenomenon as "the hijacked sense of self in the aftermath of trauma". It is critical that individuals are developed and nurtured in a secure, predictable, consistent social environment, where a secure attachment develops during a sensitive development period, because the sense of self is not only a base for individual human functioning but also for orienting oneself in space and time, and relating to others with healthy boundaries (Lanius, 2020). This information holds significance in clinical implications for helping professionals because attachment whose foundational base was developed early in life, in the relationship with a parental figure, may not be something explicitly observable or obvious to either the helped or the helper, but otherwise it may affect varied domains of one's functions in life.

In clinical settings, helping professionals, particularly mental health professionals, often witness clients who have experienced trauma early in life facing seemingly endless internal battles that shake core beliefs about themselves. Additionally, research also suggests that it is prevalent that many individuals with trauma experience suffer from cognitive alterations, such as enduring negative beliefs about oneself, others, or the world, and repeated, colored blame of self or others for what has caused a traumatic event or what such event resulted in (Cox et al., 2014). Moreover, this prevalence was higher among those with lifetime experience in traumatic distress than among those who were exposed to a traumatic event but did not have prolonged traumatic distress.

Somatically, trauma can leave a persistent representation in varying ways. This includes an experience in somatic disturbances, such as general aches and pains in muscle, lower back pain, burping, or a feeling of unfinished bowel movement (Graham et al., 2019). It is documented that these somatic disturbances can substantially perturb the sense of self (Graham et al., 2019). In addition, many individuals with a diagnosis of PTSD endorse somatic alterations pertaining to self-experience, felt disembodiment, and accordant identity disturbances (Frewen & Lanius, 2015). As trauma can lead to a lack of or an altered development of the secure and sustained sense of self, both cognitively and somatically, individuals who experience traumatic events or series of events are vulnerable to profound, persistent disturbances and their attributes (Lanius, 2020). These may include seemingly endless captivity in the traumatic experience; fragmented memories of this experience; subsequent challenges to being present in the here and now to explore the full potential of themselves for optimal life; or developing and sustaining healthy social interactions and relationships in adulthood.

Neurobiology of the Sense of Self: The Default Mode Network

Before the sense of self is viewed from a neurobiological perspective, let's think more about the functions of our brains at rest. Have you ever thought about the human brain's function at rest? Daydreaming? Temporarily zoning out? What does the brain do when it is not actively engaged in cognitive tasks or goal-oriented behavior? Marcus Raichle, an American neurologist, coined the term default-mode to describe brain function at a resting state (Raichle et al., 2001). In relation to this, the DMN is one of the major resting state networks in the brain. Over the past two decades, neuroimaging methods have fueled research to explore the anatomy of the DMN system as well as its functions.

Functions of the DMN

The DMN in the brain is most active when individuals are in dialogue and reflection with themselves with minimal disruptions or stimuli from the external environment. Furthermore, brain regions in the DMN present an attenuation during the initiation of goal-oriented, cognitive tasks from a resting state. The DMN is characterized by low-frequency neuronal oscillations (< .01 Hz) that lead to temporal synchronization between functionally connected regions in the brain (Broyd et al., 2009). These oscillations are assumed to arise mostly from variations in metabolic processes during rest while seemingly managing independence of cardiac and respiratory processes (Sonuga-Barke & Castellanos, 2007).

Now, let's take some time to exercise this resting-state, passive activity. Please gently invite yourself to have a seat in a place where you and your body feel comfortable and safe. While you are practicing this activity, please distance yourself from a place where there are pronounced external stimuli, such as a disturbing noise, too much visual stimulation, a distinctive scent, the intake of food or beverage, and overt physical touch. Next, take a few minutes to think about each of the following questions on your own, maybe in silence.

- What was your childhood dream? (autobiographical memory)

- Can you draw a timeline in your mind where you can mark the milestones of your personal or professional accomplishments? (self-reflection/self-awareness)

- How would you describe your current professional identity as a helping professional? (self-reflection/self-awareness)

- While you are exercising this activity, how are you feeling? (experience of having an embodied sense of self existing in space)

- How would you describe your social network at present? In the past? (perceiving the perspectives of others/social interaction)

- How do you think your close friends describe your personality? (perceiving the perspectives of others/social interaction)

- In 5 years, where do you see yourself in your career journey? (continued experience of self across time and into the future)

- What was it like for you to practice this exercise? (self-reflection/self-awareness)

This exercise was designed to help you, as a reader of this textbook, better understand your inner environment. You were invited to think to yourself while undisturbed or minimally disturbed by your external environment. The DMN in your brain is most active at a resting state, and when you are left to look into yourself; recall your past; reflect on yourself in the past, at present or in the future; or feel and explore your emotional experience. These properties suggest that "the DMN functions to allow flexible mental explorations or stimulations that provide a means to prepare for upcoming, self-relevant events before they happen" (Buckner et al., 2008, p. 30).

Anatomy of the DMN

Anatomically, the DMN mostly comprises cortical regions across the brain's midline that include the PCC, the precuneus, and the medial prefrontal cortex (Buckner et al., 2008; Lanius et al., 2020). Located in the rear region of the brain, the PCC and precuneus are pertaining to our experience of having an embodied self that is existing in space and recalling the past experience (Lanius et al., 2020). The mPFC in the frontal region of the brain is involved in our awareness of thoughts and emotions related to the self (Lanius et al., 2020). Figure 6.2 illustrates the activated DMN at a resting state in healthy individuals.

The DMN is further organized into two functionally distinct subsystems—the medial prefrontal and the medial temporal subsystems (Buckner et al., 2008; Lanius et al., 2020). While both the subsystems are associated with autobiographical memory, the former is recruited during autobiographical memory construction processes, whereas the latter involves autobiographical

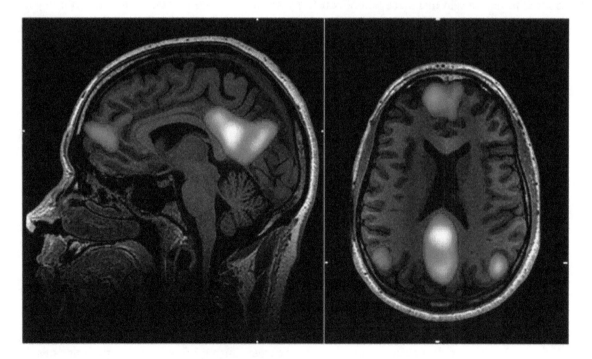

FIGURE 6.2   The Brain in the Default Mode Network

memory exploration. According to Lanius and colleagues (2020), autobiographical memory construction is "a process of forming early memory where contextual and semantic information set a stage for a particular memory to be recalled and then brought to make a mental representation" (p. 4). In particular, the DMN's medial prefrontal subsystem facilitates this process. In contrast, autobiographical memory elaboration processes are mediated by the medial temporal subsystem of the DMN (Lanius et al., 2020). This allows "a memory to be reexperienced by recalling its salient characteristics" in the presence of self-referential perspectives, in collaboration with visual imagery processes promoting these processes (Lanius et al., 2020, p. 4).

The Development and Maturation of the DMN

In this section, let's think about the development of the brain's function by default mode, including autobiographical processes of memory construction and exploration, embodied emotional experience, self-referential mentalizing/introspection, and social-cognitive relations. Fair and colleagues (2008, p. 4028) describe a young brain in childhood as having a basic ability for *episodic memory*, that is, "the ability to encode and retrieve stored information," although higher-order organization and incorporation of strategic planning develop with age in interaction with life experience. This development promotes the developing brain's performance on episodic memory tasks. In other words, the regions of the brain recruited in the DMN and its hubs are intact and functioning at relatively young ages of 7 to 9 (Fair et al., 2008). However, the maturation of the DMN and its associated functions require the progressive integration of the network and advanced strategies to improve memory processes with age (Fair et al., 2008).

In a functional connectivity MRI study, Fair et al. (2008) found that the structure of the DMN in children deviates substantially from the adult structure. For instance, the overall network in the DMN in children is only sparsely connected functionally. In contrast, in adults, the vmPFC is functionally connected with other regions (i.e., posterior cingulate and lateral parietal cortex) of the network (Fair et al., 2008). Readers are encouraged to refer to Fair et al.'s (2008) article, including a visualization of the distinct differences in the DMN network in children and adults.

The Role of the DMN in the Hijacked Sense of Self

The development and maturation of the DMN is influenced by a variety of factors. Moreover, its development is not immune to attributes of trauma experienced early in life. For instance, studies also suggest that altered neural patterns of DMN activity are seen in individuals with a number of mental disorders and neurological disorders, such as Alzheimer's disease, autism spectrum disorders, posttraumatic stress disorders, or schizophrenia spectrum disorders (Buckner et al., 2008; Lanius et al., 2020). Therefore, such individuals may be more vulnerable for dysfunction of mental processes.

Similarly, emerging research has suggested theoretical models of psychopathology for mental disorders in relation to atypical patterns of DMN activity. As an example, the default mode interference hypothesis/the default network interference hypothesis (Sonuga-Barke & Castellanos, 2007) speculates altered neural patterns exist in DMN activity compared to the normal transitioning between states of task positive and task passive. In the context of this framework, the task-positive state involves the brain's activity devoted to high levels of external, goal-oriented tasks (e.g., test taking), while the task-passive state includes the state of the brain activity recruited pertaining to internal cues (e.g., autobiographical memory processes). The interplay between these states is related to attentional performance (Sonuga-Barke & Castellanos, 2007). Thus, individuals with altered DMN activity related to attentional lapses and excessive wandering of the mind may be at risk for psychopathology, such as attention deficit/hyperactivity disorder (Gerrits et al., 2019).

Relevantly, research supports that altered functionality in the DMN of the brain has been observed in individuals with symptoms of PTSD in both resting-state and under-threat conditions when compared to their counterparts (Lanius et al., 2020). For instance, in individuals with PTSD, the DMN shows patterns in substantially decreased functional connectivity during rest (see Figure 6.3 [a]; Lanius et al., 2020). This reduced functional connectivity is viewed in association with a deceased coherence across the network. In a similar vein, these reductions in functional connectivity during rest between DMN hubs (i.e., the mPFC, PCC, and the precuneus) and the DMN are seemingly concentrated mostly in the medial-temporal subsystem (Lanius et al., 2020). These results imply the re-experiencing of the altered autobiographical memory (Lanius et al., 2020). From these results, it does not come as a surprise that many individuals with trauma exposure may be in pronounced captivity in the traumatic re-experience or its fragmentation over and over again.

In addition to showing altered functional connectivity in the DMN under threat-related conditions compared to their counterparts, individuals with PTSD also show this under subliminal threat conditions (Lanius et al., 2020). The subliminal threat condition may be viewed as a condition in which the memory of individuals with symptoms of traumatic stress is prompted related to the trauma and experienced or re-experienced outside of conscious awareness (Lanius et al., 2020). In contrast, individuals without symptoms of PTSD demonstrate a deactivation in their DMN, which contrasts to individuals with symptoms of PTSD. Interestingly, significantly stronger functional connectivity between the periaqueductal gray (PAG) in the midbrain and the DMN in individuals with PTSD was observed during subliminal, trauma-related conditions (Terpou et al., 2019a). Anatomically, the PAG is located in the midbrain, while functionally, its activation recruits defensive responses, such as fight, flight, or faint, in response to impending threat (Terpou et al., 2019a; Terpou et al., 2019b; Terpou et al., 2019c).

It is worth noting that the DMN hubs were functionally connected to the PAG during trauma-related conditions outside of conscious awareness in individuals with symptoms of PTSD, while this connection between those areas was not shown during subliminal, non-trauma-related stimulus conditions (see Figure 6.3 [b]). Moreover, threat- or trauma-related stimuli are processed by an interconnected network consisting of thalamic, midbrain, and brainstem regions (Lanius et al., 2017; Lanius et al., 2020). This network is called the innate alarm system. This system plays a detective role at the midbrain level that is similar to a Transport Service Administration agent working at an airport to search for threat-related information. This detected information is subsequently transmitted to the cortices for information integration in relation to the contextual information, and accordant decision making at the cortex level.

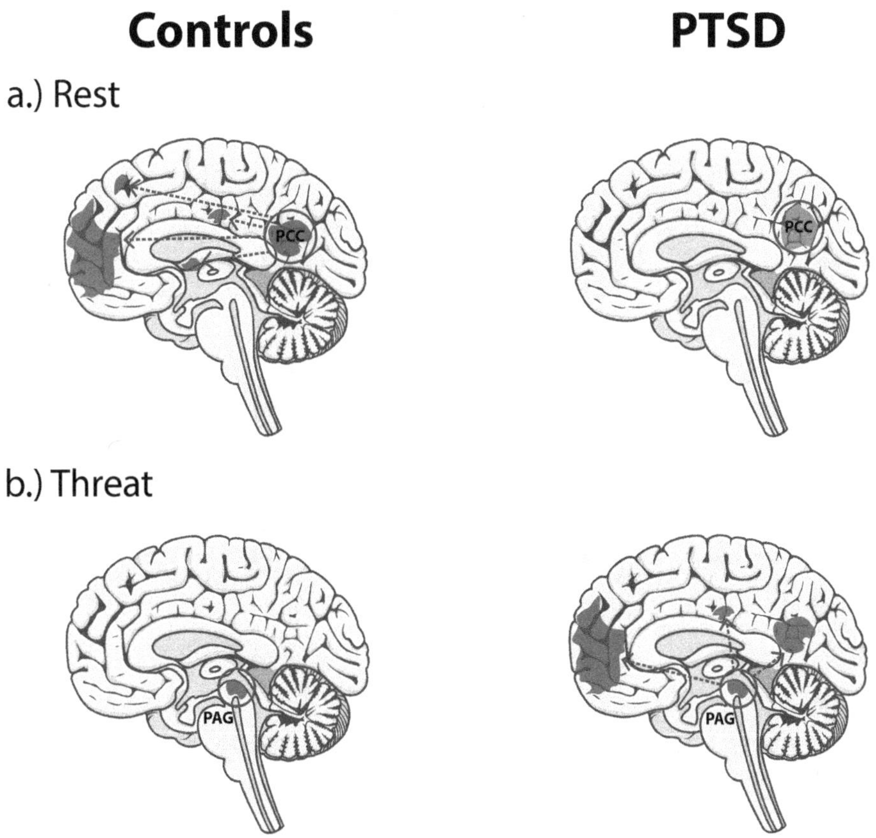

FIGURE 6.3 Functional Connectivity of the DMN in Healthy Individuals (Left) and in Individuals with PTSD (Right) at Resting (Top) and Subliminal Threat (Bottom) Conditions

These findings appear to align with the clinical reports referenced earlier in this chapter showing that individuals who have experienced trauma encounter persistent disruptions in cognitive and somatic experiences in association with the altered sense of self in both resting-state and outside of conscious awareness, trauma-related states. Given the critical role trauma plays in one's sense of self, these findings in altered functionality in the DMN in individuals with symptoms of PTSD in specific conditions may have critical clinical implications for both those with PTSD and their surrounding support systems, including their loved ones and the professionals helping them in clinical settings.

The Role of Stress in Human Function: Sensory Processing

During the Boston International Trauma Conference held in 2021, Sherain Harricharan explained that sensory processing helps us develop an internal depiction of how we interact with our surroundings. What are the sources of sensory information? As depicted in Figure 6.4 (Harricharan et al., 2021), sensory information comes in several different forms that can generally be organized in two different groups of input, including interoceptive and exteroceptive input. *Interoception*

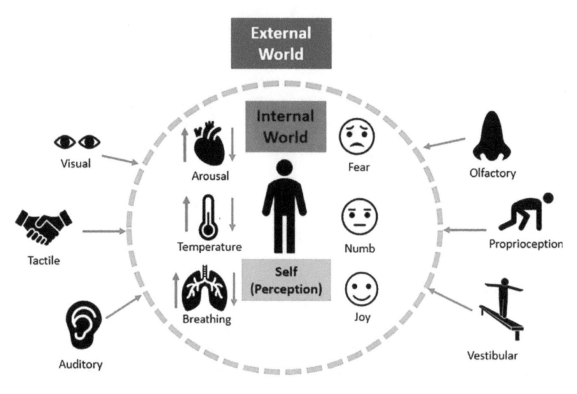

FIGURE 6.4   The Interaction Between Internal and External Worlds

refers to "the perception of the body from the inside" whereas *exteroception* is "the perception of the body from the outside" (Harricharan et al., 2021, p. 3). The functions of interoception involve sensing internal physiological states of the body and playing a role in searching for visceral sensations deriving from emotional and affective states (Harricharan et al., 2021). Specifically, the PAG, located in the midbrain, is a structure involved in a foundational primary process of emotional systems that generate raw affective sensations. These emotional systems are important for interoceptive processing at the cortex level.

By contrast, exteroception relies on multisensory stimuli stemming from the following information: sight, smell, hearing, taste, and touch, as well as orientation of the body in space. Let's practice your exteroception now! Look around your surroundings. What do you see? Maybe search through your kitchen and grab a savory snack. What does it smell like? Take a bite of your snack or take a sip of your liquid snack. What does it taste like? Are you still following me in this exercise? Then, if you are reading this book in a bound copy, can you close it up and touch its cover? What is it like to touch this book's cover?

The Role of Sensory Processing

Sensory processing is conceptualized as "the provision of a contextual framework where an individual can organize incoming salient information from the external world to shape a cohesive depiction of their inner world" (Harricharan et al., 2021, p. 3). Let's invite A depicted in the case study included in this textbook in order to better understand the neurobiological underpinnings of sensory processing in A's brain and the role of sensory processing in their decision making to adjust behavioral responses in the context where they are.

THE SCENARIO

On a sunny Saturday afternoon, A, their son-in-law, and their daughter go to the Philadelphia Flower Show that is being held in FDR Park in Philadelphia. For the first time in A's lifetime, the show is being hosted outdoors. A is a big fan of flowers and believes that they can even "talk" with flowers. As usual, A enjoys mints in their mouth while A is walking into the park. As they walk into the park, they are immediately stunned by the picturesque scene. At their first glance, the purple orchids and numerous red roses decorated around a pond catch their attention. They make a stop at those roses and lean forward to smell them. It is such a beautiful day out, and the park is extremely crowded by many visitors even though it is relatively warm and humid. All of a sudden, A's moment of enjoying the flowers appears to be disrupted by the buzzing of a bumblebee flying close by. A appears to have a frown on their face and eventually stretches their arm in full swing as if to scare the bee. A's attempt to shoo the bee away does not seem to be successful, as the roses keep attracting more bumblebees. A eventually decides to let them fly around and continues indulging in the flower show.

Now, let's see how A processes the sensory information stemming from the flower show visit illustrated above. A processes external sensations from the external world in conjunction with their inner physical and affective sensations associated with their feeling states stemming from within their body (Harricharan et al., 2021). Specifically, the sensory information coming from exteroceptive stimuli or from the surroundings of A in FDR Park include visual, auditory, tactile, vestibular, olfactory, and proprioceptive sensory information. These include what A sees in the park (e.g., flowers, bees, other visitors, and the park itself), what A smells (e.g., the flowers), what A touches, what A hears (e.g., the footsteps of themself and others, or other visitors' talk), what A tastes (e.g., the mints in their mouth), walking in balance or leaning toward the flowers without stumbling, and knowing that they are in the park without being confused, and how to orient themselves in the park. Also, affective sensations deriving from within A's body simultaneously join this exteroceptive sensory information, allowing A to monitor their inner bodily states. Examples of this interoceptive input may include A's body temperatures, sensations of blood flow, breathing, bowel movement, and affective and emotional sensations. Together, simultaneously coordinated processing of these internal and external signals is important for driving A's neural processes that help their adaptive action in response to their surroundings (Harricharan et al., 2021).

The initial phenomenological experience of this raw sensory information enters at the brainstem. The brainstem plays a critical role in receiving raw sensory information. Raw sensory information means that it is not yet integrated with contextual information and interpreted cognitively. Then, the brainstem eventually relays this information in detail to the insula and subsequently to the PFC in the brain (Harricharan et al., 2021). This allows for advanced, higher-order sensory processing that includes making interoceptive inferences from the raw internal stimuli and integrating the sensory information with contextual information in order to ultimately facilitate goal-oriented, adaptive behavioral action in response to salient stimuli (Harricharan et al., 2021). Multisensory integration (see Figures 6.5 and 6.6 [Harricharan et al., 2021]) at the PFC level is critical for understanding and interpreting varying sources of sensory information. This process contextualizes a sensory experience that promotes our embodied representation of the self in space and time, in relation to our surrounding environment (Harricharan et al., 2021).

Getting back to A's scenario, the exteroceptive and interoceptive signals simultaneously enter the brainstem in their brain and subsequently are transmitted to the insula, making them aware of the sensory experience. In particular, in the posterior insula of the brain, interoceptive inferences are made from raw interoceptive signals transmitted from the brainstem. With the contextual information (A is at the flower show in FDR Park in Philadelphia) coming into play with the internal and external sensory information, A can orient themselves in the park and continue enjoying the flower show. When A hears the buzzing of a bumblebee, based on the description of their facial expressivity of having a frown on their face, you might hypothesize that A seems to be disturbed by the bee, or associated memories related to bees if A had a relevant experience in the past. As A's attempt to shoo that bee away becomes unsuccessful, they decide to move on and allow themselves to not be bothered by the buzzing bee, but instead to continue enjoying their time in the roses. Figure 6.5 illustrates the sensory transmission in individuals who are thought to have the intact ability to process sensory information properly.

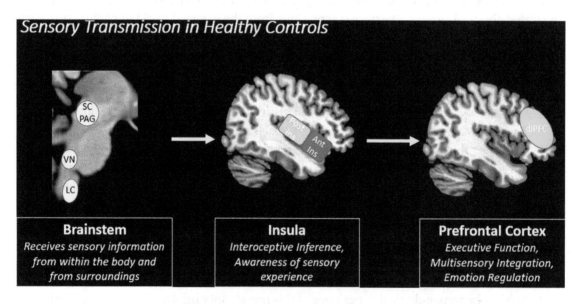

FIGURE 6.5   Sensory Transmission in Healthy Controls

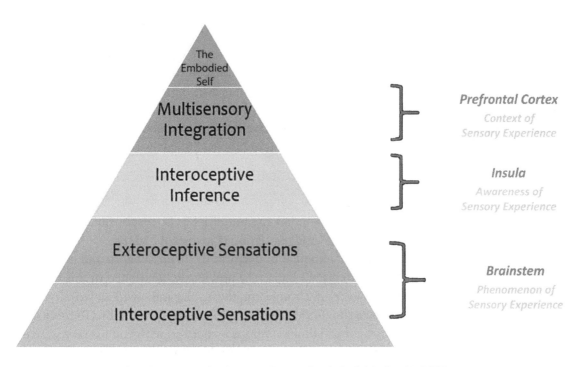

FIGURE 6.6   Theoretical Framework for Sensory Processing in Individuals with PTSD

Perception in the Aftermath of Trauma

Sherain Harricharan presented informative sessions during the 31st and 32nd Boston International Trauma Conferences to address the importance of multisensory integration in sensory processing in relation to a sustained sense of self over time. Additionally, she also described the impact of trauma on sensory processing and the sense of self in individuals with PTSD, and those with PTSD and dissociation. This latter group is described as a dissociative subtype of PTSD in her work. Relatedly, Lanius and colleagues (2010) reported that individuals with a dissociative subtype of PTSD showed unique neural presentations compared to both individuals without PTSD (so-called healthy counterparts) and individuals with PTSD and with non-dissociation.

According to Lanius and colleagues (2010), it is observed in clinical settings that individuals with symptoms of PTSD show persistent hypervigilance toward their physical and social surroundings. By contrast, individuals with a dissociative subtype PTSD experience hypoactivation of the insula, which is associated with the processing of incoming interoceptive affective sensations. This hypo-activated insula may further result in reduced emotional awareness and may also promote emotional numbing. This subtype is also associated with the demonstration of PAG connectivity with structures, such as the temporal parietal junction (TPJ) associated with passive defensive responses (dissociation) and emotional detachment (Lanius et al., 2010).

In a similar vein, research has suggested that individuals exhibiting symptoms of probable *alexithymia*, a condition characterized as "difficulty in identifying, interpreting, and describing emotions," are likely to report widespread activation and deactivation of bodily sensations throughout the body that are inadequate in intensity and in specificity (Lloyd et al., 2021, p. 2). Specifically, compared to individuals without this condition, in those who exhibit symptoms of alexithymia, bodily intensity maps show less activation in intensity of activation sensations across emotions and are less discernible in activational patterns across emotions (Lloyd et al., 2021). For instance, bodily sensation maps appear similar for the emotions of anxiety, anger, fear, happiness, love, pride, and surprise in such individuals. Similarly, the lack of specificity in somatosensory information aligns with altered interoception in this condition (Lloyd et al., 2021). Individuals who have difficulty and struggle with interoceptive awareness are likely to face difficulty identifying emotional states, such as feeling hungry or thirsty, or hot or cold. Therefore, this impairment in interoception has the potential to be responsible for severely altered emotional experience, expression, and regulation (Lloyd et al., 2021).

In order to investigate these neurobiological underpinnings, Harricharan and colleagues (2021) proposed the integrative model (see Figure 6.6) previously mentioned in this chapter. This model uses a hierarchy that involves the brainstem, the insula, and the PFC. In individuals with PTSD, neural alterations have shown that there are substantial aberrations in brainstem functional connectivity with cortical and limbic regions associated with emotional reactivity (Harricharan et al., 2021). This may influence how such individuals process sensory information stemming from both internal and external sensations in cortical regions of the brain. Specifically, when compared to individuals without PTSD, individuals with PTSD tend to show widespread PAG connectivity with areas involved in emotional reactivity at resting states (Harricharan et al., 2016). Such individuals might be vulnerable to persistently engaging in heightened states with the redirection of incoming sensory information to alternative brain regions under threat (Harricharan et al., 2016, 2021). This persistent, heightened physiological state can affect how exteroceptive sensory information is processed (Harricharan et al., 2021).

In addition, the transmission of raw sensory information coming from the brainstem to the insula aids in making an interoceptive inference (Harricharan et al., 2021). This inference may trigger higher-order cortical regions in the central executive network (CEN) to carry out multisensory integration (Harricharan et al., 2021). This process is coupled with the activation of overlapping brain structures responsible for emotional regulation that help with re-integration of a traumatic memory through conscious, top-down reappraisal (Harricharan et al., 2021).

In individuals with dissociative subtype PTSD, limited vestibular nuclei connectivity with the TPJ within the parieto-insular vestibular cortex is observed (Harricharan et al., 2021). Thus, it was postulated that this neural aberration may have a negative effect on the ability to understand self-orientation in space, likely leading to feelings of disembodiment (Harricharan et al., 2021). *Embodiment* refers to "how an individual's perception of the world can shape how the body meaningfully interacts with their environment" (Harricharan et al., 2021, p. 13). In this state, one is compromised in the ownership of their body while their mental agency to make an adaptive movement is also limited (Blanke et al., 2015). In addition, interestingly, the PTSD dissociative subtype manifests increased insula subregion connectivity with posterior brain structures (e.g., occipital cortex; Harricharan et al., 2021). Figure 6.7 (Harricharan et al., 2021)

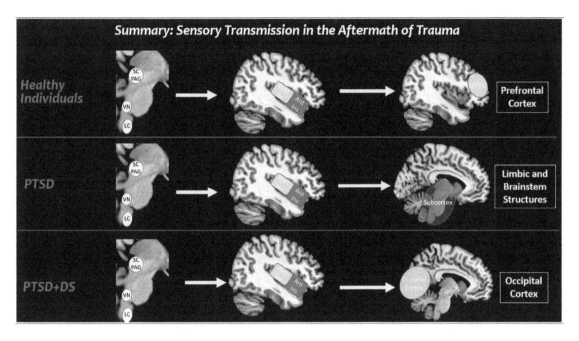

FIGURE 6.7   Sensory Transmission in the Aftermath of Trauma

summarizes the sensory transmission in individuals with PTSD and with PTSD in addition to dissociation when compared to their counterparts.

Summary

It is imperative for helping professionals to have a good understanding of the human brain and its intricate networks with other organs and organ systems in the body, as they are intimately related to overall human health. When it comes to the development of the healthy brain, the first few years as well as the prenatal period are sensitive periods in life. The human brain is known to be susceptible to varying factors, including internal and external environmental stimuli, such as caregiving experiences, attachment, or safety in surrounding environments (Malan-Muller et al., 2018). Additionally, the human brain is organized broadly in three distinct functional networks known as the central executive network, DMN, and salience network (Sridharan et al., 2008). Each of these networks consists of specific regions in the brain, and they are responsible for different functions. The details of this knowledge appear in Table 6.1 of this chapter.

As addressed earlier, early caregiving experiences hold significance in healthy brain development. For instance, developing the stable sense of self as one of the functions of the brain originates from the attachment relationship with a parental figure (Lanius, 2020). Furthermore, the development of secure attachment is important for the development and maintenance of the social engagement system, as addressed in Stephen Porges's polyvagal system (Porges, 2011). Similarly, a secure attachment develops during a sensitive development period and generates a base for individual human functioning, helping orient oneself in space and time, and relate to others with healthy boundaries (Lanius, 2020). However, adversity early in life or trauma can lead to developmental disruptions, resulting in immediate and long-lasting effects on the health and function of the brain. Specifically, trauma can have a substantial, developmental effect on the sense of self and leave a signature on the cognitive and somatic domains of an one's sense of self (Lanius, 2020). Relevantly, research has suggested that many individuals with trauma experience suffer from cognitive alterations (e.g., enduring negative beliefs about oneself, others, or the world; repeated, colored blame of self or others; Cox et al., 2014). In addition, trauma can also leave a persistent physical representation in those who undergo traumatic life events that is associated with somatic disturbances (e.g., general muscle aches and pains, back pain, or feeling of unfinished bowel movement; Graham et al., 2019). In a similar vein, research suggests that many individuals with a diagnosis of PTSD deal with somatic alterations related to feelings of disembodiment and identity disturbances (Frewen & Lanius, 2015). This holds significant clinical implications for helping professionals who are particularly working with clients with developmental trauma and complex trauma. Specifically, this chapter addressed the importance of multisensory integration in sensory processing related to a sustained sense of self over time. The impact of trauma on sensory processing and the sense of self in individuals with symptoms of trauma- and stressor-related disorders is substantial and developmentally disruptive. Similarly, research has shown that individuals with symptoms of PTSD present persistent hypervigilance toward their physical and social surroundings, while those with PTSD and dissociation experience alterations in processing interoceptive affective sensations (Lanius et al., 2020). This hypoactivation in the insula, a region of the brain, is responsible for reduced emotional awareness and may promote emotional numbing (Lanius et al., 2020). This chapter addressed the findings from relevant studies supporting evidence for neural aberrations in such individuals.

Informative Resources

- A video series by Sebern Fisher and Ruth Lanius, *At Least I Felt Alive*

  https://www.youtube.com/watch?v=PvrrWY3EOIY

- A video series by Sebern Fisher and Ruth Lanius, *Just Getting to the Here and Now*

  https://www.youtube.com/watch?v=vTpVudIkZDI

Experiential Questions

1. What information from the case study do you think would describe effects of A's gut-brain interaction in relation to their current experience in a health state addressed?

2. What stressors do you think are affecting A's brain function described in the case study?

3. What do you think exists between A's current stress level and homeostasis in their gut health?

References

Sense of Self

Broyd, S. J., Demanuele, C., Debener, S., Helps, S. K., James, C. J., & Sonuga-Barke, E. J. S. (2009). Default-mode brain dysfunction in mental disorders: A systematic review. *Neuroscience & Biobehavioral Reviews, 33*(3), 279–296. https://doi.org/10.1016/j.neubiorev.2008.09.002

Buckner, R. L., Andrews-Hanna, J. R., & Schacter, D. L. (2008). The brain's default network. *Annals of the New York Academy of Sciences, 1124*(1), 1–38. https://doi.org/10.1196/annals.1440.011

Cox, K. S., Resnick, H. S., & Kilpatrick, D. G. (2014). Prevalence and correlates of posttrauma distorted beliefs: Evaluating *DSM*-5 PTSD expanded cognitive symptoms in a national sample. *Journal of Traumatic Stress, 27*(3), 299–306. https://doi.org/10.1002/jts.21925

Fair, D. A., Cohen, A. L., Dosenbach, N. U. F., Church, J. A., Miezin, F. M., Barch, D. M., Raichle, M. E., Petersen, S. E., & Schlaggar, B. L. (2008). The maturing architecture of the brain's default network. *Proceedings of the National Academy of Sciences, 105*(10), 4028–4032. https://doi.org/10.1073/pnas.0800376105

Felice, M. D., Eyde, N., Dodick, D., Dussor, G. O., Ossipov, M. H., Fields, H. L., & Porreca, F. (2013). Capturing the aversive state of cephalic pain preclinically. *Annals of Neurology, 74*(2), 257–265. https://doi.org/10.1002/ana.23922

Frewen, P. A., & Lanius, R. A. (2015). *Healing the traumatized self: Consciousness, neuroscience, treatment.* W. W. Norton & Company.

Graham, K., Searle, A., Van Hooff, M., Lawrence-Wood, E., & McFarlane, A. (2019). The associations between physical and psychological symptoms and traumatic military deployment exposures. *Journal of Traumatic Stress, 32*(6), 957–966. https://doi.org/10.1002/jts.22451

Gerrits, B., Vollebregt, M. A., Olbrich, S., van Dijk, H., Palmer, D., Gordon, E., Pascual-Marqui, R., Kessels, R. P.C., & Arns, M. (2019). Probing the "default network interference hypothesis" with EEG: An RDoC approach focused on attention. *Clinical EEG and Neuroscience, 50*(6), 404–412. https://doi.org/10.1177/1550059419864461

Lanius, R. A., Rabellino, D., Boyd, J. E., Harricharan, S., Frewen, P. A., & McKinnon, M. C. (2017). The innate alarm system in PTSD: Conscious and subconscious processing of threat. *Current Opinion in Psychology, 14*, 109–115. https://doi.org/10.1016/j.copsyc.2016.11.006

Lanius, R. A., Terpou, B. A., & McKinnon, M. C. (2020). The sense of self in the aftermath of trauma: Lessons from the default mode network in posttraumatic stress disorder. *European Journal of Psychotraumatology, 11*(1). https://doi.org/10.1080/20008198.2020.1807703

Raichle, M. E., MacLeod, A. M., Snyder, A. Z., Powers, W. J., Gusnard, D. A., & Shulman, G. L. (2001). A default mode of brain function. *Proceedings of the National Academy of Sciences, 8*(2), 676–682. https://doi.org/10.1073/pnas.98.2.676

Sonuga-Barke, E. J. S., & Castellanos, F. X. (2007). Spontaneous attentional fluctuations in impaired states and pathological conditions: A neurobiological hypothesis. *Neuroscience and Biobehavioral Reviews, 31*(7), 977–986. https://doi.org/10.1016/j.neubiorev.2007.02.005

Terpou, B. A., Densmore, M., Théberge, J., Thome, J., Frewen, P., McKinnon, M. C., & Lanius, R. A. (2019a). The threatful self: Midbrain functional connectivity to cortical midline and parietal regions during subliminal trauma-related processing in PTSD. *Chronic Stress*, 3, 1–12. https://doi.org/10.1177/2470547019871369

Terpou, B. A., Densmore, M., Thome, J., Frewen, P., McKinnon, M. C., & Lanius, R. A. (2019b). The innate alarm system and subliminal threat presentation in posttraumatic stress disorder: Neuroimaging of the midbrain and cerebellum. *Chronic Stress*, 3, 1–13. https://doi.org/10.1177/2470547018821496

Terpou, B. A., Harricharan, S., McKinnon, M. C., Frewen, P., Jetly, R., & Lanius, R. A. (2019c). The effects of trauma on brain and body: A unifying role for the midbrain periaqueductal gray. *Journal of Neuroscience Research*, 97(9), 1110–1140. https://doi.org/10.1002/jnr.24447

Sensory Processing

Blanke, O., Slater, M., & Serino, A. (2015). Behavioral, neural, and computational principles of bodily self-consciousness. *Neuron*, 88, 145–166. https://doi.org/10.1016/j.neuron.2015.09.029

Harricharan, S., Mckinnon, M. C., & Lanius, R. A. (2021). How processing of sensory information from the internal and external worlds shape the perception and engagement with the world in the aftermath of trauma: Implications for PTSD. *Frontiers in Neuroscience*, 15, 625490. https://doi.org/10.3389/fnins.2021.625490

Harricharan, S., Rabellino, D., Frewen, P. A., Densmore, M., Théberge, J., McKinnon, M. C., Schore, A. N., & Lanius, R. A. (2016). fMRI functional connectivity of the periaqueductal gray in PTSD and its dissociative subtype. *Brain Behavior*, 6(12), e00579. https://doi.org/10.1002/brb3.579

Lanius, R. A., Vermetten, E., Loewenstein, R. J., Brand, B., Schmahl, C., Bremner, J. D., & Spiegel, D. (2010). Emotion modulation in PTSD: Clinical and neurobiological evidence for a dissociative subtype. *American Journal of Psychiatry*, 167, 640–647. https://doi.org/10.1176/appi.ajp.2009.09081168

Lloyd, C. S., Stafford, E., McKinnon, M. C., Rabellino, D., D'Andrea, W., Densmore, M., Thome, J., Neufeld, R. W. J., & Lanius, R. A. (2021). Mapping alexithymia: Level of emotional awareness differentiates emotion-specific somatosensory maps. *Child Abuse & Neglect*, 113. https://doi.org/10.1016/j.chiabu.2020.104919

Sridharan, D., Levitin, D. J., & Menon, V. (2008). A critical role for the right fronto-insular cortex in switching between central-executive and default-mode networks. *Proceedings of the National Academy of Sciences*, 105(34), 12569–12574. https://doi.org/10.1073/pnas.0800005105

General

Agrawal, M., Sabino, J., Frias-Gomes, C., Hillenbrand, C. M., Soudant, C., Axelrad, J. E., Shah, S. C., Ribeiro-Mourão, F., Lambin, T., Peter, I., Colombel, J.-F., Narula, N., & Torres, J. (2021). Early life exposures and the risk of inflammatory bowel disease: Systematic review and meta-analyses. *EClinicalMedicine*, 36, 100884. https://doi.org/10.1016/j.eclinm.2021.100884

Bastiaanssen, T. F. S., Cussotto, S., Claesson, M. J., Clarke, G., Dinan, T. G., & Cryan, J. F. (2020). Gutted! Unraveling the role of the microbiome in major depressive disorder. *Harvard Review of Psychiatry*, 28(1), 26–39. https://doi.org/10.1097/HRP.0000000000000243

Callaghan, B. L., Fields, A., Gee, D. G., Gabard-Durnam, L., Caldera, C., Humphreys, K. L., Goff, B., Flannery, J., Telzer, E. H., Shapiro, M., & Tottenham, N. (2019). Mind and gut: Associations between mood and gastrointestinal distress in children exposed to adversity. *Development and Psychopathology*, *32*(1), 309–328. https://doi.org/10.1017/s0954579419000087

Capuron, L., & Miller, A. H. (2011). Immune system to brain signaling: Neuropsychopharmacological implications. *Pharmacology & Therapeutics*, *130*(2), 226–238. https://doi.org/10.1016/j.pharmthera.2011.01.014

Carlson, A. L., Xia, K., Azcarate-Peril, M. A., Goldman, B. D., Ahn, M., Styner, M. A., Thompson, A. L., Geng, X., Gilmore, J. H., & Knickmeyer, R. C. (2018). Infant gut microbiome associated with cognitive development. *Biological Psychiatry, 83*(2), 148–159. https://doi.org/10.1016/j.biopsych.2017.06.021

Cowan, C. S. M., Dinan, T. G., & Cryan, J. F. (2020). Annual research review: Critical windows—the microbiota–gut–brain axis in neurocognitive development. *The Journal of Child Psychology and Psychiatry, 61*(3), 353–371. https://doi.org/10.1111/jcpp.13156

Desbonnet, L., Garrett, L., Clarke, G., Kiely, B., Cryan, J. F., & Dinan, T. G. (2010). Effects of the probiotic bifidobacterium infantis in the maternal separation model of depression. *Neuroscience, 170*(4), 1179–1188. https://doi.org/10.1016/j.neuroscience.2010.08.005

Jacka, F. N., Ystrom, E., Brantsaeter, A. L., Karevold, E., Roth, C., Haugen, M., Meltzer, H. M., Schjolberg, S., & Berk, M. (2013). Maternal and early postnatal nutrition and mental health of offspring by age 5 years: A prospective cohort study. *Journal of the American Academy of Child and Adolescent Psychiatry*, *52*(10), 1038–1047. https://doi.org/10.1016/j.jaac.2013.07.002

Foster, J. A., Rinaman, L., & Cryan, J. F. (2017). Stress & the gut-brain axis: Regulation by the microbiome. *Neurobiology of Stress, 7*, 124–136. https://doi.org/10.1016/j.ynstr.2017.03.001

Garcia-Cabrerizo, R., Carbia, C., O'Riordan, K. J., Schellekens, H., & Cryan, J. F. (2021). Microbiota-gut-brain axis as a regulator of reward processes. *Journal of Neurochemistry, 157*, 1495–1524. https://doi.org/10.1111/jnc.15284

Gershon, M. D. (1999). *The second brain*. Harper Perennial.

Hill, J. H., & Round, J. L. (2021). SnapShot: Microbiota effects on host physiology. *Cell, 184*(10), 2796–2796. e1. https://doi.org/10.1016/j.cell.2021.04.026

Logan, A. C., Jacka, F. N. & Prescott, S. L. (2016). Immune-microbiota interactions: Dysbiosis as a global health issue. *Current Allergy Asthma Rep, 16*, 13. https://doi.org/10.1007/s11882-015-0590-5

Malan-Muller, S., Valles-Colomer, M., Raes, J., Lowry, C. A., Seedat, S., & Hemmings, S. M. J. (2018). The gut microbiome and mental health: Implications for anxiety- and trauma-related disorders. *OMICS: A Journal of Integrative Biology*, *22*(2), 90–107. https://doi.org/10.1089/omi.2017.0077

Mayer, E. (2018). *The mind-gut connection: How the hidden conversation within our bodies impacts our mood, our choices, and our overall health*. Harper Wave.

Park, S. H., Videlock, E. J., Shih, W., Presson, A. P., Mayer, E. A., & Chang, L. (2016). Adverse childhood experiences are associated with irritable bowel syndrome and gastrointestinal symptom severity. *Neurogastroenterology and Motility, 28*, 1252–1260. https://doi.org/10.1111/nmo.12826

Petersen, C., & Round, J. L. (2014). Defining dysbiosis and its influence on host immunity and disease. *Cellular Microbiology, 16*(7), 1024–1033. https://doi.org/10.1111/cmi.12308

Porges, S. W. (2011). *The polyvagal theory: Neurophysiological foundations of emotions, attachment, communication, and self-regulation*. W. W. Norton & Company.

Sender, R., Fuchs, S., & Milo, R. (2017). Revised estimates for the number of human and bacterial cells in the body. *bioRxiv.* https://doi.org/10.1371/journal.pbio.1002533

Raichle, M. E. (2011). The restless brain. *Brain Connectivity, 1*(1), 3–12. https://doi.org/10.1089/brain.2011.0019

Roceri, M., Cirulli, F., Pessina, C., Peretto, P., Racagni, G., & Riva, M. R. (2004). Postnatal repeated maternal deprivation produces age-dependent changes of brain-derived neurotrophic factor expression in selected rat brain regions. *Biological Psychiatry, 55*(7), 708–714. https://doi.org/10.1016/j.biopsych.2003.12.011

Figure Credits

CHAPTER SEVEN

Heart, Immune System, and Human Microbiome

The key points addressed in this chapter are

- the impact of heart health on mental health and mental illness

- the use of the heart rate variability as an index of heart health and its other clinical implications

- the immune system and its attributes to mental health and mental illness

- the interplay between gut microbes and the immune system via a variety of mechanisms, including the intestinal barrier

---

The Association Between Heart Health and Mental Illness

> "When the heart is affected it reacts on the brain; and the state of the brain again reacts through the pneumo-gastric (vagus) nerve on the heart; so that under any excitement there will be much mutual action and reaction between these, the two most important organs of the body."
>
> *Darwin (1872, p. 69)*

Among other factors, it has been identified that ischemic heart disease is the primary cause of increased mortality in those with mental disorders (Goldstein et al., 2015; Ösby et al., 2001). Compared to the general population, those with mood disorders (e.g., depressive disorders or bipolar disorders) experience more than 2 to 2.5 times higher mortality due to ischemic heart disease (Angst et al., 2002). This risk is more pronounced in individuals with a bipolar disorder than in those with a major depressive disorder. Specifically, in the United States, adults with a bipolar disorder have a five-fold increased risk of cardiovascular disease (Goldstein et al., 2015). It has also been identified that individuals with a bipolar disorder have shorter life expectancies and are likely to experience the comorbidities of diabetes, smoking, or obesity (Angst et al., 2002; Murray et al., 2009).

In addition, an extensive body of evidence has suggested that autonomic imbalance alongside other factors is associated with disease and death (Thayer et al., 2010). In this context, *autonomic imbalance* is characterized by "a hyperactive sympathetic system and a hypoactive parasympathetic system" (Thayer et al., 2010, p. 122). As one index of cardiac autonomic function, heart rate variability (HRV) has been identified and employed by researchers (Villareal et al., 2002). HRV is a physiological marker to index health; higher values of HRV represent the physiology of a healthier autonomic nervous system (Villareal et al., 2002). Measures of HRV are organized into time and frequency domains to indicate vagal activity. In the time domain, the following measures—the standard deviation of the interbeat intervals, standard deviation of R to R intervals, root mean square successive differences, and measures of baroreflex sensitivity—have proved the ability and usefulness to indicate vagal activity (Thayer et al., 2010). Despite debate over the autonomic system affecting the measures, the frequency domain of HRV involves low frequency (0.04–0.15 Hz) and high frequency (0.15–0.40 Hz) spectral powers (Thayer et al., 2010). While people with a high level of adaptability demonstrate a high degree of HRV, associated with the ability to promptly adapt to environmental demands, decreased HRV has been associated with numerous consequences, such as myocardial infarction and sudden cardiac death (Villareal et al., 2002). In addition, there is evidence linking HRV to risk factors (e.g., hypertension, obesity, family history, and work stress) for cardiovascular disease (Thayer et al., 2010).

For example, Ortiz and colleagues (2021) conducted a study to investigate the association between HRV measures and several variables related to perceived illness burden in 53 adults with a primary diagnosis of bipolar I or II in any phase of the illness. The factors characterizing illness burden of bipolar disorders included lifetime depressive episodes; lifetime number of manic, hypomanic, or mixed episodes; lifetime number of all types of episodes; durations of the most severe depressive and hypomanic/manic episodes; duration of current episode; the age at onset; a history of suicide attempts; psychotic symptoms during episodes; comorbidity of anxiety disorders; and a family history of mental disorders or suicide (Ortiz et al., 2021). Results indicated reduced HRV was associated with a high level of perceived illness burden in bipolar disorder when controlling for age, sex, years of education, marital status, medication use, body mass index, and functional cardiovascular status (Ortiz et al., 2021). The authors emphasized that these findings were important because HRV is a reliable index of overall functional cardiovascular status, and a decreased HRV is predictive of an elevated risk of cardiovascular disease and mortality (Ortiz et al., 2021).

Also, in children and adolescents, alongside major depressive disorder, attempted suicide, and anxiety, bipolar disorder has been linked to increased risk of premature cardiovascular disease or related deaths (Goldstein et al., 2015). Mood disorders are highly prevalent among adolescents, and early intervention can prevent a severe illness course or relevant consequences from a developmental perspective; thus, it is critical to perform improved identification, monitoring, and treatment of these conditions for both mental and cardiovascular benefits (Goldstein et al., 2015). In this context, the use of HRV measures can be an empirically supported, helpful marker.

According to the American Heart Association, pathophysiological mechanisms of the high risk of cardiovascular disease among adults with mental disorders include several factors: HPA axis and SAM hyperactivity, increased platelet reactivity, decreased HRV, vascular inflammation, oxidative stress, and endothelial dysfunction (Goldstein et al., 2015). The adoption of unhealthy lifestyle behaviors (e.g., sedentary lifestyle or early substance use) may promote these processes. In addition, there is empirical support for shared genetic pathways between depression and cardiovascular disease (McCaffery et al., 2009).

Additionally, physiological regulation is paramount and implicated in health and disease. In a similar vein, the regulation of physiological systems has been associated with vagal function and HRV (Thayer & Lane, 2009). Specifically, in mammals, vagal tone is the greatest during unchallenged situations (e.g., sleep), and it is actively withdrawn in situations, such as exercise, stress, attention, and information processing (Thayer & Lane, 2009). These activities are adaptive and responsive to external demands. The vagus nerve in mammals is described as acting as a brake to allow speedy inhibition and disinhibition of vagal tone to the heart to facilitate behavioral mobilization or self-soothing in individuals (Porges, 2011). Thus, the vagal brake plays a pivotal mediating role in cardiac output by decelerating or accelerating the inhibitory vagal control of the heart to influence heart rate (Porges, 2011). These processes subsequently help fine-tune metabolic resources to buttress either behavioral mobilization or social engagement behaviors (Porges, 2011).

In research, findings have suggested support for the concept of the vagal brake to examine individuals' differences in ability to speedily change their physiological state (Calkins et al., 2007). For instance, children with externalizing problems showed less vagal braking while children with a combination of externalizing and internalizing behaviors showed with the greatest suppression of respiratory sinus arrhythmia and an increased heart rate (Calkins et al., 2007). Similarly, the neurovisceral integration model (Thayer & Lane, 2000) proposes that cardiac vagal tone is associated with the integrity of prefrontal and subcortical circuits. As HRV is a reliable index of cardiac vagal tone, an increased HRV can be related to optimal functioning of prefrontal-subcortical circuits (Thayer & Lane, 2009). Considering the physiology of the heart and its relationships with the brain, the neurovisceral integration model further supports the relationship between HRV and the regulation of critical cognitive, emotional, and physiological functions (Thayer & Lane, 2009). In this context, HRV as an index demonstrates the ability to meet environmental demands in a flexible system of neural structures optimally and dynamically (Thayer & Lane, 2009).

Summary
It is evident that many individuals with mood disorders are at higher risk for mortality compared to the general population in the United States due to ischemic heart disease (Angst et al., 2002).

Specifically, adults with a bipolar disorder have up to five-fold increased risk of cardiovascular disease (Goldstein et al., 2015). Similarly, autonomic imbalance in addition to other varied factors is responsible for disease and death in humans (Thayer et al., 2010).

HRV has been used as one biomarker of cardiac autonomic function (Villareal et al., 2002). Research has found that HRV has a predictive capacity for a greater risk of cardiovascular disease and death (Ortiz et al., 2021). Additionally, in children and adolescents, bipolar disorder has been associated with heightened risk of premature and cardiovascular disease or related deaths (Goldstein et al., 2015). When considering the prevalence of mood disorders, such as bipolar disorders, among adolescents, early invention can hold significance in preventing a severe illness course, or developmental consequences and complications through strengthened case identification, monitoring, and treatment of those conditions (Goldstein et al., 2015). In doing so, the use of HRV measures as an index of heart health can be a helpful marker. Moreover, physiological regulation is critical and implicated in human health and disease. Furthermore, this has been linked to vagal function and HRV (Thayer & Lane, 2009). Research has found that examining the vagal brake is paramount in unraveling individual differences in the ability to rapidly change physiological states. Similarly, cardiac vagal tone is associated with the integrity of prefrontal and subcortical circuits in the neurovisceral integration model (Thayer & Lane, 2000).

The Role of Stress in the Immune System

> "Inflammation presents one feasible mechanism through which diet may affect the risk of mental disorders."
>
> *Firth et al. (2019, p. 3)*

> "Early life exposures impact immune system development and therefore the risk of immune-mediated diseases, including inflammatory bowel disease."
>
> *Agrawal et al. (2021, p. 1)*

In recent years, research has revealed that severe mental illnesses (SMI), such as mood disorders (depressive and bipolar disorders), and schizophrenia, are associated with increased inflammation. Specifically, the associated inflammation processes have been observed at levels of both peripheral inflammation (Goldsmith et al., 2016) and systemic inflammation (Wang & Miller, 2017). Alongside poor mental health, a study suggests that people with SMIs experience noticeable, disproportionate physical health problems, including cardiometabolic disorders, diabetes, and higher rates of obesity (Firth et al., 2019). The comorbidity of poor physical health and SMIs leads to vulnerability in those who suffer. Furthermore, alongside the increasing depression in younger populations, research has suggested that neurodevelopmental and neurodegenerative diseases, such as autism spectrum disorder and Alzheimer's disease, have been on the rise (Weinberger et al., 2018). Nevertheless, emergent research has pointed to a common factor in these metabolic, cognitive, mental, and neurological illnesses; that is, the gut microbiome (Mayer, 2021).

It is well documented from extensive research over the past decade that the gut microbiome is closely in bidirectional dialogue with the immune system in our bodies through the lifespan. Chronic inflammation stemming from the effects of alterations in this interplay is seen in individuals with the aforementioned metabolic, cognitive, mental, and neurological illnesses, and increases them. For example, in recent years, research has suggested that individuals with cardiovascular, metabolic, and mood disorders (e.g., depressive disorders and anxiety disorders) have an increased risk of developing neurodegenerative disorders (Giacobbo et al., 2019). Given the significance of the immune system's interplay with the gut microbiome and health, general knowledge on the immune system will be addressed in the following section.

Immune System

The majority of cells in the human body are red blood cells (Sender et al., 2017). In contrast, white blood cells, also called leukocytes, make up a small percentage of the entire cells in the human body, although they serve a significant role, such as protecting us from infection, foreign invasion, or disease. The immune system in the body consists of a vast network of different types of cells, tissues, and organs, and coordinates in an intricate manner with other systems, such as the nervous system, gastrointestinal system, endocrine system and the human microbiome, to list a few. Furthermore, the immune system functions as a primary safeguard that fights against threats. White blood cells are further classified into two cell type groups, including the phagocyte and lymphocyte. While phagocytes have the ability to consume foreign invaders (e.g., pathogenic viruses, bacteria, or toxins), lymphocytes consist of B cells and T cells, which collaborate to activate an immune response to protect us from varying events in the long term. For those who are interested in learning more about the immune system and its accordant functions, *The Anatomy Coloring Book* by Wynn Kapit and Lawrence Elson might be a good resource to use.

The immune system also plays other roles beyond its significant protective role for human development and health. For instance, the immune system positions us in constant interplay with the environment through a critical sensory experience (Logan et al., 2016). Microorganisms serve an important role in this dialogue between the host and its environment. Moreover, vertebrates and more complex immune systems have evolved together (Logan et al., 2016). It is now thought the adaptive immune system provides vertebrates with advanced, specific immune responses while they interface with the environment (Logan et al., 2016). Originally, researchers considered that this sophisticated immune system was beneficial for defense against bad guys, preventing disease. However, it is now considered likely that this advantage enabled the host to selectively promote beneficial microorganisms for metabolic and physiological gain (Logan et al., 2016). Consequently, increased capacity for symbiosis may have been obtained in evolutionary processes. It is remarkable that this enhanced immune specificity of the adaptive immune system was evolutionarily driven by the bidirectional dialogue between microbes and the immune system (Hooper et al., 2012).

Immune Signaling Between the Gut and Brain

In the bidirectional dialogue between the gut and brain, the immune system plays a significant, mediating role in a dynamic process of homeostasis (Ghosh et al., 2020). In particular, the function of the intestinal barrier is responsible for general homeostasis of the gut (Ghosh et al., 2020). The gut is involved with numerous microorganisms and nutrient components via ingested diet. Therefore, the intestinal barrier is vital for maintaining gut homeostasis that requires a complex system responsible for several functions: detoxifying bacteria-derived endotoxins, reducing direct contact with harmful bacteria and other pathogens, regulating the absorption of nutrients while limiting the transport of harmful bacteria or substances, and modulating a proper immune response (Ghosh et al., 2020). According to Ghosh and colleagues (2020), the intestinal barrier has evolved as a functional unit in a multilayer system. Thus, this barrier provides not only a physical but also a functional barrier. Readers who are interested in learning more about the structure and function of the intestinal barrier, and its associated disease and development, can refer to Ghosh et al. (2020).

By contrast, the dysfunction of this barrier is related to local and systemic consequences (e.g., inflammation) related to direct contact of bacteria and bacteria products with the intestinal barrier (Ghosh et al., 2020). Locally, explicit contact with bacteria and bacterial products results in activated immune cells via signaling routes by interaction with lipopolysaccharide (LPS), a gut-bacteria component and endotoxin (Ghosh et al., 2020). This subsequently leads to the secretion of proinflammatory mediators that perpetuate local inflammation (Ghosh et al., 2020). Local intestinal inflammation is an underlying contributor to the development of varying gastrointestinal diseases (e.g., inflammatory bowel disease, Crohn's disease, and ulcerative colitis; Ghosh et al., 2020). Readers are encouraged to refer to Ghosh et al.'s (2020) article, which illustrates the intact intestinal barrier and disrupted barrier in a comparative manner.

Systemically, intestinal barrier disruption leads to the greater paracellular transport of LPS into systemic circulation via the blood (Ghosh et al., 2020). Consequently, this results in the activated proinflammatory transcription factor NF-kB that subsequently leads to the production of cytokines (e.g., TNFa, IL-1ß, IL-6), functioning as proinflammatory mediators, resulting in local inflammation, such as tissue inflammation (Ghosh et al., 2020). This cascade eventually involves the infiltration of immune cells in response to this proinflammatory state, and thus it perpetuates systemic inflammation that alters tissue homeostasis (Ghosh et al., 2020). Importantly, it has been found that the existence of LPS in systemic circulation is a causal or complicating factor in numerous neurodevelopmental (autism spectrum disorder), neurodegenerative (Alzheimer's disease and Parkinson's disease), and autoimmune (arthritis and asthma) conditions (Ghosh et al., 2020).

Consequences of the immune signaling can also be manifested behaviorally. For instance, in animal studies, research has shown that infectious microorganisms affect behavioral measures via the immune signaling, sending the message from the body to the nervous system (Foster et al., 2017). Thus, dysbiosis caused by disturbance or alternations in the composition of gut microbiota may promote a state of chronic inflammation. This chronic inflammation can lead to negative consequences, such as maladaptive changes in mood and behavior that include increased stress responses and further stress-related health conditions (e.g., depressive disorders; Foster et al., 2017).

The Interplay Between the Immune System and Human Microbiome

Given the significance of the immune system in relation to the overall human health, it is critical for helping professionals to understand what factors play a pivotal role in contributing to disturbances and alterations in the immune system and its attributes, and thus to disease in humans. For instance, in recent years, emerging evidence supports the importance of the microbiota to human development. Furthermore, changes in microbial composition are speculated to be contributing factors to the onset and/or persistence of many diseases and chronic health conditions (e.g., inflammatory bowel diseases, such as Crohn's and ulcerative colitis; diabetes; asthma; allergies; autistic spectrum disorder; and neurodegenerative diseases, such as Alzheimer's disease and Parkinson's disease; Mayer 2021; Petersen & Round, 2014).

A number of factors can influence the structure of the microbial community in the body, such as the host's genetics, epigenetic programming, diet, infection, or the use of antibiotics (Petersen & Round, 2014). Given the importance of microbiota to the development and maturation of appropriate intestinal immune responses, many studies have been conducted to support this notion (Petersen & Round, 2014). Furthermore, emerging evidence has begun to identify the organisms and their mechanisms equipped to trigger immune development within the host (Petersen & Round, 2014).

Intestinal Microbiota Colonization in Infants

It is known that the developing immune system is substantially dependent on microbial stimulation through interactions with the environment. Thus, diminished contact with biodiversity in early life has been implicated in the increasing risk for the development of early-onset inflammatory diseases (e.g., infant allergic diseases; Logan et al., 2016). Additionally, this declining biodiversity is implicated in the increasing risk of inflammatory diseases later in life (Logan et al., 2016).

The Role of Chronic Stress and Microbiome-Gut-Brain Network

The concept of a bidirectional dialogue taking place along the microbiome-gut-brain axis was introduced earlier in this chapter. The significance of systematic approaches to science, in relation to human health and disease, is also called network science. The two-way conversation between the brain, gut, and microbiome is seen in the brain-gut-microbiome (BGM) network, a term first coined by Emeran Mayer in his recent book (2021), titled *The Gut-Immune Connection*. The BGM network is a part of the larger network in the body, and its communication should be considered dynamic, complex, and circular rather than simple or linear. According to Mayer (2021), information is transferred in multiple feedback loops along two major trajectories, including from the gut and its microbiome to the brain (this loop is called "bottom-up communication"), and from the brain to the gut and microbiome (this trajectory is called "top-down communication").

Needless to say, this two-way interplay significantly affects the health of both brain and gut alongside the diversity and abundance of microbes residing in the gut.

Numerous factors contribute to the work of the BGM network and its consequences. Chronic and acute inflammation is associated with varying adverse effects on the architecture and function, which seems to adversely affect cognitive performance (Capuron & Miller, 2011; Kanoski & Davidson, 2011). Furthermore, low-grade inflammation is recognized as a common underlying pathophysiological mechanism for the co-existence of the steadily increasing non-communicable diseases and mental disorders (Logan et al., 2016). Another factor includes that acute and chronic stress lead to a reduction in the magnitude of *Lactobacillus*, known to be a pivotal microbial genus for sustaining healthy gut (Wang et al., 2019).

In addition, in the bottom-up communication of the BGM network, stress mediators (e.g., norepinephrine) released into the gut can activate genes of gut microbes that promote bacterial engagement with the gut immune system (Mayer, 2021). Moreover, stress affects an increase in intestinal permeability that can result in low-grade activation of the gut immune system (Ghosh et al., 2020). This condition is generally known as "leaky gut." In the top-down communication of the BGM network, chronic stress sends signals to the gut from the brain that alter gut microbial signaling molecules (Mayer, 2021). Subsequently, the feedback informed by these signals is sent to the brain to respond accordingly. Also, lifestyle factors, such as unhealthy diet and lack of physical activity or regular exercise, that are combined with chronic stress, can exert a synergistic detrimental effect on gut health as well as on brain health (Mayer, 2021). Other contributing factors include exposure to environmental toxins, pesticides, our own genetic information, and the interaction with the environment, affecting epigenetic programming in the components of the BGM network and the network itself (Mayer, 2021). Thus, individual vulnerability to neurological, neurodegenerative, neurodevelopmental, and mental illnesses must involve a comprehensive, systematic perspective on human health and disease, perhaps through systematic approaches to science and integrative, interdisciplinary endeavors (Mayer, 2021).

Children Exposed to Toxic, Chronic Stress

It is now well recognized that children exposed to toxic, chronic stress are vulnerable to mental (e.g., depressive disorders, stress-related disorders, substance use disorders) and physical (e.g., coronary heart disease, cancers, autoimmune conditions) problems across the lifespan. Due to a lack of the biological and behavioral pathways underlying risk for this heterogeneous nature of health conditions, Nusslock and Miller proposed a neuroimmune network hypothesis (Nusslock & Miller, 2016). This hypothesis as a framework describes that under normal physiological conditions, brain circuits involved in emotion regulation engage in bidirectional interplay with peripheral immune cells that mediate inflammation (Miller et al., 2020; Nusslock & Miller, 2016). What is hypothesized in the framework is that toxic, chronic stress in childhood augments this two-way communication and initiates positive feedback loops between peripheral inflammatory activity and the developing cortico-amygdala and cortico-striatal circuits in the brain (Miller et al., 2020; Nusslock & Miller, 2016). The former is associated with threat processing while the latter mediates reward processing (Miller et al., 2020; Nusslock & Miller, 2016). Due to the enhanced bidirectional dialogue, children with early stress exposure are hypothesized to present a phenotype showing chronic low-grade inflammatory activity (Miller et al., 2020; Nusslock & Miller, 2016). This is accompanied by increased threat responsivity and increased reward processing (Miller et al., 2020; Nusslock & Miller, 2016). Without early proper intervention, components of this phenotype are hypothesized to escalate the neuro-immuno-physiological pathology, resulting in inflammation-induced health conditions (Miller et al., 2020; Nusslock & Miller, 2016).

In recent years, Miller, Nusslock, and their colleagues examined the validity of the hypothesis with a sample of 207 urban children from diverse socioeconomic backgrounds.

For the measures, the researchers measured serum levels of five inflammatory biomarkers (i.e., C-reactive protein [CRP], interleukin-6 [IL-6], interleukin-8 [IL-8], interleukin-10 [IL-10], and tumor necrosis factor-a [TNF-a]. Two functional MRI tasks measuring amygdala responsivity to angry facial expressions and ventral-striatum response to monetary rewards were performed in the children. Results from this study show that amygdala-threat responsivity was positively associated with low-grade inflammation among children living in poverty (Miller et al., 2020). Contrary to the study's hypothesis, the same pattern was observed in the relationship between striatal-reward responsivity and low-grade inflammation (Miller et al., 2020). These observed relationships were independent of other socioeconomic or developmental indexes (i.e., age, sex, racial and ethical identity, and pubertal status; Miller et al., 2020). Furthermore, economically disadvantaged children also showed markers of a proinflammatory phenotype (Miller et al., 2020). These results provide preliminary support for the neuroimmune network hypothesis that exposure in children to stress, such as poverty, increases interplay between peripheral inflammation and brain circuits engaged in threat and reward processing (Miller et al., 2020). Despite the importance of these findings, we cannot assume these results imply causal effects, due to the observational nature of the study design. Nevertheless, the study findings can offer an important message for helping professionals that it is critical to have a deep understanding of how early stress contributes to the increasing risk for the development of a varying set of health conditions across the lifespan through neural-immune pathways. Also, early intervention and proactive prevention practices become even more critical.

The Role of Dietary Inflammation in Human Disease

Extensive research has suggested over the past decade that nutrients play a pivotal role in the host's innate immune system to promote or inhibit inflammation. Nutrients modulate energy homeostasis and orchestrate metabolic health and disease (Nobs et al., 2020). For instance, poor diet increases the risk of health conditions such as cardiovascular issues and diabetes (Firth et al., 2018). Furthermore, in recent years, emerging research suggests the role of dietary triggers in initiating intestinal barrier dysfunction (Ghosh et al., 2020). The intersection between diet and innate immunity happens at the intestinal barrier, in particular at the mucosal barrier (Nobs et al., 2020). In this cross talk between the immune system and metabolism in the gastrointestinal tract, the microbiota play a mediator role. The gut microbiota are critical for increasing or decreasing energy extraction from nutrients (Nobs et al., 2020). Furthermore, they also have the capacity to alter metabolic signaling and inflammation (Nobs et al., 2020). As noted earlier in this chapter, an increasing body of research has shown that metabolic diseases are associated with immune processes. Thus, as diet contributes to the health of the immune system, it is contributing to the development of detrimental health conditions (See Figure 7.1; adapted from Nobs et al., [2020]), such as cardiovascular, neurodegenerative, neurodevelopmental, and psychiatric consequences (Nobs et al., 2020).

It is well recognized that Western diets containing high fat, high cholesterol, high sugar, high sodium, and highly processed foods, are a big contributor to the increasing obesity epidemic and metabolic syndrome (Nobs et al., 2020). Alongside other factors (e.g., chronic stress, environmental toxins, and lack of regular exercise), these diets have been associated with the increase in intestinal permeability that leads to the release of LPS into systemic circulation, which in turn leads to metabolic consequences (Ghosh et al., 2020).

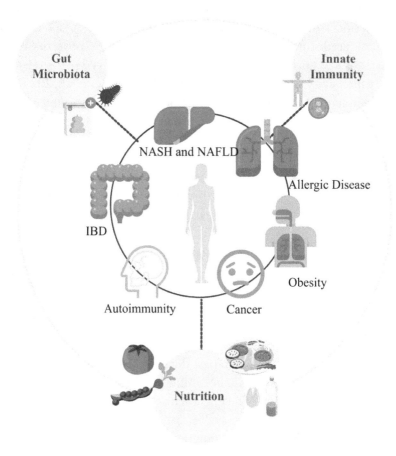

FIGURE 7.1   The Interplay Between Nutrition, the Microbiome, and Innate Immunity Regulates Many Multifactorial Diseases

Note. IBD = inflammatory bowel disease; NAFLD = non-alcoholic fatty liver disease; NASH = non-alcoholic steatohepatitis.

Moreover, a chronic, low-grade inflammation stemming from dietary practices common in the industrialized society often leads to the emergence of or contribution to numerous metabolic consequences (Firth et al., 2019; Nobs et al., 2020). Additionally, excessive consumption of a high-fat diet may lead to structural and functional reformations to innate immune cells and their immune mediators in numerous metabolic organs (e.g., arterial vasculature, central nervous system, liver, muscle, and pancreas; Nobs et al., 2020). These topics go beyond the scope of this chapter; thus, readers interested in pursuing an in-depth understanding of immunological mechanisms may find they are comprehensively reviewed elsewhere (Nobs et al., 2020). In summary, considering that SMI is associated with elevated levels of peripheral inflammation, it is important to have a deep understanding of effects of dietary inflammation in human disease, with focus given to mental illness.

Summary

In recent years, research has shown that SMIs (e.g., mood disorders or schizophrenia spectrum disorders) are linked to increased inflammation. Additionally, it is documented that individuals with poor mental health tend to experience disproportionate poor physical health (Firth et al., 2019). Also, emergent research has suggested that a common factor in cognitive, mental, metabolic, and neurological illnesses is the gut microbiome (Mayer, 2021). Extensive research over the past decade has revealed that the gut microbiome is intimately dialoguing with the immune system in the human body over its life course.

The immune system in our bodies involves several different functions, such as protecting us from threats and allowing us to interplay with the environmental demands through a sensory experience. In addition, microorganisms play a significant role in this interplay between the host and its surroundings. Although it was considered that the advanced immune system was beneficial for defense against harmful pathogens, it is now also understood that this advantage enabled the host to selectively promote helpful microorganisms for metabolic and physiological gain (Logan et al., 2016). Additionally, the immune system plays a critical role in mediating a dynamic process of homeostasis between the gut and brain (Ghosh et al., 2020).

In animal studies, it has been suggested that infectious microorganisms affect behavioral measures via immune signaling (Foster et al., 2017). The activation of this system sends the message from the body to the nervous system, implying a state of chronic inflammation. Unfortunately, this chronic inflammation can further lead to negative consequences (e.g., maladaptive changes in mood and behavior) that include increased stress responses and subsequent stress-induced negative health conditions (e.g., depression; Foster et al., 2017).

The function of the intestinal barrier is paramount in the immune system's mediating role in bidirectional dialogue between the gut and brain and maintaining gut homeostasis (Ghosh et al., 2020). However, the dysfunction of this barrier is linked to both local and systemic consequences, such as inflammation, from direct contact between bacteria and their products and the intestinal barrier (Ghosh et al., 2020). Furthermore, chronic and acute inflammation in the BGM network is associated with varying adverse effects, including cognitive performance (Capuron & Miller, 2011). Similarly, stress—especially chronic stress—can effect an increase in intestinal permeability that can result in low-grade activation of the gut immune system (Ghosh et al., 2020). Additionally, extensive research has revealed that nutrition also plays a critical role in the host innate immune system to facilitate or inhibit inflammation (Nobs et al., 2020).

Alongside other factors (e.g., chronic stress, a lack of regular exercise, and environmental toxins), Western diets containing high fat, high cholesterol, high sugar, high sodium, and highly processed foods are considered big contributors to the increasing obesity epidemic, metabolic syndrome (Nobs et al., 2020), and intestinal permeability (Ghosh et al., 2020). Considering the association between severe mental illnesses and elevated levels of peripheral inflammation, helping professionals should have a good understanding of effects of dietary inflammation in human disease.

Experiential Questions

1. What information from the case study do you think is important for understanding the role of stress in A's immune health in relation to their current health-related experience?

2. What additional information do you think will be helpful for you to gain to better understand the role of dietary inflammation in A pertaining to their current mental health state?

References

Heart

Angst, F., Stassen, H. H., Clayton, P. J., & Angst, J. (2002). Mortality of patients with mood disorders: Follow-up over 34–38 years. *Journal of Affective Disorders, 68*(2–3), 167–181. https://doi.org/10.1016/S0165-0327(01)00377-9

Calkins, S., Graziano, P. A., & Keane, S. P. (2007). Cardiac vagal regulation differentiates among children at risk for behavior problems. *Biological Psychology, 74*(2), 144–153. https://doi.org/10.1016/j.biopsycho.2006.09.005

Darwin, C. (1872). *The expression of emotions in man and animals.* Appleton.

Goldstein, B. I., Carnethon, M. R., Matthews, K. A., McIntyre, R. S., Miller, G. E., Raghuveer, G., Stoney, C. M., Wasiak, H., & McCrindle, B. W. (2015). Major depressive disorder and bipolar disorder predispose youth to accelerated atherosclerosis and early cardiovascular disease: A scientific statement from the American Heart Association. *Circulation, 132*(10), 965–986. https://doi.org/10.1161/CIR.0000000000000229

McCaffery, J. M., Duan, Q. L., Frasure-Smith, N., Barhdadi, A., Lesprance, F., Throux, P., Rouleau, G. A., & Dube, M. P. (2009). Genetic predictors of depressive symptoms in cardiac patients. *American Journal of Medical Genetics Neuropsychiatric Genetics, 150B*, 381–388. https://doi.org/10.1002/ajmg.b.30824

Murray, D. P., Weiner, M., Prabhakar, M., & Fiedorowicz, J. G. (2009). Mania and mortality: Why the excess cardiovascular risk in bipolar disorder? *Current Psychiatry Reports, 11*, 475. https://doi.org/10.1007/s11920-009-0072-3

Ortiz, A., Bradler, K., Moorti, P., MacLean, S., M. Husain, M. I., Sanches, M., Goldstein, B. I., Alda, M., Benoit H., & Mulsant, B. H. (2021). Reduced heart rate variability is associated with higher illness burden in bipolar disorder. *Journal of Psychosomatic Research*, *145*, 110478. https://doi.org/10.1016/j.jpsychores.2021.110478

Ösby, U., Brandt, L., Correia, N., Ekbom, A., & Sparén P. (2001). Excess mortality in bipolar and unipolar disorder in Sweden. *Archives of General Psychiatry*, *58*(9), 844–850. https://doi.org/10.1001/archpsyc.58.9.844

Porges, S. W. (2011). *The polyvagal theory: Neurophysiological foundations of emotions, attachment, communication, and self-regulation*. W.W. Norton & Company.

Thayer, J. F., & Lane, R. D. (2000). A model of neurovisceral integration in emotion regulation and dysregulation. *Journal of Affective Disorders*, *61*(3), 201–216. https://doi.org/10.1016/S0165-0327(00)00338-4

Thayer, J. F., & Lane, R. D. (2009). Claude Bernard and the heart–brain connection: Further elaboration of a model of neurovisceral integration. *Neuroscience and Biobehavioral Reviews*, *33*(2), 81–88. https://doi.org/10.1016/j.neubiorev.2008.08.004

Thayer, J. F., Yamamoto, S. S., & Brosschot, J. F. (2010). The relationship of autonomic imbalance, heart rate variability and cardiovascular disease risk factors. *International Journal of Cardiology*, *141*(2), 122–131. https://doi.org/10.1016/j.ijcard.2009.09.543

Villareal, R. P., Liu, B. C., & Massumi, A. (2202). Heart rate variability and cardiovascular mortality. *Current Atherosclerosis Reports*, *4*, 120–127. https://doi.org/10.1007/s11883-002-0035-1

Immune System

Agrawal, M., Sabino, J., Frias-Gomes, C., Hillenbrand, C. M., Soudant, C., Axelrad, J. E., Shah, S. C., Francisco Ribeiro-Mourão, F., Lambin, T., Peter, I., Colombel, J.-F., Narula, N., & Torres, J. (2021). Early life exposures and the risk of inflammatory bowel disease: Systematic review and meta-analyses. *EClinicalMedicine*, *36*, 100884. https://doi.org/10.1016/j.eclinm.2021.100884

Capuron, L., & Miller, A. H. (2011). Immune system to brain signaling: Neuropsychopharmacological implications. *Pharmacology & Therapeutics*, *130*(2), 226–238. https://doi.org/10.1016/j.pharmthera.2011.01.014

Firth, J., Stubbs, B., Teasdale, S. B., Ward, P. B., Verones, N., Shivappa, N., Herbert, J. R., Berk, M., Yung, A. R., & Sarris, J. (2018). Diet as a hot topic in psychiatry: A population-scale study of nutritional intake and inflammatory potential in severe mental illness. *World Psychiatry*, *17*(3), 365–367. https://doi.org/10.1002/wps.20571

Firth, J., Veronese, N., Cotter, J., Shivappa, N., Hebert, J. R., Ee, C., Smith, L., Stubbs, B., Jackson, S. E., & Sarris, J. (2019). What is the role of dietary inflammation in severe mental illness? A review of observational and experimental findings. *Frontiers in Psychiatry*, *10*, 350. https://doi.org/10.3389/fpsyt.2019.00350

Foster, J. A., Rinaman, L., & Cryan, J. F. (2017). Stress & the gut-brain axis: Regulation by the microbiome. *Neurobiology of Stress*, *7*, 124–136. https://doi.org/10.1016/j.ynstr.2017.03.001

Ghosh, S. S., Wang, J., Yannie, P. J., & Ghosh, S. (2020). Intestinal barrier dysfunction, LPS translocation, and disease development. *Journal of the Endocrine Society*, *4*(2), bvz039. https://doi.org/10.1210/jendso/bvz039

Goldsmith, D., Rapaport, M., & Miller, B. (2016). A meta-analysis of blood cytokine network alterations in psychiatric patients: Comparisons between schizophrenia, bipolar disorder and depression. *Molecular Psychiatry*, *21*(12), 1696–1709. https://doi.org/10.1038/mp.2016.3

Giacobbo, B. L., Doorduin, J., Klein, H. C., Dierckx, R. A. J. O., Bromberg, E., & de Vries, E. F. J. (2019). Brain-derived neurotrophic factor in brain disorders: Focus on neuroinflammation. *Molecular Neurobiology, 56*(5), 3295–3312. https://doi.org/10.1007/s12035-018-1283-6

Hooper, L. V., Littman, D. R., & Macpherson, A. J. (2012). Interactions between the microbiota and the immune system. *Science, 336*(6086), 1268–1273. https://doi.org/10.1126/science.1223490

Kanoski, S. E., & Davidson, T. L. (2011). Western diet consumption and cognitive impairment: Links to hippocampal dysfunction and obesity. *Physiology & Behavior, 103*(1), 59–68. https://doi.org/10.1016/j.physbeh.2010.12.003

Logan, A. C., Jacka, F. N., & Prescott, S. L. (2016). Immune-microbiota interactions: Dysbiosis as a global health issue. *Current Allergy Asthma Reports, 16*(13). https://doi.org/10.1007/s11882-015-0590-5

Mayer, E. (2021). *The gut-immune connection: How understanding the connection between food and immunity can help us regain our health.* Harper Wave.

Miller, G. E., White, S. F., Chen, E., & Nusslock, R. (2020). Association of inflammatory activity with larger neural responses to threat and reward among children living in poverty. *The American Journal of Psychiatry, 178*(4), 313–320. https://doi.org/10.1176/appi.ajp.2020.20050635

Nobs, S. P., Zmora, N., & Elinav, E. (2020). Nutrition regulates innate immunity in health and disease. *Annual Review of Nutrition, 40*, 189–219. https://doi.org/10.1146/annurev-nutr-120919-094440

Nusslock, R., & Miller, G. E. (2016). Early-life adversity and physical and emotional health across the lifespan: A neuroimmune network hypothesis. *Biological Psychiatry, 80*, 23–32.

Petersen, C., & Round, J. L. (2014). Defining dysbiosis and its influence on host immunity and disease. *Cellular Microbiology, 16*(7), 1024–1033. https://doi.org/10.1111/cmi.12308

Sender, R., Fuchs, S., & Milo, R. (2017). Revised estimates for the number of human and bacterial cells in the body. *bioRxiv.* https://doi.org/10.1371/journal.pbio.1002533

Wang, H., Braun, C., Murphy, E. F., & Enck, P. (2019). Bifidobacterium longum 1714™ strain modulates brain activity of healthy volunteers during social stress. *American Journal of Gastroenterology, 114*(7), 1152–1162. https://doi.org/10.14309/ajg.0000000000000203

Wang, A. K., & Miller, B. J. (2017). Meta-analysis of cerebrospinal fluid cytokine and tryptophan catabolite alterations in psychiatric patients: Comparisons between schizophrenia, bipolar disorder, and depression. *Schizophrenia Bulletin, 44*(1), 75–83. https://doi.org/10.1093/schbul/sbx035

Weinberger, A., Gbedemah, M., Martinez, A., Nash, D., Galea, S., & Goodwin, R. (2018). Trends in depression prevalence in the USA from 2005 to 2015: Widening disparities in vulnerable groups. *Psychological Medicine, 48*(8), 1308–1315.

Zabetian-Targhi, F., Srikanth, V. K., Smith, K. J., Oddy PhD, W. H., Beare, R., Moran, C., Wang, W., Shivappa, N., Hébert, J. R., Breslin, M., van Weel, J. M., & Callisaya, M. L. (2021). Associations between the dietary inflammatory index, brain volume, small vessel disease, and global cognitive function. *Journal of the Academy of Nutrition and Dietetics, 121*(5), 915–924.e3. https://doi.org/10.1016/j.jand.2020.11.004

Figure Credit

Fig. 7.1: 1) Generated with Visme. Copyright © by Easy WebContent, Inc. 2) Adapted from Samuel Philip Nobs, Niv Zmora, and Eran Elinav, "Nutrition Regulates Innate Immunity in Health and Disease," *Annual Review of Nutrition*, vol. 40. Copyright © 2020 by Annual Reviews.

PART III

Healing and Prevention Actions and Practices for Helping Professions

Healing and Prevention Actions and Practices at Microbial, Individual, and Relationship Levels

The key points addressed in this chapter are

- to apply the biopsychosocial and lifestyle approach, with focus given to lifestyle factors that are influential in human development, health, and disease

- to address information and resources regarding services and programs for prevention and healing

- to provide information on screening and assessment

"There is growing appreciation that a successful well-care system must expand its scope beyond the traditional realm of individualized, clinical practice to address the complex social, economic, cultural, environmental, and developmental influences that lead to population-based health disparities and unsustainable medical care expenditures."

Shonkoff et al. (2012, p. e233)

"Nutrition may therefore represent an important public health target for strategies to address childhood mental well-being."

Hayhoe et al. (2021, p. 458)

In Chapter 2 of this textbook, the Social-Ecological Model (SEM; Centers for Disease Control and Prevention, n.d.) was presented as adapted and modified into the Social-Ecological Model for Prevention—Modified (SEMP-M). This textbook will use it to help guide suggestions and recommendations for prevention actions and practices among helping professionals. Also, this chapter will provide information regarding healing practices to help alleviate human suffering, such as negative effects of toxic stress on human disease. In the following section, suggestions and recommendations, mostly supported by scientific investigation, will be provided at each of the following five levels: microbial, individual, relationship, community, and societal. Furthermore, given that the agency of healing and prevention actions and practices is focused on us as humans, those at the microbial level will be combined with those at the individual level in the following section.

At the Microbial and Individual Levels

Strategies to promote prevention actions and practices, and healing at these levels, may include learning to increase conscious awareness and relevant knowledge regarding microbial and individual factors increasing vulnerabilities in people for negative health. Some examples of such influential factors involve a lack of diversity and abundance in gut microorganisms; the microbial composition in the gut; factors known to affect microbial functions, such as antibiotic use, medication use, or the use of psycho-probiotics; pathogenic microbial infection; and microbial genetic programming. Furthermore, clinical interventions and health-related programs that incorporate content about the human microbiome, and a sustainable, healthy lifestyle (e.g., adaptive and sustainable diet) will be explored.

Biopsychosocial and Lifestyle Approaches

It is imperative for helping professionals to identify and understand a wide array of influencing factors and determinants that put individuals at high risk for compromised health across the lifespan. As addressed in Chapter 2, it can be instrumental to apply comprehensive models such as the ecobiodevelopmental framework—modified (EBD-M), which emphasizes the comprehensive, developmental lens to human development. To reiterate, the model comprises building blocks including biology and systems biology, human microbiome, ecology, and phenomenology, all of which are closely intertwined with each other to influence human development across the lifespan. In alignment with such a point of view, the biopsychosocial and lifestyle framework (Malhi et al., 2015) could also be applicable and instrumental, particularly for mental health professionals. In this way of guiding actions and practices for human health, selective lifestyle factors (e.g., diet, nutrition, and exercise) will be delineated in depth in this chapter to tailor the prevention toward human health and healing from human suffering (e.g., negative effects of toxic stress).

Diet

Certain ingredients of modern lifestyles—particularly of those who live in industrialized societies such as the United States—can be a contributing factor to negative health states and conditions, such as autoimmune, metabolic, neurodevelopmental, neurodegenerative, and mental consequences. All these conditions have a common underlying factor, the microbiome (Mayer, 2018; Nobs et al., 2020). The loss of gut microbial diversity in industrialized societies is related to negative health conditions like chronic diseases (Wibowo et al., 2021).

Also, extensive research has suggested that interplay between diet and innate immunity in our bodies helps regulate and govern energy homeostasis and metabolic health (Nobs et al., 2020). Consequently, disruptions in this relationship can result in negative health states, such as the emergence and development of metabolic diseases (e.g., cardiometabolic disease; Nobs et al., 2020). Similarly, emerging evidence suggests that nutrition can also influence the development of allergic diseases (e.g., asthma, food allergies, and eczema; Nobs et al., 2020). Among many influential factors on this development, the mother's nutrition during pregnancy and that of infants substantially impact allergy development and worsen allergic inflammation (Nobs et al., 2020).

Furthermore, emerging research has demonstrated that poor diet is associated with adverse health outcomes, including chronic mental disorders, albeit there is a recognition that this association will have to be further elucidated to explore relevant mechanisms. However, some research has demonstrated that diet plays a pivotal role in modulating inflammatory processes in our bodies. Considering the association between severe mental illnesses (e.g., major depressive disorder, bipolar disorder, and schizophrenia spectrum disorders) and inflammation, emphasizing a healthy diet is paramount in all, particularly in those with a mental health condition.

For instance, a sizeable study conducted in the UK that included 7,750 adolescents aged between 11 and 18, and 1,253 children with an age of 8 to 11, and used the Norfolk Children and Young People Health and Well-Being Survey, emphasized the significance of good-quality nutrition for childhood mental health (Hayhoe et al., 2021). Specifically, findings showed the weekly frequency of consumption of fruit and vegetables was significantly associated with high levels of mental well-being in the adolescents (Hayhoe et al., 2021). Also, this association presented as a linear pattern, indicating that those consuming five portions were associated with higher mental well-being than those consuming three or four. In turn, those with consumption of three or four had higher scores on mental well-being than those consuming one or two (Hayhoe et al., 2021).

In the same study, the type of breakfast or lunch consumption was also associated with noticeable differences in well-being; those who did not eat any breakfast had lower scores on well-being compared to those who consumed a conventional type of breakfast. Similarly, children who did not eat any lunch had lower well-being when compared to those who consumed a packed lunch (Hayhoe et al., 2021). However, the data used in the study indicated that on average, in a class of 30 adolescents, about 21 adolescents or 70% would have consumed a conventional-type breakfast, while at minimum, four adolescents would have had nothing to eat or drink before classes would start (Hayhoe et al., 2021). Given the aforementioned association between breakfast or lunch consumption and mental well-being, these data are quite concerning when we think through it in consideration of healthy growth and development in children and adolescents. The authors of the study suggest that nutrition may be a critical avenue to target strategies to address childhood mental health (Hayhoe et al., 2021).

In contrast, food choices in those who reside in North America appear to be dominated by *ultra-processed food*, defined as "industrially manufactured, ready-to-eat/heat formulations that are made with multiple additives and largely devoid of whole foods" (Juul et al., 2021, p. 1). Such foods are characterized as nutrient-deficient and excessively dense in calories. In a study conducted in Canada, individuals studied reported that 48% of calories came from ultra-processed food in 2004, regardless of all socioeconomic groups (Moubarac et al., 2017). Furthermore, the findings from this study suggested that a significant positive association was observed between the dietary share of ultra-processed foods and the content in macronutrients (e.g., carbohydrates, free sugars, and saturated fats), while there was a negative relationship between dietary content in proteins, fiber, vitamins, and minerals (Moubarac et al., 2017). Similar to this study, in a study conducted in the United States, 57% of adults studied consumed ultra-processed foods in 2018, and this was an increase from 53.5% observed during the year of 2001 to 2002 (Juul et al., 2021). The trend in high ultra-processed consumption in North America is concerning because it has been linked to cancer, cardiometabolic diseases, and obesity (Juul et al., 2021). Such foods are not only associated with physical health concerns but also with the increased inflammation seen in those with severe symptoms of a mental disorder (Firth et al., 2019).

It was previously described in Chapters 7 and in this chapter that nutrition plays as a mediator between innate immunity and gut microbiome. As an example, it is recognized that nutrition modulates innate immunity in the context of food allergy (Nobs et al., 2020). Alterations in response to food-derived antigens have profoundly increased over recent decades in Western countries (Eiwegger et al., 2019). As a major contributing factor to this phenomenon, changes in diet are raised. For instance, emerging research has suggested that calorie-dense diets that are high in saturated fats and simple carbohydrates seem to boost peripheral inflammation. In contrast, a diet high in fiber and a variety of vegetables help reduce inflammation (Hlebowicz et al., 2011; Kastorini et al., 2011).

Dietary and Nutritional Practices

Thus, helping professionals may take advantage of the potential use of nutritional and dietary practices (e.g., nutritional interventions and nutrition education) for improving mental health outcomes and employing them as prevention to reduce the risk for human diseases. In relation to this, it is evident that diet has the modulatory ability to influence the microbiota-gut-brain axis (Foster et al., 2017). In an animal study, alongside a diet high in fat and sugar, chronic stress exposure exacerbated alterations in the intestinal tight junction protein, linked to altered behavior and biomarkers in inflammation within the hippocampus (de Sousa Rodrigues et al., 2017). This may suggest the association among the hippocampal function, behavioral effects, and diet (de Sousa Rodrigues et al., 2017).

As extensively addressed in Chapter 6, it is known that groups of microorganisms or certain individual species are associated with specific phenotypic diseases in humans (Nobs et al., 2020). Despite the advances made in understanding of how diet hugely impacts disease at a molecular level, little is known about how nutrition influences the dialogue between immune mediators and the microbiome (Nobs et al., 2020). Because of high variation among humans, metabolic responses to dietary interventions can be robustly diverse and dependent on an array of individual parameters (e.g., genetic programming and microbial characteristics), and other environmental and cultural factors (Nobs et al., 2020). As a result, the application of precision nutrition could enable better dietary planning and further the vision of modifying individual features (e.g., the microbiota) in order to match and optimize the effect of diet on the human immune system (Nobs et al., 2020). In addition, other therapeutic methods (e.g., probiotics) targeting the gut microbiota have the potential for enhancing mental health, although a systematic review and meta-analysis suggested that most probiotics studied did not influence anxiety, depression, and distress when compared to placebo (Le Morvan de Sequeira et al., 2022).

Physical Activity

In addition, physical activity may be another modifiable factor in lifestyles that relates to human health and human disease. For instance, findings from a study have shown that dietary patterns in children, alongside other health regimens on exercise and screen time, were predictive of prospective referrals during the age range of 10 to 11 years for a diagnosis of mental disorder in the subsequent two years (Loewen et al., 2019). These findings emphasize the significance of lifestyle recommendations not only to promote healthy physical development in children but also to prevent chronic diseases later in life (Loewen et al., 2019). Thus, during child visits and services, highlighting the importance of adherence to lifestyle guidelines could have the potential to enhance adolescent mental health (Loewen et al., 2019).

Similarly, in older adults, research has unraveled that physical activity in late life is related to brain health characterized using markers of brain tissue synaptic integrity (Casaletto et al., 2022). The findings of the study suggest that physical activity may play a supportive role in building synaptic health in a dynamic manner (Casaletto et al., 2022). Therefore, there may be optimal therapeutic windows for physical activity interventions to be used for positive synaptic outcomes, and they may be particularly effective in older adults in transitional cognitive states (Casaletto et al., 2022).

Clinical Interventions for Healing and Prevention

The Use of Heart Rate Variability

Previously addressed in Chapter 7, the heart as an organ is substantially intertwined both with physical and mental health in humans. Furthermore, increased heart rate variability or high frequency heart rate variability at a resting state is associated with psychological adjustment outcomes (e.g., attachment security, executive functioning, and empathic responding to others who are in distress) among children, adolescents, and adults (Beauchaine & Thayer, 2015). Inversely, low resting high frequency heart rate variability is linked to a wide array of psychopathology (e.g., anxiety, depression, bipolar disorders, schizophrenia, and attention difficulty; Beauchaine & Thayer, 2015). Additionally, robust evidence has documented that decreased heart rate variability precedes the onset of numerous risk factors (e.g., obesity, hypertension, familiar history, and work stress) for cardiovascular diseases (Thayer et al., 2010). Thus, the use of heart rate variability can be an index of mental health resilience, where *resilience* is characterized as "a dynamic process wherein an organism displays a positive and functional adaptation in the face of stress events and adversity, while preserving its stability" (Perna et al., 2020, p. 754).

The Integration of Sensory Processing

Emerging studies investigating the impact of sensory-oriented therapeutic interventions and approaches are noteworthy. Some examples, including findings from a study have suggested that a sensory-based fear pathway is seated in the primary olfactory cortex (You et al., 2021; You et al., 2022). Additionally, a sensory-based threat memory pathway in the olfactory cortex presents hyperactivation in those with anxiety disorders (You et al., 2022). Similarly, it was substantially addressed in Chapter 6 of this textbook that sensory-based psychotherapeutic practices can be effective for trauma treatment (Harricharan et al., 2021). These findings highlight the importance of integrating sensory processing to help individuals with maladaptive responses to fear and threat process trauma memories (You et al., 2022; Harricharan et al., 2021). As opposed to traditional psychotherapeutic modalities, sensory-based approaches, such as Somatic Experiencing (Brom et al., 2017) and art therapy (Malchiodi, 2020), may be more effective mechanisms that invite the prefrontal cortex online via sensory input that is critical for multisensory integration and emotional regulation (Harricharan et al., 2021).

Neurofeedback

Neurofeedback is characterized as "an emerging neuroscience-based clinical application based on the general principles of biofeedback" (Gunkelman & Johnstone, 2005, p. 93). Albeit both pharmacological and neuroscience-informed interventions help improve attentional and behavioral states in individuals, long-term use of medications may be more expensive than neuroscience-informed interventions (Gunkelman & Johnstone, 2005). Furthermore, neuroscience-informed interventions have less likelihood of leading to unwanted side effects than do medications (Gunkelman & Johnstone, 2005). For instance, emerging research in an animal study suggested that a long-term use of benzodiazepines, particularly in older people at risk for dementia, can lead to cognitive impairments (Shi et al., 2022). Mechanism-wide, brain immune cells known as microglia bind to a specific protein (i.e., the translocator protein [TSPO]) on the surface of the microglia (Shi et al., 2022). The activated microglia via this binding plays a role in degrading and recycling connections, also known as synapses, between nerve cells (Shi et al., 2022).

It is well established that through the concept of brain plasticity, the brain is malleable across one's lifespan albeit its activities are most active early in life, particularly the first 2 to 3 years (Gunkelman & Johnstone, 2005; Shonkoff et al., 2012). From the perspective of the brain, when it learns, it presents structural changes (Gunkelman & Johnstone, 2005). In particular, electroencephalogram (EEG) neurofeedback, as a type of neurofeedback, is helpful for the brain's learning (Gukelman & Johnstone, 2005). The brain's communication via electrical patterns that can be modified through operant conditioning was first discovered in the 1960s by Barry Sterman (Gunkelman & Johnstone, 2005) in animal studies, and later in human studies beginning in the 1970s (Sterman, 2000). Electrical activity in the brain recorded from the scalp with EEG is a summative outcome of populations of local field potentials (LFPs; Raichle, 2011).

LFPs refer to "signals coming from the integrated electrical activity in pre- and post-synaptic terminals of the brain" (Raichle, 2011, p. 6).

Specifically, EEG neurofeedback involves the technique amplified from the micro-voltages and attached on the scalp of the brain with special equipment to control a computer game (Gunkelman & Johnstone, 2005). The clinician or technician makes an adjustment following an individualized protocol informed by a variety of factors, such as the initial presentation of symptoms and brain mapping that shows the baseline of brain activity. Thus, the EEG neurofeedback helps noninvasively the brain's electrical patterns following an individualized plan for reward presented to the individual and subsequently adjust their brain's activity into a more regulated pattern (Gunkelman & Johnstone, 2005).

The efficacy and effectiveness of EEG neurofeedback for numerous states and conditions (e.g., ADHD, anxiety disorders, stress- and trauma-related disorders, etc.) has been extensively documented. As a resource, the International Society for Neuroregulation and Research provides a comprehensive bibliography of neurofeedback research—https://isnr.org/isnr-comprehensive-bibliography.

Screening and Assessment
Depression Screening in Women During Perinatal Period

Evidence has shown that approximately 20% of women are affected by depression during pregnancy (Sha et al., 2022). The guidelines set forth by the American College of Obstetricians and Gynecologists (ACOG) recommend that health providers screen for depression and anxiety once at minimum during the perinatal period by employing a validated instrument (ACOG, 2005). Furthermore, the United States Preventive Services Task Force has also recommended that depression screening be conducted in the general population, including perinatal women (Siu, 2016).

Despite the need for the biological mechanisms to be elucidated, some scholars view that depression during pregnancy could be "a specific type of inflammation-induced depression" (Sha et al., 2022, p. 1); fetal development involves immune system changes, and thus, this may lead to fluctuations in pro-inflammatory factors and tryptophan metabolites throughout pregnancy. The findings from this study suggest that inflammatory cytokines (i.e., IL-6 and IL-1ß) and kynurenine metabolites in the blood sample in the second trimester were predictive of depression in the third trimester in 114 women participating in the study (Sha et al., 2022). Furthermore, with 83% accuracy, a set of 15 biomarkers was predictive of women who were vulnerable for severe depression during the perinatal period (Sha et al., 2022).

These findings have significant clinical implications for helping professionals. It is imperative to screen and identify those who may be at risk for this type of depression during the perinatal period and refer them for appropriate care throughout pregnancy (Sha et al., 2022). Despite the importance of clinician-reported assessment using a tool to screen for depression in women during pregnancy or of self-assessment, it is possible that some women may feel reluctant to report depressive symptoms during and after pregnancy for a variety of reasons, such as feelings of shame due to stigma. Therefore, the addition or availability of using biological markers as empirically validated tools to predict future potential depression during pregnancy could help helping professionals deliberately schedule needed follow-up visits (Sha et al., 2022). Additionally, at-risk pregnant women proactively may be intervened with using psychosocial methods such as stress reduction programs or increased social support (Sha et al., 2022). Additionally, previously addressed in this chapter, preventative measures (e.g., diet and physical exercise) can be helpful for inflammation reduction, leading to the alleviation of risk for depression (Sha et al., 2022).

Trauma or Toxic Stress Screening

When helping professionals work with children, they may typically rely on self-reported or parent-reported questionnaires for adversity in childhood. Despite its importance, data from this type of screening and assessment may be affected by the subjective nature of human memory that can be influenced by levels of stress at times. Furthermore, evidence has shown that some people may manifest symptoms of PTSD or trauma responses without relevant trauma memory (May et al., 2022). It is worth emphasizing that helping professionals know that such individuals may have more difficulty accessing needed treatment and services and perceive them as less applicable to themselves (May et al., 2022). In addition, it is also possible that some individuals may not want to share trauma narratives for varied reasons.

As a result, biomarkers suggestive of adverse experiences and exposure can be used or supplement the credibility of data as a more objective measure of physiological memory. Some health researchers use blood, saliva, or urine samples to assess levels of a steroid hormone (e.g., cortisols) in humans. Teeth may offer another biomarker. For instance, findings from a study of 70 children from the Avon Longitudinal Study of Parents and Children Birth Cohort have suggested that human teeth may record events early in life (Mountain et al., 2021). A detailed description of their use will be addressed in the section of this chapter for prevention actions and practices at the relationship level. In the meantime, these measures may be suitable clinically when they are used as an index of measuring a child's current stress level.

Gastrointestinal Health Screening

The findings of a study (Park et al., 2016) suggested that a history of ACEs is associated with a higher risk for the development of irritable bowel syndrome (IBS). These authors also provide evidence that IBS status can be predicted by a history of emotional abuse, and household stressors (e.g., a family member with a mental disorder or incarceration; Park et al., 2016). Additionally, they documented that both overall IBS symptoms and the perceived severity of abdominal pain are associated with ACE scores (Park et al., 2016). As a result, it may be useful for helping professionals to identify and assess gastrointestinal health using subjective measures and pre-designed instrumentation. Such instrumentation includes bowel symptom questionnaires designed to measure the presence of IBS and other gastrointestinal symptoms; for example, Rome III poses questions about IBS symptom severity and pain severity using a 0–20 numeric rating scale over the past week (Park et al., 2016).

Assessment in Race-Based Stress

Mounting research has supported that racial trauma, as a form of race-based stress, is associated with physical outcomes (e.g., hypertension and a risk for heart disease) and an increased risk for other negative health outcomes that can increase substantial psychological and emotional disturbances (Carter, 2007; Williams et al., 2018). Thus, helping professionals may consider making intentional efforts to render services (e.g., racial trauma assessment such as the Race-Based Traumatic Stress Symptom Scale [Carter et al., 2013]) to people from various races (Carter, 2007).

Summary

This chapter addresses the importance of identifying and understanding a wide variety of influential factors that place individuals and families at risk for negative health states and conditions across the lifespan. In alignment with the EBD-M framework delineated in Chapter 2 of this textbook, the application of comprehensive, developmental lenses to examining human development is paramount. To be consistent with this point of view, the biopsychosocial and lifestyle framework (Malhi et al., 2015) can be useful in helping tailor helping professionals' approaches to prevention and healing actions and practices. In this chapter, selective lifestyle factors, such as diet, nutrition, and physical activity, are substantially addressed, particularly to help prevent negative effects of human suffering, specifically life stressors causing toxic stress.

To summarize, mounting research has supported the interrelation between diet and immunity in human bodies, and this helps human function (e.g., regulation and governance of energy homeostasis and metabolic health; Nobs et al., 2020). Consequently, disruption in this relationship can lead to health problems, including metabolic diseases (Nobs et al., 2020). In addition, diet also plays a key role in an intimate dialogue between the immune system, microbiota, gastrointestinal system, and the nervous system. Although more research is needed to further elucidate its mechanisms, poor diet has been shown to be hugely related to adverse health outcomes (e.g., physical and mental health). Thus, it is imperative to exercise healthy and sustainable dietary and nutritional practices. The application of precision nutrition could better allow dietary planning in order to match and optimize the effect of diet on the human immune system (Nobs et al., 2020). Additionally, other therapeutic methods targeting the gut microbiota (e.g., probiotics) may have the potential for augmenting mental health, albeit a meta-analysis of studies did not support favorable outcomes of the influence of probiotics on negative mental health states (e.g., anxiety and depression) when compared to placebo (Le Morvan de Sequeira et al., 2022). In a similar vein, physical activity (e.g., exercise) is another modifiable factor in lifestyles that is closely associated with human health and disease. Subsequently, the importance of lifestyle recommendations by qualified professionals are suggested not only to facilitate healthy physical development in youth but also prevent chronic diseases in adulthood (Loewen et al., 2019). In addition, physical activity in older adults is related to brain health characterized as brain tissue synaptic integrity that may be effective in this population in transitional cognitive states (Casaletto et al., 2021).

To explore neurobiology-informed approaches to prevention and healing, this chapter addressed the use of heart rate variability, the integration of sensory processing, and biofeedback, particularly EEG neurofeedback. Furthermore, as a part of the comprehensive services for risk identification and treatment in relation to effects of stress on human health, it is important for helping professionals to utilize and maximize appropriate and timely screening and assessment. As one example, this chapter emphasizes the importance of depression screening in women during the perinatal period, given that about 20% of women during this period are vulnerable for depression (Sha et al., 2022). It is critical to screen and detect those who may be at risk for this type of depression during pre- and post-pregnancy, and subsequently refer them for appropriate care and necessary follow-ups (Sha et al., 2022). It is also important that helping professionals practice toxic stress screening and assessment, particularly when working with children, by employing a wide range of applicable measures (e.g., self-report questionnaires, parental reports, and biomarkers). In a similar vein, it is documented that a history of adverse experiences early in life may manifest as an increased risk for the development of IBS (Park et al., 2016). Thus, it may be useful to target and assess gastrointestinal health using subjective measures as a part of prevention and healing practices among helping professionals. Moreover, mounting research has suggested that racial trauma is associated with physical and mental health (Carter, 2007; Williams et al., 2018). This warrants that helping professionals consider making intentional efforts to render screening and assessment in individuals and families from various races (Carter, 2007).

Informative Resources

- Learn Self-Regulation Skills for Anxiety & Stress by Dr. Tim Culbert through HeartMath: https://www.heartmath.com/webinars/health-professionals/health-professional-education-series-tim-culbert/?tfa_next=%2Fresponses%2Flast_success%26sid%3D131bb-c5fbb36b880003bf2c55331a692

- TED Ed on *How the Food You Eat Affects Your Gut* by Shilpa Ravella: https://ed.ted.com/lessons/how-the-food-you-eat-affects-your-gut-shilpa-ravella

- TED Ed on *How the Food You Eat Affects Your Brain* by Mia Nacamulli: https://ed.ted.com/lessons/how-the-food-you-eat-affects-your-brain-mia-nacamulli#review

- TED Ed on *How Sugar Affects the Brain* by Nicole Avena: https://ed.ted.com/lessons/how-sugar-affects-the-brain-nicole-avena

At the Relationship Level

"One strategy to prevent mental illness may be to target interventions toward children who are exposed to adversity, particularly during sensitive periods when these adversities may have even more enduring effects."

Davis et al. (2020, p. 502)

Strategies to promote prevention actions and practices and healing at the relationship level may include eliminating or minimizing the risk of being exposed to toxic stress in surrounding relationships. One's surroundings typically include a social circle consisting of peers, parents, family members, loved ones, educators, co-workers, or close professionals working in a relevant field. Therefore, these strategies pertaining to helping professionals may include parent-child stress prevention programs, peer support, mentoring programs, healing-centered professional-client relationship programs, and interdisciplinary collaboration in human service fields. These strategies are to promote and augment relational communication and healing in relationships, and to help alleviate the risk for longstanding effects of adversity.

Women During Perinatal Pregnancy and Their Children

As addressed throughout this textbook, numerous factors influence and facilitate the healthy development of children. Similarly, some factors (e.g., children's exposure to maternal psychosocial stressors such as stressful life events) can impact disrupted development and health across the life course. In particular, maternal psychosocial stress can result in lifelong neurobiological and physiological disruptions via biological mechanisms (Mountain et al., 2021). By contrast, increased maternal social support is a protective factor against inflammation in their children during the first year of life (Mountain et al., 2021).

Biomarkers

Mountain and colleagues (2021) argue that detailed prenatal medical records are frequently unavailable, and this leads to relying on retrospective maternal self-reports. Despite some validity of these data, they may be susceptible to memory and recall biases (Mountain et al., 2021). Furthermore, retrospective reports are disadvantaged in tailoring preventive efforts to help prevent offspring from being negatively influenced by maternal psychosocial stress because they may lack timely information regarding maternal psychosocial stress exposure (Mountain et al., 2021). Therefore, new approaches are needed, including the use of measurement tools that can more objectively and timely provide information about children's exposure to maternal stress during the prenatal period (Mountain et al., 2021). In the following section, the teeth as a specific example of a biomarker will be described in greater detail.

The TEETH (Teeth Encoding Experiences and Transforming Health; Davis et al., 2020; see Figure 8.1) is a conceptual model proposed for the use of teeth as biomarkers of early life adversity and subsequent mental health risk in children. In this model, primary and permanent teeth are proposed to serve as dual markers of both post–psychosocial stress exposure and prospective mental health risk (Davis et al., 2020). Specifically, it was promised in the model that disruptions induced by early life psychosocial stress may be responsible for alterations at macro- and micro-levels, leading to changes in tooth dimensions as well as microstructure and chemical compositions manifested in stress lines (Davis et al., 2020). Specifically, it is known that the neonatal line in teeth can be used to characterize the overall stress of the birth process (Mountain et al., 2021). Similarly, it is evident that wider neonatal lines have been associated with

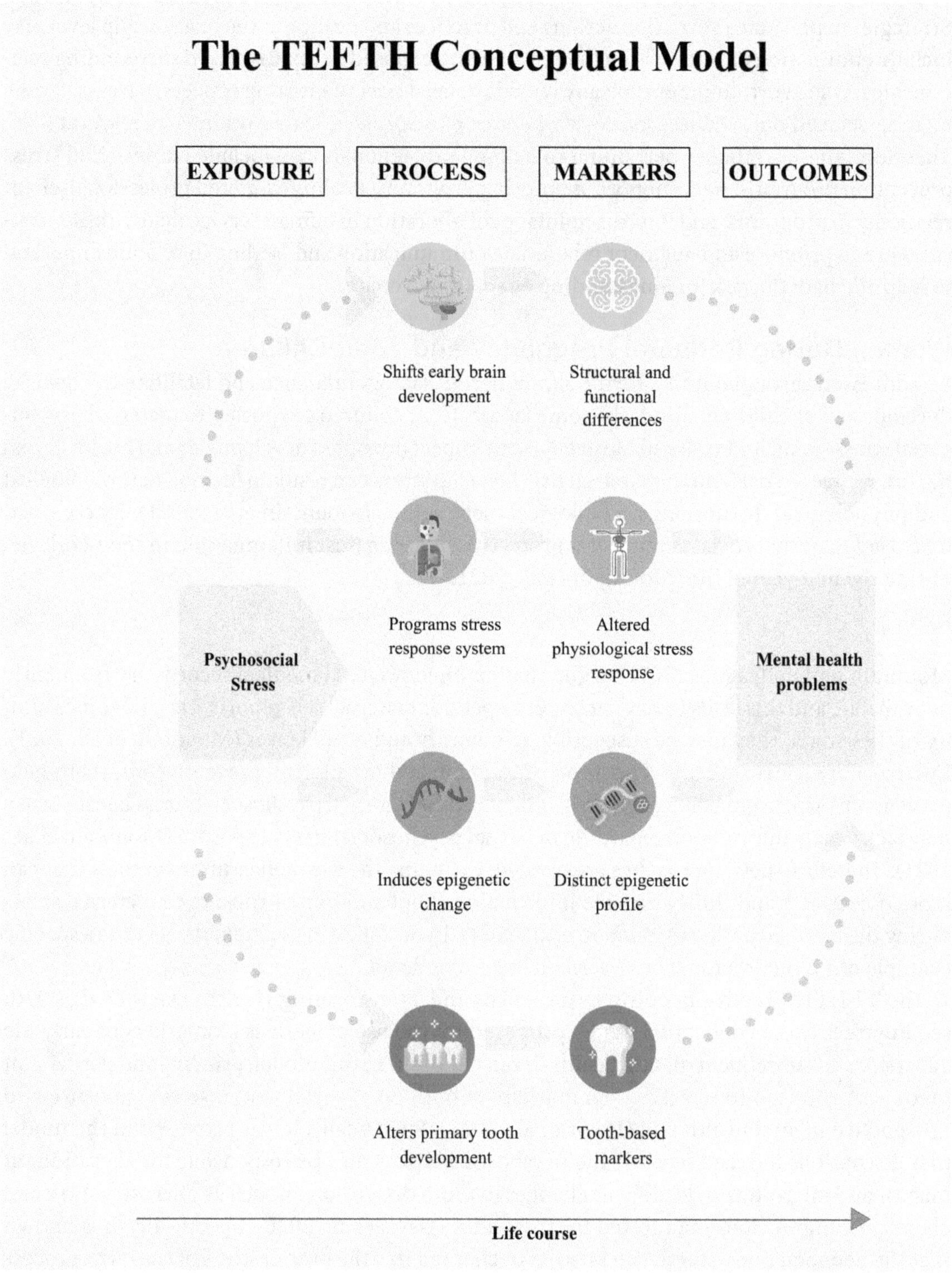

The TEETH Conceptual Model

EXPOSURE	PROCESS	MARKERS	OUTCOMES

Shifts early brain development

Structural and functional differences

Programs stress response system

Altered physiological stress response

Psychosocial Stress

Mental health problems

Induces epigenetic change

Distinct epigenetic profile

Alters primary tooth development

Tooth-based markers

Life course →

FIGURE 8.1   TEETH Conceptual Model

some known maternal stress prenatal and perinatal conditions, such as complicated delivery, longer duration of delivery, and preterm births (Mountain et al., 2021).

A study suggested that exposure to maternal psychosocial stress has biological embedding in teeth development in children. Strong associations were found between increased maternal depressive and anxiety symptoms, particularly at 32 weeks' gestation, and neonatal line width in the offspring's primary eye teeth (Mountain et al., 2021). However, these associations were not observed at 18 weeks' gestation (Mountain et al., 2021). The authors address that one possible hypothesis is that the neonatal line in offspring's teeth forms and reflects "experiences at the time of birth and shortly thereafter" (Mountain et al., 2021, p. 7). As a result, teeth could be used in prevention programs to help screen at-risk children for future mental disorders that typically develop any time during middle childhood or later (Davis et al., 2020).

The Development of Gut Microbiota

In addition, varied factors are known to influence the development of microbiota during infancy (see Figure 8.2; Kapourchali et al., [2020]). Specifically, the composition of gut microbes begins during the gestational period and is influenced by an array of factors (Desbonnet et al., 2010):

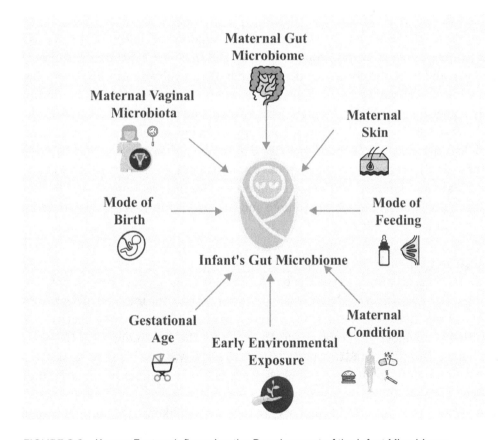

FIGURE 8.2   Known Factors Influencing the Development of the Infant Microbiome

the gestational age of the mother, mode of delivery (e.g., natural delivery or Cesarean delivery), and mode of feeding (e.g., breastfeeding). Furthermore, maternal conditions, such as maternal body weight and lifestyles (e.g., diet) during gestation and lactation, and material microorganisms in the vagina on the surface of the skin are also influential factors in the development of the microbial composition in offspring (Desbonnet et al., 2010).

Parental Emotional Socialization Behavior

It is evident that changes in brain activity are associated with depression in adults. Among many mechanisms, alterations in reward-brain function may be one mechanism pertaining to the development of this mental state (Morgan et al., 2022). In addition, research has suggested that parental social behaviors (e.g., maternal warmth and encouragement) are responsible for healthy reward function (Morgan et al., 2022). *Parental socialization of emotion* is defined as "parent behaviors (e.g., modeling, contingent responding) that either support or discourage child emotion expressions via implicit or explicit means" (Morgan et al., 2022, p. 4). Parental emotional-socialization behaviors, such as acknowledgement, elaboration of a child's positive emotion expression, and imitation, tend to support positive emotion expression in children, while dismissive, invalidating, or punitive parental responses can disrupt a child's positive emotion expression (Morgan et al., 2022).

To examine mechanisms of how maternal positive-emotion socialization may be associated with reward-related neural disruptions in high-risk children with a maternal history of depression, Morgan and her colleagues conducted a study that involved forty-nine 6- to 8-year-old children without a lifetime history of mental disorders (Morgan et al., 2022). Findings from this study suggested that children at high risk for depression presented decreased brain activity in the ventral striatum to winning reward, but only when low maternal encouragement or high maternal discouragement of a child's positive emotion expression was at play (Morgan et al., 2022). These findings emphasize the importance of maternal positivity in a child's socioemotional and brain development and suggest that preventive interventions should be focused on maternal socialization of emotion to promote and sustain healthy reward-related development in children (Morgan et al., 2022).

Complicated Grief Prevention

As of May 27, 2022, according to the Centers for Disease Control and Prevention (CDC, 2022; https://www.cdc.gov/nchs/covid19/mortality-overview.htm), the total toll of deaths attributed to COVID-19 was 1,003,865 in the United States. In at least 90% of these deaths, COVID-19 was recorded as an underlying cause of death, while for the remainder, COVID-19 was listed as contributing causality of the mortality (CDC, 2022). Given the concerning death toll, it is not uncommon that the pandemic will likely leave behind a number of bereaved individuals and families.

Consequently, the emotional burden of bereavement will likely have noticeable mental and physical health consequences that will warrant urgent action pertaining to preventive and supportive interventions for such individuals and families in need (Kokou-Kpolou et al., 2020).

Before recommendations are provided, readers are encouraged to think about the following questions. How would everyone adapt to the loss of a loved one? Would everyone's adaptation patterns during grieving over time look the same?

These questions were answered in bereavement studies such as the Changing Lives of Older Couples study conducted at the University of Michigan. In this study, approximately 1,500 older adults were interviewed across different points in time before and after the death of a spouse aged 65 years or older (Galatzer-Levy & Bonanno, 2012). The researchers interviewed the participants first when both members of the couple were alive and neither of the spouses was ill (Galatzer-Levy & Bonanno, 2012). When one of the spouses in the couple died, the surviving spouse was interviewed again at 6, 18, and 48 months after the death (Galatzer-Levy & Bonanno, 2012).

Galatzer-Levy and Bonanno found in the study that there were four trajectories, categorizing older individuals' grieving as follows: *resilient* ("characterized by little or no depression"; 66.3%), *chronic grieving* ("characterized by depression following loss and alleviated by 4 years post-loss"; 9.1%), *pre-existing chronic depression* ("ongoing high pre- through post-loss depression"; 14.5%), and *depressed improved* ("characterized by high pre-loss depression that decreases following loss"; 10.1%; Galatzer-Levy & Bonanno, 2012, p. 1987; see Figure 8.3). The findings from the study remind us as helping professionals that more than half of the spouses who lost a spouse fell into the resilience category, indicating that adaptation to the loss may be the most frequent pattern of grieving in older adults (Galatzer-Levy & Bonanno, 2012).

However, it is noteworthy that those who followed the chronic grieving trajectory demonstrated full recovery in depressive symptoms by 4 years after the death of their spouse, although they experienced elevated scores on depression at 6 months and 18 months post-loss (Galatzer-Levy & Bonanno, 2012). Similarly, approximately 1 in 10 bereaved people do not appear to adapt

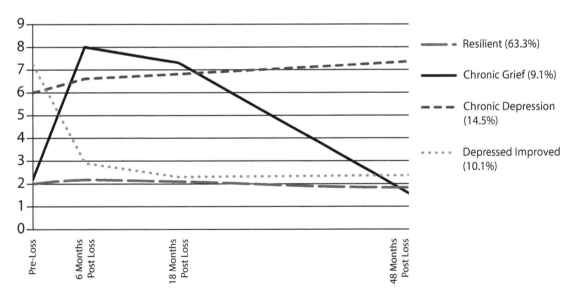

FIGURE 8.3   4-Class Unconditional Trajectory Model of CED-S scores (*N* = 301)

over a long period of time. This phenomenon is termed as *complicated grief,* characterized as "debilitating recurrent pangs of painful emotions, with intense yearning, longing and searching for the deceased, and preoccupation with thoughts for the loved one" (O'Connor et al., 2008, p. 969). Furthermore, M. Katherine Shear and her colleagues argue that complicated grief as a stress response syndrome is underrecognized as a public health issue that affects numerous people in the United States, especially in older adults (Shear et al., 2014).

In a more recent study using an event-related functional magnetic resonance imaging scan, the bereaved presented activated brain regions (i.e., the anterior cingulate cortex and the insula) pertaining to the importance (e.g., a death of a loved one), and they presented particularly a neural activity related to social pain in response to reminders of the deceased (O'Connor et al., 2008). Furthermore, this study has also suggested that only those with complicated grief presented reward-related neural activity in the nucleus accumbens, compared to those without complicated grief (O'Connor et al., 2008). O'Connor (2022) argues that reward used in this context is not something just joyful or pleasurable but involves "the encoding that means, yes, we want that, let's do that again, let's see them (the deceased) again" (O'Connor, 2022, p. 188). Getting back to the study findings, greater activation in the nucleus accumbens among those with complicated grief was positively correlated with levels of yearning by self-report, while it was not related to the length of time since the death and participant age, or even the amount of positive or negative emotion that they were experiencing (O'Connor et al., 2008). Similarly, it was speculated in the study that the greater activation in the brain area may interfere with the adaptation to the loss in the present time (O'Connor et al., 2008).

The circumstances surrounding death attributed to the pandemic involve multiple traumatic characteristics; experiencing the likely multiple deaths could relate to overwhelming bereavement and subsequently the capacity of healthy coping could be disturbed due to a profound overflow of grieving. The social restrictions instituted as preventative measures due to the pandemic prohibited some individuals and families from visiting their loved ones at intensive care units or hospitals, which in turn might trigger or worsen feelings of guilt (Kokou-Kpolou et al., 2020). Despite the necessity of elucidating a better understanding of what exactly pathological grief is (i.e., grief disorder or prolonged grief disorder), it is imperative that helping professionals identify those at high risk who are vulnerable for the development of complicated grief or a prolonged grief disorder, as they might benefit from prevention. At present, in the *DSM-5* (APA, 2013), persistent complex bereavement disorder is listed in the section of conditions for further study and is characterized as persistent yearning for the deceased, intense emotional pain in response to the death, preoccupation with the deceased, or preoccupation with the circumstances of the death. Furthermore, reactive distress following the death selectively includes substantial difficulty accepting the death, disbelief or emotional numbness over the loss, anger related to the loss, or a diminished sense of one's identity; these disturbances are attributable to clinically significant distress or functional impairment in important areas of life of the bereaved (APA, 2013). Additionally, prolonged grief disorder is now included in the *International Statistical Classification of Diseases and Related Health Problems* (11th ed.; World Health Organization, 2019), and is also listed in the *DSM-5, Text Revision* (APA, 2022).

Biomarkers

To detect those who are at high risk for the development of complicated grief, measuring changes in known biomarkers after the death of a loved one may enable helping professionals to understand the mechanisms that may lead to bereavement-related morbidity and mortality (O'Connor, 2019). For instance, cardiovascular biomarkers have displayed consistent changes during bereavement when comparing acute grief (less than 6 weeks in a period of time after the death) and complicated grief (O'Connor, 2019). As described in the article (O'Connor, 2019), these biomarkers encompass heart rate variability and blood pressure. Furthermore, changes in neuroendocrine biomarkers have also shown that higher levels of cortisol and dysregulated activity in the HPA axis are consistently presented (Ong et al., 2011).

Complicated Grief Treatment

In addition to the aforementioned prevention efforts, it is also critical that helping professionals are well-versed in complicated grief treatment. It is imperative that they recognize the existing literature on complicated grief that recognizes that those who are depressed before bereavement may need different interventions from those whose onset of depression occurs only after the loss (O'Connor et al., 2019). Also, the comprehensive interventions for complicated grief should incorporate not only biological factors but also psychosocial factors that include emotional expression and meaning-making (Stroebe et al., 2002).

As one example, Katherine Shear and colleagues developed a complicated grief treatment now known as the prolonged grief disorder therapy (PGDT), whose efficacy has been supported in a randomized clinical trial (Shear et al., 2014). Specifically, this treatment aims at resolving or alleviating grief complications while it helps facilitate adaptive coping (e.g., natural mourning; Shear et al., 2014). The dual-process model of grief (Stroebe & Schut, 1999) was employed to design the treatment model, and each session encompasses both loss-focused and restoration-focused elements (Shear et al., 2014). Given the limited space in this textbook, readers are encouraged to seek the following resource for the details of the treatment: the Center for Prolonged Grief (https://prolongedgrief.columbia.edu/professionals/complicated-grief-professionals/overview/).

Relevantly, it is noteworthy to acknowledge that not every expert in grief and bereavement work agrees that a form of grief may be pathological, as the diagnostic classification systems suggest. Such professionals rather see that grief is a normal response to the loss and a part of the lifespan. Furthermore, grieving is an individualized process and warrants cultural considerations. However, unquestionably, helping professionals must be equipped to render grief-informed services when they are needed. Donna L. Schuurman and Monique B. Mitchell at The Dougy Center, the national grief center for children and families, have conducted remarkable work (i.e., the Understand Grief movement) that in part created the following core ten principles of being *grief-informed*:

- natural

- complex and nonpathological

- contextual

- disruptive
- relational connection and perceived support
- personal empowerment and agency
- safety
- person-centered
- dynamic
- nonfinite

They have also provided the ten concrete action items that ask helping professionals to take on action from the understanding of grief, death, and dying.

Social Isolation and Loneliness Prevention

The Alzheimer's Association estimates that approximately 6.5 million Americans aged 65 and older were affected by Alzheimer's disease and other dementias in 2022 (Alzheimer's Association, 2022). Deaths due to Alzheimer's disease between 2000 and 2019 have more than doubled and increased by 145% (Alzheimer's Association, 2022). According to the report, it is estimated that one in three American seniors dies with Alzheimer's or another dementia (Alzheimer's Association, 2022). Furthermore, a special report titled "Race, Ethnicity and Alzheimer's in America" (Alzheimer's Association, 2021) also examines the detrimental impact of the COVID-19 pandemic on people living with Alzheimer's disease (Alzheimer's Association, 2021); there was a 6% increase in mortality from Alzheimer's and other dementias compared with averages from the previous 5 years. Additionally, findings in the report suggest that non-White racial or ethnic populations living in the United States experience more barriers compared to their White counterparts when accessing medical care such as dementia care; and they indicate less confidence that they have access to health professionals who fully understand their cultural background and relevant experiences (Alzheimer's Association, 2021). Specifically, approximately 66% of Black or African Americans believe that it is harder for them to access and experience excellent care for Alzheimer's disease or other dementias, while 40% of Native Americans, 39% of Latinx Americans, and 34% of Asian Americans believe that they face similar barriers due to their race or ethnicity (Alzheimer's Association, 2021).

Importantly, it is evident that Alzheimer's disease develops due to multiple factors. The known risk factors for the disease and other dementias include older age, genetics (apolipoprotein e4 gene [*APOEe4*]), and a family history (first-degree relative; Alzheimer's Association, 2021). While these risk factors are not changeable, other risk factors can change or be modified to decrease the risk for cognitive decline or the development of Alzheimer's disease and other dementias. Examples of such factors involve lifestyle factors, such as diet, physical activity, smoking, education, and social and cognitive engagement (Alzheimer's Association, 2021). It is critical that prevention practices and actions are actively promoted to reduce those risk factors, because it is suggested in the 2020 Lancet Commission on Dementia Prevention, Intervention, and Care that they might prevent or delay the onset of dementia in up to approximately 40% of such cases (Livingston et al., 2020).

Although the biological processes or mechanisms have yet to be elucidated, research has found evidence that staying socially and mentally active over the lifespan may support and subsequently reduce the risk of cognitive decline and developing Alzheimer's and other dementias (James et al., 2011). Conversely, recent research has revealed that lonely individuals younger than 80 years old who live in the United States face a three-fold increase in risk of prospective Alzheimer's and other dementias (Salinas et al., 2022). Furthermore, perceived loneliness was associated in the study with lower total cerebral volume and a greater volume of white matter hyperintensities indicative of greater small vessel cerebrovascular injury (Salinas et al., 2022).

Specifically, this research was derived from the retrospective data of the population-based Framingham Study, and data analysis was based on 2,308 participants who were free of dementia at baseline and an average age of 73 (Salinas et al., 2022). These individuals were expected to be at low risk for cognitive decline and onset of dementias based on the known risk factors (i.e., age and inherent generic risk or an *APOEe4* allele; Salinas et al., 2022). These findings are alarming when considering the prevalence of loneliness increased from 11% to 14% in a U.S. population–based sample from 2018 to 2020, partly due to social isolation (McGinty et al., 2020) and predating the pandemic's increased isolation. This study reminds us as helping professionals to emphasize the significance of the role of psychosocial factors such as loneliness and social environments. The authors of the study suggest that it may be beneficial to employ tools to efficiently screen for loneliness in routine clinical care and ask the following question: "In the past, how often have you felt lonely?" (Salinas et al., 2022, p. 21).

Summary

The strategies to facilitate prevention and healing actions and practices can be exercised at the relationship level and guided by the Socio-Ecological Model for Prevention—Modified (SEMP-M; CDC, n.d.). This chapter focused on strategies for helping professionals to exercise, including parent-child services and programs, as well as an increase in appropriate, relational communication between the two to help reduce the risk for lifelong effects of adversity.

Relevantly, maternal psychosocial stress can lead to enduring neurobiological and physiological disruptions via biological mechanisms (Mountain et al., 2021). However, enhanced maternal social support plays a protective role in reducing inflammation in the offspring during the first year of life (Mountain et al., 2021). Due to the difficulty in accessing medical records, and the overuse of maternal self-reports susceptible to memory and recall biases, it is necessary that helping professionals invest in new approaches, such as using biomarkers (e.g., child teeth and inflammatory markers) that may more objectively and timely provide information about children's exposure to maternal stress during the perinatal period (Mountain et al., 2021).

In addition, it is also imperative to provide education on the impact of parental social behavior, such as maternal warmth and encouragement, on healthy child development and child function (e.g., healthy reward function; Morgan et al., 2022). In particular, the findings from a study have suggested that positive maternal emotion socialization is highly related to socioemotional development as well as brain development in their offspring (Morgan et al., 2022). These findings suggest that preventive interventions for those who may be at risk for negative effects of maternal depression during the perinatal period should be tailored toward the increase in maternal socialization of emotion as a means to promote and maintain healthy reward-related development in children (Morgan et al., 2022).

In addition, this chapter highlights the importance of prevention for effects of complicated grief given the insurmountable death toll related to COVID-19 in the nation. Similarly, the emotional burden of bereavement will likely have a sizeable impact on physical and mental health among the bereaved and their surrounding supports. Thus, this calls for urgent action related to preventive and supportive resources and services (Kokou-Kpolou et al., 2020). One index to identify those at high risk for the development of complicated grief, measuring changes in supported biomarkers, such as cardiovascular biomarkers (e.g., heart rate variability and blood pressure) and neuroendocrine biomarkers (e.g., high levels of cortisol and dysregulated activity in the HPA axis), may be useful among the bereaved after the death of a loved one (Ong et al., 2011). In addition to preventive practices, it is also imperative that helping professionals are equipped for grief treatment by recognizing the existing complicated grief literature and employing relevant treatment programs, such as the PGDT (Shear et al., 2014).

Moreover, this chapter emphasized the prevention of social isolation and loneliness. Research has supported that staying socially and mentally active over one's life course may support and then decrease the risk of cognitive decline (James et al., 2011). By contrast, study findings have shown that lonely individuals younger than 80 years living in the United States are vulnerable for a three-fold increased risk of prospective Alzheimer's and other dementias (Salinas et al., 2022). These findings remind helping professionals to better understand the role of psychosocial factors (e.g., loneliness and the social environment) on human health. Thus, it may be important for helping professionals to effectively screen for loneliness in routine clinical care (Salinas et al., 2022).

Informative Resources

- The importance of being grief-informed: https://www.dougy.org/assets/uploads/Being-Grief-Informed-from-Understanding-to-Action.pdf

- Dougy Dialogues, Episode 7: The Importance of Becoming Grief-Informed: https://www.dougy.org/videos/dougy-dialogues-episode-7

- General resources center: https://www.dougy.org/get-involved/join-in/understandgrief/understandgrief-resources

- Complicated grief public resources: https://prolongedgrief.columbia.edu/professionals/resources-pro/

Experiential Questions

1. What dietary and nutritional practices do you think may be helpful to alleviate A's health-related state?

2. Based on your primary professional role, is it necessary for you to utilize some screening and/or assessment to strengthen your understanding of A's current health state? If so, what measures of such would you use, with what rationale?

3. From the case study, what risk factor(s) do you identify that may put A at high risk for neurodegeneration and a potential cognitive decline?

References

At the Microbial and Individual Level

The American College of Obstetricians and Gynecologists Committee Opinion. (2005). Screening for perinatal depression, no 631. *Obstetrics & Gynecology, 125*, 1272–1275.

Beauchaine, T. P., & Thayer, J. F. (2015). Heart rate variability as a transdiagnostic biomarker of psychopathology. *International Journal of Psychophysiology, 98*(2), 338–350. https://doi.org/10.1016/j.ijpsycho.2015.08.004

Brom, D., Stokar, Y., Lawi, C., Nuriel-Porat, V., Ziv, Y., Lerner, K., & Ross, G. (2017). Somatic experiencing for posttraumatic stress disorder: A randomized controlled outcome study. *Journal of Traumatic Stress, 30*(3), 304–312. https://doi.org/10.1002/jts.22189

Carter, R. T. (2007). Racism and psychological and emotional injury: Recognizing and assessing race-based traumatic stress. *The Counseling Psychologist, 35*(1), 13–105. https://doi.org/10.1177/0011000006292033

Carter, R. T., Mazzula, S., Victoria, R., Vazquez, V., Hall, S., Smith, S., Sant-Barket, S., & Forsyth, J. (2013). Initial development of the Race-Based Traumatic Stress Symptom Scale: Assessing the emotional impact of racism. *Psychological Trauma: Theory, Practice, and Policy, 5*(1), 1–9. https://doi.org/10.1037/a0025911

Casaletto, K., Ramos-Miguel, A., VandeBunte, A., Memel, M., Buchman, A., Bennett, D. & Honer, W. (2022). Late-life physical activity relates to brain tissue synaptic integrity markers in older adults. *Alzheimer's & Dementia.* Advance online publication. https://doi.org/10.1002/alz.12530

Centers for Disease Control and Prevention. (n.d.). The social-ecological model: A framework for prevention. https://www.cdc.gov/violenceprevention/about/social-ecologicalmodel.html

Davis, K. A., Mountain, R. V., Pickett, O. R., Den Besten, P. K., Bidlack, F. B., & Erin C. Dunn, E. C. (2020). Teeth as potential new tools to measure early-life adversity and subsequent mental health risk: An interdisciplinary review and conceptual model. *Biological Psychiatry, 87*(6), 502–513. https://doi.org/10.1016/j.biopsych.2019.09.030

Desbonnet, L., Garrett, L., Clarke, G., Kiely, B., Cryan, J. F., & Dinan, T. G. (2010). Effects of the probiotic bifidobacterium infantis in the maternal separation model of depression. *Neuroscience, 170*(4), 1179–1188. https://doi.org/10.1016/j.neuroscience.2010.08.005

de Sousa Rodrigues, M. E., Bekhbat, M., Houser, M. C., Chang, J., Walker, D. I., Jones, D. P., Oller do Nascimento, C. M. P., Barnum, C. J., & Tansey, M. G. (2017). Chronic psychological stress and high-fat high-fructose diet disrupt metabolic and inflammatory gene networks in the brain, liver, and gut and promote behavioral deficits in mice. *Brain, Behavior, and Immunity, 59*, 158–172. https://doi.org/10.1016/j.bbi.2016.08.021

Eiwegger, T., Hung, L., San Diego, K. E., O'Mahony, L., & Upton J. (2019). Recent developments and highlights in food allergy. *Allergy, 74*, 2355–2367. https://doi.org/10.1111/all.14082

Firth, J., Veronese, N., Cotter, J., Shivappa, N., Hebert, J. R., Ee, C., Smith, L., Stubbs, B., Jackson, S. E., & Sarris, J. (2019a). What is the role of dietary inflammation in severe mental illness? A review of observational and experimental findings. *Frontiers in Psychiatry, 10*, 350. https://doi.org/10.3389/fpsyt.2019.00350

Foster, J. A., Rinaman, L., & Cryan, J. F. (2017). Stress & the gut-brain axis: Regulation by the microbiome. *Neurobiology of Stress, 7*, 124–136. https://doi.org/10.1016/j.ynstr.2017.03.001

Gunkelman, J. D., & Johnstone, J. (2005). Neurofeedback and the Brain. *Journal of Adult Development,* 12, 93–98 (2005). https://doi.org/10.1007/s10804-005-7024-x

Hayhoe, R., Rechel, B., Clark, A. B., Gummerson, C., Smith, S. J. L., & Welch, A. A. (2021). Cross-sectional associations of schoolchildren's fruit and vegetable consumption, and meal choices, with their mental well-being: A cross-sectional study. *BMJ Nutrition, Prevention & Health*, e000205. https://doi.org/10.1136/bmjnph-2020-000205

Harricharan, S., Mckinnon, M. C., & Lanius, R. A. (2021). How processing of sensory information from the internal and external worlds shape the perception and engagement with the world in the aftermath of trauma: Implications for PTSD. *Frontiers in Neuroscience, 15*, 625490. https://doi.org/10.3389/fnins.2021.625490

Hlebowicz, J., Persson, M., Gullberg, B., Sonestedt, E., Wallström, P., & Drake, I., Nilsson, J., Hedblad, B., & Wirfält, E. (2011). Food patterns, inflammation markers and incidence of cardiovascular disease: The Malmö Diet and Cancer study. *Journal of Internal Medicine, 270*(4), 365–376.

Juul, F., Parekh, N., Martinez-Steele, E., Monteiro, C. A., & Chang, V. W. (2021). Ultra-processed food consumption among US adults from 2001 to 2018. *The American Journal of Clinical Nutrition, 305*, 1–11. https://doi.org/10.1093/ajcn/nqab305

Kapourchali, F. R., & Cresci, G. A. M. (2020). Early-life gut microbiome—The importance of maternal and infant factors in its establishment. *Nutritional in Clinical Practice, 35*(3), 386–405. https://doi.org/10.1002/ncp.10490

Kastorini, C-M., Milionis, H. J., Esposito, K., Giugliano, D., Goudevenos, J. A., & Panagiotakos, D. B. (2011). The effect of Mediterranean diet on metabolic syndrome and its components: A meta-analysis of 50 studies and 534,906 individuals. *Journal of American College of Cardiology, 57*(11), 299–313. https://doi.org/10.1016/j.jacc.2010.09.073

Le Morvan de Sequeira, C., Hengstberger, C., Enck, P., & Mack, I. (2022). Effect of probiotics on psychiatric symptoms and central nervous system functions in human health and disease: A systematic review and meta-analysis. *Nutrients, 14*, 621. https://doi.org/10.3390/nu14030621

Loewen, O. K., Maximova, K., Ekwaru, J. P., Faught, E. L., Asbridge, M., Ohinmaa, A., & Paul J. Veugelers, P. J. (2019). Lifestyle behavior and mental health in early adolescence. *Pediatrics, 143*(5), e20183307. https://doi.org/10.1542/peds.2018-3307

Malchiodi, C. A. (2020). *Trauma and expressive arts therapy: Brain, body, and imagination in the healing process*. Guilford Publications.

Malhi, G. S., Bassett, D., Boyce, P., Bryant, R., Fitzgerald, P. B., Fritz, K., Hopwood, M., Lyndon, B., Mulder, R., Murray, G., Porter, R., & Singh, A. B. (2015). Royal Australian and New Zealand College of Psychiatrists clinical practice guidelines for mood disorders. *Australian & New Zealand Journal of Psychiatry, 49*(12), 1087–1206. https://doi.org/10.1177/0004867415617657

May, H., Paskell, R., Davies, C., & Hamilton-Giachritsis, C. (2022). Having permission not to remember: Perspectives on interventions for post-traumatic stress disorder in the absence of trauma memory. *European Journal of Psychotraumatology, 13*, 1, 2055295. https://doi.org/10.1080/20008198.2022.2055295

Mayer, E. (2018). *The mind-gut connection: How the hidden conversation within our bodies impacts our mood, our choices, and our overall health*. Harper Wave.

Moubarac, J.-C., Batal, M., Louzada, M. L. E., Steele, E. M., & Monteiro, C. A. (2017). Consumption of ultra-processed foods predicts diet quality in Canada. *Appetite, 108*(1), 512–520.

Mountain, R. V., Zhu, Y., Pickett, O. R., Lussier, A. A., Goldstein, J. M., Roffman, J. L., Bidlack, F. B., & Dunn, E. C. (2021). Association of maternal stress and social support during pregnancy with growth markers in children's primary tooth enamel. *JAMA Network Open, 4*(11), e2129129. https://doi.org/10.1001/jamanetworkopen.2021.29129

Nobs, S. P., Zmora, N., & Elinav, E. (2020). Nutrition regulates innate immunity in health and disease. *Annual Review of Nutrition, 40*, 189–219. https://doi.org/10.1146/annurev-nutr-120919-094440

Park, S. H., Videlock, E. J., Shih, W., Presson, A. P., Mayer, E. A., & Chang, L. (2016). Adverse childhood experiences are associated with irritable bowel syndrome and gastrointestinal symptom severity. *Neurogastroenterology and Motility, 28*, 1252–1260. https://doi.org/10.1111/nmo.12826

Perna, G., Riva, A., Defillo, A., Sangiorgio, E., Nobile, M., & Caldirola, D. (2020). Heart rate variability: Can it serve as a marker of mental health resilience? Special section on "Translational and Neuroscience Studies in Affective Disorders." *Journal of Affective Disorders, 263*, 754–761. https://doi.org/10.1016/j.jad.2019.10.017

Raichle, M. E. (2011). The restless brain. *Brain Connectivity, 1*(1), 3–12. https://doi.org/10.1089/brain.2011.0019

Sha, Q., Madaj, Z., Keaton, S., Galvis, M. L. E., Smart, L., Kryzanowski, S., Fazleabas, A. T., Leach, R., Postolache, T. T., Achtyes, E. D., & Brundin, L. (2022). Cytokines and tryptophan metabolites can predict depressive symptoms in pregnancy. *Translational Psychiatry, 12*, 35. https://doi.org/10.1038/s41398-022-01801-8

Shi, Y., Cui, M., Ochs, K., Brendel, M., Strübing, F. L., Briel, N., Eckenweber, F., Zou, C., Banati, R. B., Liu, G.-J., Middleton, R. J., Rupprecht, R., Rudolph, U., Ulrich Zeilhofer, H., Rammes, G., Herms, J., & Dorostkar, M. M. (2022). Long-term diazepam treatment enhances microglial spine engulfment and impairs cognitive performance via the mitochondrial 18 kDa translocator protein (TSPO). *Nature Neuroscience, 25*, 317–329. https://doi.org/10.1038/s41593-022-01013-9

Siu, A. L. (2016). Screening for depression in adults: US Preventive Services Task Force recommendation statement. *JAMA, 315*, 380–387.

Sterman, M. B. (2000). Basic concepts and clinical findings in the treatment of seizure disorders with EEG operant conditioning. *Clinical Electroencephalography, 31*(1), 45–55. https://doi.org/10.1177/155005940003100111

Thayer, J. F., Yamamoto, S. S., & Brosschot, J. F. (2010). The relationship of autonomic imbalance, heart rate variability and cardiovascular disease risk factors. *International Journal of Cardiology*, *141*(2), 122–131. https://doi.org/10.1016/j.ijcard.2009.09.543

You, Y., Brown, J., & Li, W. (2021). Human sensory cortex contributes to the long-term storage of adverse condition. *Journal of Neuroscience*, *41*(14), 3222–3233. https://doi.org/10.1523/JNEUROSCI.2325-20.2021

You, Y., Novak, L. R., Clancy, K. J., & Li, W. (2022). Pattern differentiation and tunning shifts in human sensory cortex underlie long-term threat memory. *Current Biology*, *32*(9), 2067–2075.e4.

Wibowo, M. C., Yang, Z., Borry, M., Hubner, A., Huang, K. D., Tierney, B. T., Zimmerman, S., Barajas-Olmos, F., Contreras-Cubas, C., Garcia-Ortiz, H., Martinez-Hernandez, A., Luber, J. M., Kirstahler, P., Blohm, T., Smiley, F. S., Arnold, R., Ballal, S. A., Pamp, S. J., Russ, J., Maixner, F., Rota-Stabelli, O., ... Kostic, A. D. (2021). Reconstruction of ancient microbial genomes from the human gut. *Nature*, *594*, 234–239. https://doi.org/10.1038/s41586-021-03532-0

Williams, M. T., Printz, M. B., & DeCapp, R. C. T. (2018). Assessing racial trauma with the Trauma Symptoms of Discrimination Scale. *Psychology of Violence*, *8*(6), 735–747. http://dx.doi.org/10.1037/vio0000212

At the Relationship Level

Alzheimer's Association. (2021). *Race, Ethnicity and Alzheimer's in America*. https://www.alz.org/media/Documents/alzheimers-facts-and-figures-special-report-2021.pdf

Alzheimer's Association. (2022). *2022 Alzheimer's Disease Facts and Figures*. https://www.alz.org/media/Documents/alzheimers-facts-and-figures.pdf

Centers for Disease Control and Prevention. (n.d.). The social-ecological model: A framework for prevention. https://www.cdc.gov/violenceprevention/about/social-ecologicalmodel.html

Galatzer-Levy, I. R., & Bonanno, G. A. (2012). Beyond normality in the study of bereavement: Heterogeneity in depression outcomes following loss in older adults. *Social Science & Medicine*, *74*(12), 1987–1994. https://doi.org/10.1016/j.socscimed.2012.02.022

James, B., Wilson, R., Barnes, L., & Bennett, D. (2011). Late-life social activity and cognitive decline in old age. *Journal of the International Neuropsychological Society*, *17*(6), 998–1005. https://doi.org/10.1017/S1355617711000531

Kapourchali, F. R., & Cresci, G. A. M. (2020). Early-life gut microbiome—The importance of maternal and infant factors in its establishment. *Nutritional in Clinical Practice*, *35*(3), 386–405. https://doi.org/10.1002/ncp.10490

Kokou-Kpolou, C. K., Fernández-Alcántara, M., & Cénat, J. M. (2020). Prolonged grief related to COVID-19 deaths: Do we have to fear a steep rise in traumatic and disenfranchised griefs? *Psychological Trauma: Theory, Research, Practice, and Policy*, *12*(S1), S94–S95. http://dx.doi.org/10.1037/tra0000798

Livingston, G., Huntley, J., Sommerlad, A., Ames, D., Ballard, C., Banerjee, S., Brayne, C., Burns, A., Cohen-Mansfield, J., Cooper, C., Costafreda, S. G., Dias, A., Fox, N., Gitlin, L. N. Howard, R., Kales, H. C., Kivimaki, M., Larson, E. B., Ogunniyi, A., ... Mukadam, N. (2020). Dementia prevention, intervention, and care: 2020 report of the *Lancet* Commission. *The Lancet*, *396*(10248), 413–446. https://doi.org/10.1016/S0140-6736(20)30367-6

McGinty, E. E., Presskreischer, R., Han, H., & Barry, C. L. (2020). Psychological distress and loneliness reported by US adults in 2018 and April 2020. *JAMA*, *321*(1), 93–94. https://doi.org/10.1001/jama.2020.9740

Morgan, J. K., Eckstrand, K. L., Silk, J. S., Olino, T. M., Ladouceur, C. D., & Forbes, E. E. (2022). Maternal response to positive affect moderates the impact of familial risk for depression on ventral striatal response to winning reward in 6- to 8-year-old children. *Biological Psychiatry: Cognitive Neuroscience Neuroimaging*, *7*(8), 824–832. https://doi.org/10.1016/j.bpsc.2021.12.014

O'Connor, M.-F. (2019). Grief: A brief history of research on how body, mind, and brain adapt. *Psychosomatic Medication*, *81*(8), 731–738. https://doi.org/10.1097/PSY.0000000000000717

O'Connor, M.-F. (2022). *The grieving brain: The surprising science of how we learn from love and loss*. HarperOne.

O'Connor, M.-F., Wellisch, D. K., Stanton, A. L., Eisenberger, N. I., Irwin, M. R., & Lieberman, M. D. (2008). Craving love? Enduring grief activates brain's reward center. *NeuroImage*, *42*, 969–972. https://doi.org/10.1016/j.neuroimage.2008.04.256

Ong, A. D., Fuller-Rowell, T. E., Bonanno, G. A., & Almeida, D. M. (2011). Spousal loss predicts alterations in diurnal cortisol activity through prospective changes in positive emotion. *Health Psychology*, *30*(2), 220–227. https://doi.org/10.1037/a0022262

Salinas, J., Beiser, A. S., Samra, J. K., O'Donnell, A., DeCarli, C. S., Gonzales, M. M., Aparicio, H. J., & Seshadri, S. (2022). Association of loneliness with 10-year dementia risk and early markers of vulnerability for neurocognitive decline. *Neurology*, *98*(13). https://doi.org/10.1212/WNL.0000000000200039

Shear, M. K., Wang, Y., Skritskaya, N., Duan, N., Mauro, C., & Ghesquiere, A. (2014). Treatment of complicated grief in elderly persons: A randomized clinical trial. *JAMA Psychiatry*, *71*(11), 1287–1295. https://doi.org/10.1001/jamapsychiatry.2014.1242

Stroebe, M., & Schut, H. (1999). The dual process model of coping with bereavement: Rationale and description. *Death Studies*, *23*(3), 197–224. https://doi.org/10.1080/074811899201046

Stroebe, M., Stroebe, W., Schut, H., Zech, E., & van den Bout, J. (2002). Does disclosure of emotions facilitate recovery from bereavement? Evidence from two prospective studies. *Journal of Consulting and Clinical Psychology*, *70*(1), 169–178. https://doi.org/10.1037/0022-006X.70.1.169

World Health Organization. (2019). *International statistical classification of diseases and related health problems* (11th ed.).

Figure Credits

Fig. 8.1: 1) Generated with Visme. Copyright © by Easy WebContent, Inc. 2) Adapted from Kathryn A. Davis, et al., "Teeth as Potential New Tools to Measure Early-Life Adversity and Subsequent Mental Health Risk: An Interdisciplinary Review and Conceptual Model," *Biological Psychiatry*, vol. 87, no. 6. Copyright © 2020 by Elsevier B.V.

Fig. 8.2: 1) Generated with Visme. Copyright © by Easy WebContent, Inc. 2) Adapted from Fatemeh Ramezani Kapourchali and Gail A. M. Cresci, "Early-Life Gut Microbiome? The Importance of Maternal and Infant Factors in Its Establishment," *Nutritional in Clinical Practice*, vol. 35, no. 3, p. 387. Copyright © 2020 by John Wiley & Sons, Inc.

Fig. 8.3: Source: https://www.sciencedirect.com/science/article/pii/S0277953612001967#fig1.

CHAPTER NINE

Healing and Prevention Actions and Practices at Community and Society Levels

---

The key points addressed in this chapter are

- to emphasize the importance of examining communities where social relationships are created and maintained to prevent risk factors of the root causes of toxic stress

- to introduce an asset-driven model as opposed to a deficit model for collective healing from adverse experiences and social environments

- to investigate concepts influencing existing policies for early child development and seek opportunities for new concepts to expand efforts for prevention actions and practices, particularly for early child development

---

At the Community Level

Guided by the SEMP-M (CDC, n.d.), toxic stress prevention at the community level examines settings such as neighborhoods, schools, workplaces, and community centers in which social relationships are formed and maintained. In particular, intentional and proactive seeking is necessary at this level in order to identify the characteristics and conditions of these settings to decrease and prevent risk factors associated with toxic stress. Concurrently, it is also critical for helping professionals to acknowledge and honor the existing assets (e.g., strengths and resources), and practices in such settings, as opposed to applying a deficit approach.

At the community level, prevention and healing strategies center around improving the physical and social environment in these settings through collective and communal efforts, actions,

132

and practices to create places where all community members live, learn, work, interact, and play with safety at all levels—psychological, physical, and emotional.

Healing-Centered Engagement

This section will describe an approach to prevention actions and practices as well as healing at the community level (i.e., healing-centered engagement, or HCE). First, *healing-centered* as an approach may be understood as being focused on the healing from adversity, whereas trauma-informed may be understood as being focused on the effects of adversity. Healing-centered is "holistic involving culture, spirituality, civic action, and collective healing" (Ginwright, 2018, para. 10). Despite the significance of trauma-informed care as an approach to treat symptoms of effects of adverse experiences in life, Shawn Ginwright calls for action that promotes a holistic healing from adverse experiences and social environments for those who are exposed to adversity, particularly in youth. Briefly, his view on trauma-informed care is that they are rather deficit approaches because they focus on pathology of trauma manifestations. Also, their focus is put on individual experiences, when traumatic life experiences and their effects often affect the collective realm of those who have experienced trauma, and the social and physical environment in which such individuals and families interact. Furthermore, trauma-informed care gives limited insight into how the root causes of trauma in families, neighborhoods, and schools are addressed. Therefore, despite the importance of trauma-informed care, he views it as incomplete, and thus requiring a new approach.

By contrast, *healing-centered engagement* (HCE; Ginwright, 2018), as a lens, intentionally expands the ways people perceive responses to trauma and serves as a practical, holistic approach to foster collective well-being. Furthermore, HCE intends to "[advance] a collective view of healing and [re-center] culture as a central feature in well-being" (Ginwright, 2018, para. 11). Four key elements of HCE are as follows (Ginwright, 2018):

- HCE is explicitly political, rather than clinical.
- HCE is culturally grounded and views healing as the restoration of identity.
- HCE is asset-driven and focuses on the well-being we want, rather than symptoms we want to suppress.
- HCE supports adult providers with their own healing.

By now, some readers of this textbook may ask themselves, "How do we apply and build HCE in our community?" Ginwright (2016, 2018) provides concrete tools to help build HCE. Foremost, it is necessary for helping professionals to shift their focus from a treatment model to an engagement model that does not view trauma and its effects as an isolated experience, but promotes collective healing and well-being (Ginwright, 2018).

- Start by building empathy.
- Encourage young people to dream and imagine.
- Build critical reflection and take love action.

One specific example has adapted this model as a part of the principles for a U.S.-government-funded interprofessional training program in conjunction with a counselor education program in the Philadelphia area. Jeanne Felter, director of the Department of Counseling and Behavioral Health at Thomas Jefferson University, shared her training experience in an interview that will follow later in this chapter.

At the Society Level

At this level, a broad scope of societal factors include cultural and social norms, systems, structures, and collective practices (CDC, n.d.). These are subject to close attention and exploration to generate and sustain a culture where prevention and healing actions and practices are encouraged to deal with effects of toxic stress. It is important that helping professionals identify and examine these factors because they may inadvertently perpetuate the root causes of toxic stress. Other important societal factors to explore for prevention actions and practices include educational, health-related, economic, social, judicial, and corrective policies that deepen and perpetuate inequalities between groups in society (CDC, n.d.). Healing and prevention strategies at this level may include collective and communal efforts that carefully critique existing societal norms and promote societal norms and collective practices that prevent risk factors leading to toxic or chronic stress.

State-Level Trauma Prevention Initiatives

As one example of a statewide initiative to promote awareness about mental health and work against stigma, a "Trauma-Informed PA" plan will be described in this section. The Office of Advocacy and Reform in Pennsylvania under Governor Tom Wolf released this plan as guidance for the commonwealth and service providers to become trauma-informed and healing-centered across different sectors in Pennsylvania. The mission of the plan is "to make Pennsylvania a Trauma-Informed State to better serve all residents" while the vision is that "Pennsylvania is a state where prevention is the norm" (Office of Governor, 2020, p. 11). "When people do experience emotional and psychological trauma, they feel respected, safe, empowered, and supported to recover and heal" (Office of Governor, 2020, p. 11). One way to achieve the initiative's goals is to help promote collective efforts to detect and decrease risk factors, and increase protective factors (e.g., peer support programs) for individuals and families in the commonwealth in order to enhance their human rights (e.g., the cessation of cycles of different types of trauma). In doing so, the plan puts focus on the following selective areas: building and supporting community-based efforts across all sectors to become trauma-informed in the commonwealth; and preventing and healing from different types of trauma, such as racial trauma, community trauma, and historical trauma. For details, readers may refer to the Trauma-Informed PA report (https://www.scribd.com/document/470553274/2020-Trauma-Informed-PA-Plan?secret_password=AcWbQ2CvooqQQ8w20WZO).

Policy Development, Implementation, and Evaluation

As noted previously in this chapter, social and judicial policies at the local, regional, and national level are societal factors that can reduce the risk of effects of toxic stress and propel the prevention of this type of stress while society promotes protective factors, such as resiliency or stress management. It is necessary that helping professionals collaborate to increase collective and communal efforts that first identify and carefully critique existing societal policies pertaining to human development or lifespan development, human health, and human rights. The existing policies must not worsen and sustain deepening inequalities between social groups in the United States. Furthermore, an expansion of the existing policies may be needed, and advances in the science of trauma and adaptability can offer new opportunities for more effective strategies to address and respond to the pressing mental health needs of U.S. society (Shonkoff, 2022).

As one example, in a report dated January of 2022, Jack P. Shonkoff (2022, p. 1) at the Center on the Developing Child at the Harvard University addressed that one of the pressing needs of the U.S. society in terms of early childhood development is "to expand the longstanding focus of the early childhood ecosystem on poverty and educational achievement to also address the critically important issues of systemic racism and lifelong health." He also argued that responding to the aforementioned need requires new approaches that promote healthy child development and that align with unique assets and needs of families raising youth in a wide array of cultural contexts and circumstances (Shonkoff, 2022).

Relevantly, the current lens for policies is informed by the following three core concepts of early childhood development: a) the impact of early experiences on brain architecture; b) the importance of responsive, severe, and return interactions for healthy development; and c) the disruptive effects of toxic stress on the developing brain and early learning (Shonkoff, 2022, p. 2). However, the prolonged pandemic of the past 2 years has worsened inequalities and thwarted critical health services (Shonkoff, 2022). Furthermore, the enduring inequities of institutional and systemic racism in U.S. society have led to synergistic challenges, increasing the need for a shift in ways of thinking for the future of the early childhood development field, particularly, and for the helping professions at large (Shonkoff, 2022). Guided by the advances in the biological and microbiological sciences, three additional concepts are to provide a new model to re-envision early childhood development in a post-pandemic era (Shonkoff, 2022). These additional concepts include connecting the brain to the rest of the body, supporting universal needs and individual variation, and providing what young children need when they need it most (Shonkoff, 2022, p. 2).

The concept of connecting the brain to the rest of the body should not come as a surprise to readers of this textbook, given that Chapters 6 and 7 have extensively provided support for this, informed by numerous, rigorous scientific studies. Furthermore, as delineated in Chapter 2, the modified ecobiodevelopmental framework of human development and human diseases also supports this concept. In addition, the second new concept, supporting universal needs and individual variation, calls for more investment in understanding differentiations in sensitivity to traumatic experiences, and variation in "what services work for whom and how context and circumstances influence outcomes" (Shonkoff, 2022, p. 3). Related to this concept, predicting health and behavioral outcomes for youth based solely on traumatic experiences is highly problematic and can result in inaccurate labeling (e.g., a wrongful diagnosis) followed by further unmatched services (Shonkoff, 2022). As addressed earlier in this chapter, HCE takes a similar view, although the focus of the lens is put on collective healing and well-being, as opposed to policies related to individual child development, and individual child health and suffering.

The third new concept about providing what young children need when they need it most presents exciting opportunities for helping professionals to promote policies and programs that affect well-being during infancy and pregnancy (Shonkoff, 2022). Additionally, persistent, pervasive, longstanding racial and ethnic disparities in mental health compel the need to confront the effects of institutional and systemic racism as early as possible (Shonkoff, 2022). In a similar vein, Shawn Ginwright (2019, para. 9) argues that in order for us to attempt to solve the problem of racial and ethnic disparities in mental health, we must focus on "building a shared understanding of how racial inequality, hidden attitudes, biases, policies, and practices have created" the problem that we are facing. Furthermore, it is critical to understand that a shared understanding warrants "an engagement in deeper reflection about their own biases" and examines "how their racial bias shows up" in the work they do (Ginwright, 2019, para. 10).

Summary

This chapter addresses the significance of examining neighborhoods, schools, workplaces, and communities in which social relationships are established and sustained in order to identify risk factors of the root causes of toxic stress for prevention purposes. In doing so, asset-driven models are worth investing in, as opposed to a deficit model, for treatment of trauma. As one specific example, HCE (Ginwright, 2018) is introduced and described briefly in the chapter.

In addition, strategies for healing and prevention at a societal level include examining a wide scope of societal factors, such as social norms, systems, structures, collective practices, and policies. It is critical that helping professionals pay close attention to existing policies that perpetuate the root causes of toxic stress, remove such policies, and subsequently constitute new policies as a means of collective advocacy for prevention actions and practices in terms of early childhood development.

Experiential Questions

1. How might healing-centered engagement as a framework be applicable to your actions and practices based on your primary professional role when working with A?

2. What state-level trauma prevention practices are there in effect or planned in the area of your residence?

VOICES BY EXPERTS

Interview held on April 12, 2022, with Dr. Jeanne Felter

Yoon Suh Moh: I will have this opportunity to ask you a couple interview questions. My first question for you is, **how would you describe your professional identity and training background?**

Jeanne Felter (she/her): I am a licensed professional counselor and I have a master's in counseling but a doctoral degree in education psychology. And I was very interested early on in working with children, adolescents, and families within the school setting but I didn't want to be a school counselor, largely because the role of a school counselor was really not appealing to me. I wanted to be a mental health provider within the community, and specifically within schools, and so very early on in my career, I spent a lot of time within Philadelphia, in school-based mental health, always employed by a community agency, but working full time in schools. I worked, both in the school district of Philadelphia, and in a number of different charter schools throughout the city. Really, that's where so much of my learning and inspiration, you know, for the work that I do in higher education, came from, was really being a community-based provider specifically within a very vulnerable system, which is the schools in Philadelphia.

Yoon Suh Moh: I'm glad you said the very vulnerable system instead of putting it on individuals who are in that system. My next question for you is, **can you please tell me about the background of developing a counselor education program in the Greater Philadelphia area that infuses trauma, cultural humility, and community engagement across the program curriculum?**

Jeanne Felter (she/her): When I was working in school-based mental health, I had an opportunity to teach at, I was asked to kind of come in and adjunct at a university up in Philadelphia. And when I was teaching, it was within a counselor education program (a master's counseling program), and I was teaching the standardized curriculum, where I would teach a theories class here, and I would teach an ethics class, and, you know, in my spare time, and what I was doing was, I was bringing my clinical experience into the classroom and I was talking a lot to the students about the impact of trauma on my clients, and how it was showing up in their behaviors, in their functioning within their families, within their communities. And I noticed that the students were just leaning in; these were all master's-level students that were in clinical internships. And this was so relevant and exciting for them, and they hadn't been taught it anywhere else in the curriculum, so I was teaching one class and a 60-credit curriculum, and they were begging for more. And so I went to the program leadership and I said, how about we develop, and how about we infuse this throughout the curriculum, and the leader at the time said no. They said that we have a waiting list of students and we're not going to change our curriculum, but you go ahead and talk about it in the classes that you teach. And so I was a little bit frustrated by that because I knew that when I was working in community mental health, with the degrees that I had, there was no talk about trauma except reserved for veterans.

And I was very ill-prepared to work with the children I was serving, and I made a lot of clinical errors early on, such as misdiagnosing and ill-informed treatment planning, largely because I wasn't conceptualizing the whole client, I was really very focused on pathology. And I made a very concerted effort, as I was feeling really unskilled in my work, to get training in an area that I knew that I didn't receive, and we were lucky enough in Philadelphia to have some extraordinary experts here. Dr. Sandy Bloom, Steve Berkowitz, and others throughout the city that were accessible to me, and I was able to get not only the hands-on training, but also, I dove into reading. I was just absorbing as much as I could and that's what I was bringing to the students in the university setting. And so, you can imagine that that wasn't a great response from the program leader, because I really felt passionate about trying to provide the education that I think people need. And so simultaneously another university in Philadelphia was very intelligently looking to develop a program that integrated trauma throughout the curriculum, and I was fortunate enough to be offered the position to develop and lead that program. And you know that's where it started, and the beautiful thing about that opportunity was that I built the program from the ground up; that I wasn't trying to revise an existing curriculum. We really were able to build what we believed was most relevant and necessary. And again, those really important people in Philadelphia that had helped to train me as a young clinician were part of the building of the program. And they were psychiatrists, social workers, and nurse practitioners that had been working in different areas across professions and across disciplines, that had incredible trauma knowledge, and it was really great to pull their knowledge into the development of a counselor education curriculum.

Yoon Suh Moh: Can you please tell me a little bit more about the frameworks that were used in guiding the process of developing the program?

Jeanne Felter (she/her): Sure, so I can talk about it. Was your question about the building of the curriculum and how we did it? **Or was it more about when we thought about what the program needed?**

Yoon Suh Moh: The latter.

Jeanne Felter (she/her): We had our creditors to have very clear standards about the content that needs to be in the program, and we were really clear about wanting to pull the thread of trauma and social justice and emotional literacy through the entire curriculum, and we also knew that we had an opportunity to create specific courses outside of a standard CACREP curriculum that could focus more strongly on trauma content, knowledge, and competencies, and so that's really what guided the development of the curriculum. The flexibility that we had building a program from the ground up, to really provide foundational and advanced competency course-specific courses. But what we realized early on was that when you deviate from a standardized curriculum, and if you infuse really difficult content around child maltreatment right around trauma adversity and chronic stress, that's going to take a toll on the student. We also knew that our students would be working within very vulnerable communities exposed to trauma.

And that would take a toll on them, and we also realized very quickly as we started to admit students and read their personal statements and talk to them in interview processes that our students were coming with their own lived experience of trauma.

And we knew that we had to be very thoughtful about not just what we taught, but how we taught it, what our context, what our kind of learning culture would be. And we turned to the leaders of the sanctuary model and we brought them in to do a full week-long training with our faculty, and then also to serve as consultants with us, as we really got up and running as a program. And that was really important, the sanctuary model was really developed as an organizational change model for human service organizations that work with trauma impacted people, and it was really born out of the knowledge that the stress and the symptoms of the community served by the organization can show up in the within the organization, right, the parallel process between the clients' symptoms and how they show up in the organization, and so it's a very intentional model that really focuses on safety and well-being. And really promotes workforce wellness and protects the provider in many ways. And so we decided that, although we were not providing clinical services, as you know, and as a program, and we were not a human service providing organization, but our students were out in the communities, providing service. Our students needed the same kind of protections. So we worked with the leaders to adapt the model to fit kind of a higher education program and it really has served to be such an incredibly important framework for us. As we have evolved and grown as a program throughout the years.

Yoon Suh Moh: It is an amazing opportunity to work with those experts who are experienced and wise and those who helped the body of faculty and staff in the program.

My next question is that I know that you touched on it a bit earlier, but I am wondering if there's anything you would like to add as to, **why do you think it's important for helping professionals, when I say helping professionals, such as professional counselors, social workers, and psychiatrists, to be knowledgeable about the effects of adversity, in other words, traumatic stress in childhood, and its association with chronic health conditions in adulthood?**

Jeanne Felter (she/her): Well, I think, you know, it goes back to what I said earlier about when I didn't have that knowledge. I was not helpful. I was mislabeling or mis-identifying. I was using the wrong strategies and interventions. And I was also losing confidence and competence that I did not feel competent in my work because I wasn't contributing to health or healing for my clients and their families. I was missing the boat, and so the more that I learned and the more that my perspective shifted, and consequently the interventions and the approaches that I took shifted, the more I contributed to healing and health for the children and adolescents and families I worked with. You talked about the multidisciplinary piece in cities like Philadelphia—our behavioral health system is so stressed, we have enormous waiting lists. You know those who need care often don't receive it until their needs are acute, and really difficult to treat. If they do access services, it's often in a school or it's often in a primary care setting or an emergency room, right, and so it's really important that this knowledge and these skills are not reserved just for the people sitting behind a desk in an outpatient or an inpatient program, because the most vulnerable people do not access care through the usual channels. And so I'm really passionate about bringing that knowledge, not only to our counseling students, but trying to really work across disciplines and professions, to make sure that anyone who comes in contact with somebody who has been impacted by trauma, by trauma adversity, chronic stress, is met with a professional who has some competencies around being able to contribute to healing and being able to understand the whole person and contribute to healing.

Yoon Suh Moh: So I appreciate what you said related to this question. My next questions is, **what recommendations might you have for clinical training programs like yours so that they can help increase traumatic stress or trauma competencies in their clinical students or trainees?**

Jeanne Felter (she/her): So, some advice or guidance that I would have for programs that wanted to make some kind of shift, so how would I encourage somebody at an administrative level but also just a faculty member?

I'm really big on saying that anyone can make a change and everybody has a sphere of influence, right, and so often, when I go into schools and I provide consultation in schools, or when I provide trainings to, you know, K–12 educators, often—I met with my leadership, it doesn't buy into this, so I can't do this. And what I say is, you can. You can make small changes within your sphere of influence that will contribute to health and healing even in the absence of having your leadership buy in. And so, the same is true, I think, in higher education, in that all we need is one or more faculty members that really believe that this is critically important content, and they bring it to the courses that they teach, they infuse it within their courses. The beauty or the harsh reality of trauma is that it is able to be infused in every class, right? Like, how can you talk about ethics without talking about trauma? How can you talk about human development without talking about trauma? How can you talk about psychopathology without talking about trauma, right? So every single course that is required, career development, every course that is required of us, there is an opportunity, and I would say, a necessity to introduce content within that course. And so I would really inspire faculty to do that, within the courses that they have autonomy over. And I think leadership should be compelled to make these changes, as an administrator, as somebody that's really charged with strategic visioning for our department, my responsibility is to be responsive to the needs of the community. It does not matter if I build programs that attract people, if those people are not graduating and serving a necessary community need, right? If they're not helpful, then I failed. It doesn't matter how many I've graduated and how much money we've made. If they are not succeeding—and by succeeding, I mean helping—then we failed. And so administrators should really be focused on providing relevant education, and this is the most relevant clinical training.

Yoon Suh Moh: Thank you! **What are some of projects you and your team in the Department of Counseling and Behavioral Health at Thomas Jefferson University**

are working on currently or in the near future that you may share? How would you see the impact of some of those projects in the community?

Jeanne Felter (she/her): Well, one really exciting initiative that started this academic year was that we were awarded a large grant through the Health Resources and Services Administration.

Yoon Suh Moh: Congratulations!

Jeanne Felter (she/her): Thank you! It was their behavioral health workforce, education and training grant, and the goal of this grant is to ensure that helping professionals, and especially counselors, social workers, psychologists, are prepared to work on inner professional teams and also prepared to serve vulnerable children, adolescents and youth, and families. And so we were really excited that we were awarded that grant. It allows us to provide stipends to up to 30 students in their second year, in their internship, and it has also enabled us to continue to nurture or to expand community partnerships that are focused on multidisciplinary teamwork in our professional care for vulnerable children and adolescents. So that's been a really exciting project for us. It's a four-year grant; we're just finishing up year one, and we've had a lot of success so far with that. Do you want me to expand more on that, or should I talk about other projects?

Yoon Suh Moh: Maybe can you tell me about what you envision as the impact of the training?

Jeanne Felter (she/her): As I was saying, we have very stressed systems in our behavioral health system. The city is very stressed and our most vulnerable children and adolescents don't access that system. And there are different places that serve kind of as entry points to behavioral health care that often don't have behavioral health providers in those spaces, like in primary care or in hospital settings or in school settings, right? We know we have school counselors, but we often don't have a sufficient number of providers, and school counselors are often pulled to do lots of things that are not in support of counseling or health. And so, this has enabled us to develop really cool partnerships with organizations that serve as entry programs, that serve as entry points for behavioral health care for vulnerable youth. So we are working with child advocacy centers in pediatric offices. We are working in schools and college counseling centers, things like that. A really wonderful opportunity to expand some of the work of those organizations and to bring our students into them. I really believe that these are going to be sustainable relationships beyond the grant cycle, and so that's one thing. The other thing is that we've always had a focus on inner professional practice. We've had small opportunities for students to work on inner professional teams with medical students and with nurses and nursing students and with physical assistant students and occupational therapy students. This has helped us enrich that programming. And we've started a series of "lunch and learns" where students and clinical sites supervisors within the community come together. And we learn together on topics relevant to vulnerable children, adolescents, relevant to trauma, or social justice and racial literacy, and have an inner professional dialogue around those issues. And again that's very sustainable for us as a program as well, so it's given us both freedom to be creative on how we want to continue to grow these efforts within our program. And when the money goes away, I think a lot of this is sustainable, which is wonderful.

Yoon Suh Moh: That's great, and also one way to sustain the community communication and relationships built with your department may be the Jefferson Trauma Education Network that hosts annual conferences in the Greater Philadelphia area with the community partners.

Jeanne Felter (she/her): We knew early on that we had a really relevant and needed curriculum in our program, and we were limited by the fact that we would only be able to deliver this to the people that would end up in the seats in our classrooms. But we knew it was needed by so many more, and so we got a small foundation grant to develop the J-TEN, which really was born out of that desire to bring this knowledge to the community. And so, it was really a workforce development, community impact arm of our program and department, and so our first effort under J-TEN was to start an annual conference, and we called it the Philadelphia Trauma Training Conference, because we really wanted it to be for front-line providers; we did not want it to be an academic conference where we're sharing our scholarly pursuits. We really wanted to build knowledge and competencies within the people that were working directly with those in need, and it has been an incredible project and initiative and, just like, a labor of love for the J-TEN team. We're in our fifth year, we're doing a virtual conference this summer, with a focus on the youth mental health crisis. And you know it's an inner professional conference, it's awesome because it has physicians and nurses sitting next to counselors and social workers and black captains and faith leaders and foster parents and other people from juvenile justice and all over any discipline, including, of course, K–12 educators. And early childhood educators from different sectors are represented, such a rich community, and it's been a really rewarding opportunity. So that's kind of like the flagship project of J-TEN. But we have a lot of other projects that we work on, that our students get involved in. For instance, we helped a local in north Philadelphia, which is probably the poorest zip code in Philadelphia and has a tremendous amount of community violence, and just a lot of community and school violence, and there's an after-school program that has been a partner of ours, for a long time. We have provided training for their staff and trauma, we've really supported the development of a trauma-informed framework within their organization, but they wanted to develop a team of teenagers, adolescents, who would serve as youth ambassadors. And so we worked with them, with this small group of teens, to teach them about trauma, how it shows up in their own lives, and helping to develop skills within them to help to heal both themselves and others. And they are now trainers within their own communities. So they go into their regional, their local schools, and they train teachers about the impact of trauma, and how it shows up in kids. Also, they train parents, so that's been a really cool opportunity to support that community. And we're also working to develop with an organization in Philadelphia that is working with foster care. And one thing they have recognized is that the existing curriculum that trains foster parents is devoid of trauma competencies and knowledge, so we're working alongside them to develop a standardized foster parent curriculum that really infuses trauma and the understanding of trauma for foster parents. Because what we often hear from foster parents, like me, as a young physician, is that they don't understand what's going on and the kids and they don't know how to support them. And so, how do we help them to understand that? Also, we have a new project coming where we're working with Philadelphia's transit authority, the very large transit system in the city. They have noticed that, prior to the pandemic and certainly exacerbated by the pandemic, that their workforce is very stressed, resulting in high levels of conflict and altercation among their workforce. And they are looking for conflict resolution approaches that really help their workforce to understand the impact of stress and trauma on themselves, and on their peers. So that's an exciting project that we're working on. And then we have a faculty member in our program that works closely with faith leaders, and she has done this amazing work within faith communities about helping faith leaders to understand trauma and to feel more resources around that, so that they can support their faith communities again.

There are many times where people in faith communities will not turn to a medical or health professional but they'll turn to their faith leader. And so, how do we help to support them to grow their competencies? And you (Yoon Suh Moh) are somebody that's also working within the school district to help bring these competencies to counselors, to school counselors, who often are the first to identify, diagnose, and treat students. And so how do we help them to really understand, from a trauma-informed lens, what's really showing up in their students, so that we're not misdiagnosing them or we're not medicating them for things that they shouldn't be medicated for? And that we're really working on a comprehensive treatment plan that supports health and well-being? So there's that, and then we have some hospital systems and organizations within the city that are really looking to embrace more of a trauma-informed framework, and they're looking to us as consultants to support some of that work, so a lot of different things that we are involved in.

Yoon Suh Moh: Absolutely! And the list goes on and on, and how the department as a team is working with the community is just amazing, above and beyond.

Is there anything else you would like to share that you have not had a chance to yet, that readers or the audience might find helpful?

Jeanne Felter (she/her): Yeah, I think, though, the one thing that has been a challenge in the development of our program—it's been both a strength and a challenge—and that is the accreditation standards that we've been held to. The strength is certainly that we know that our curriculum is sound, because the standards are high. However, the limitation is that we are really truly only supposed to hire faculty from one unique discipline who are trained as counselor educators. There are wonderful counselor educators who are steeped in trauma, but there are a few. There are not many. Psychiatrists, social workers, play therapists, art therapists, marriage and family therapists and nurse practitioners, psychiatric nurse practitioners, and all of these folks have so much to offer our students and have the opportunity to really enrich their training, and yet we're really bound to focus on one discipline, and so I would encourage,—of course! Uphold the standards and meet the standards and perhaps exceed the standards of your creditors, but find ways to bring these other disciplines into your program. I would say, like a contained skill set.

It's not just about being good in the room with a person or a family. We need to act as social workers. We need such an expanded skill set, beyond one-to-one clinical intervention skill set, and we need an expanded knowledge base that is really enriched by inviting other professionals into your training environment.

Yoon Suh Moh: Thank you so much for sharing your insight, suggestions, and recommendations for the mental health field.

Informative Resources

- Trauma-Informed PA: https://www.scribd.com/document/470553274/2020-Trauma-Informed-PA-Plan?secret_password=AcWbQ2CvooqQQ8w20WZO

- The Center on the Developing Child: https://developingchild.harvard.edu/resources/how-early-childhood-experiences-affect-lifelong-health-and-learning/

  https://developingchild.harvard.edu/re-envisioning-ecd/

- Healing collective trauma: https://www.healingcollectivetrauma.com/neurobiology-and-transgenerational-trauma.htm

References

Centers for Disease Control and Prevention. (n.d.). The social-ecological model: A framework for prevention. https://www.cdc.gov/violenceprevention/about/social-ecologicalmodel.html

Ginwright, S. (2016). *Hope and healing in urban education: How urban activists and teachers are reclaiming matters of the heart.* Routledge/Taylor & Francis Group.

Ginwright, S. (2018). *The future of healing: Shifting from trauma informed care to healing centered engagement.* https://ginwright.medium.com/the-future-of-healing-shifting-from-trauma-informed-care-to-healing-centered-engagement-634f557ce69c

Ginwright, S., & Seigel, S. (2019). Social innovation alone can't solve racial inequity. https://ssir.org/articles/entry/social_innovation_alone_cant_solve_racial_inequity#

Office of Governor. (2020). *Trauma-informed plan: A plan to make Pennsylvania a trauma-informed, healing-centered state.* Scribd. https://www.scribd.com/document/470553274/2020-Trauma-Informed-PA-Plan?secret_password=AcWbQ2CvooqQQ8w20WZO

Shonkoff, J. P. (2022). Re-envisioning early childhood policy and practice in a world of striking inequality and uncertainty. https://developingchild.harvard.edu/re-envisioning-ecd/

CHAPTER TEN

Healing and Prevention Actions and Practices in Helping Professions

---

The key points addressed in this chapter are

- to emphasize the importance of exercising and practicing trauma-informed educational practices in clinical training and education
- to share the voice of experts

The concerning prevalence of ACEs in the U.S. general population remains a public health issue; a recent ACE survey collected data from 211,376 adults across 34 U.S. states via the Behavioral Risk Factor Surveillance System, and indicated that 57.8% experienced at least one ACE, while 21.5% encountered 3+ ACEs. This suggests that childhood adversity in the nation is common across sociodemographic groups (Giano et al., 2020). Furthermore, findings from the same data suggest that exposure to adversity early in life is disproportional among certain individuals. For instance, individuals with a multiracial identity had significantly higher ACE scores compared to all other racial or ethnic individuals; Substantially lower mean ACE scores (1.53) were seen in adults with a white racial identity compared to individuals without such identity—Black or African (1.66) or Latinx individuals (1.63). Similarly, sexual minority individuals had higher ACE scores than individuals of a non-sexual minority (Giano et al., 2020).

Further, research has suggested that the high prevalence of ACEs is also seen in many mental health professionals and students in clinical training. For example, social work students during training reported trauma histories at an astonishing rate; about 77.8% of 195 students had experienced one or more ACEs before age 18, while almost 30% noted four or more (Butler et al., 2017a). In addition, among the different categories of ACE, household mental illness (49.5%) and household substance abuse (40.5%) were the two most endorsed items (Butler et al., 2017a). Albeit these findings cannot conclude that clinical students like social work students experience higher ACEs compared to the U.S. general public, they give mental health professionals the opportunity to reflect and consider how they may lead to certain implications related to mental health and wellness.

These findings do imply an ever-increasing need for helping professionals such as mental health professionals to be adequately equipped to render human health services with stress and trauma competencies. Nonetheless, the subject of trauma is not being sufficiently taught in traditional graduate clinical programs in the United States. This gap is problematic given the alarming prevalence of ACEs in the U.S. general population and their associated effects, such as chronic health conditions in adulthood and older adulthood. This insufficient training may lead to consequences, since many mental health professional counselors, psychologists, or social workers may not be sufficiently trained to meet the needs of the U.S. public (Webber et al., 2017).

In a similar vein, although most graduate counseling programs consider trauma education an integral part of the core curriculum, it is concerning that few clinical education and training programs support the universal provision of a standalone course focusing on comprehensive trauma across programmatic or departmental systems (Black, 2006; Moh & Sperandio, 2022). However, it is critical for mental health professionals to better understand the unique needs of individuals, families, and communities impacted by trauma and to have the proper knowledge and skills to work with them effectively (Kumar et al., 2019).

Healing and Prevention Practices in Clinical Education and Training Programs

To respond to the needs of the U.S. general population, Moh and Sperandio (2022) argue that entry-level graduate clinical training programs in the United States must provide comprehensive trauma education and training. In doing so, it is also imperative that clinical educators, such as social work educators, counselor educators, and psychology educators, safely integrate trauma content into the program curriculum, i.e., in a way that minimizes potential psychological harm to students (Black, 2006; Carello & Butler, 2015; Newman, 2011). Additionally, teaching trauma material warrants culturally responsive approaches to educational practices, as trauma must be understood in a cultural context (Agllias, 2012). Cultural factors (e.g., socioeconomic background) are influential in perceptions and experiences of trauma, the ways people express and manifest trauma, and their desired healing mechanisms (Agllias, 2012).

Trauma-Informed Educational Practices

Increasingly, trauma-informed (TI) approaches to educational practices (e.g., andragogies, pedagogies, and teaching methods) have gained attention in clinical training programs. However, as addressed in Chapter 9 of this textbook, readers are invited to explore potential limitations of TI educational practices given the focus on the trauma-informed as opposed to asset-driven approaches, such as HCE. In one example of TI educational practices, Carello and Butler (2014a) argued that when clinical educators integrate information about and discussion of trauma material, they should promote TI approaches for the following reasons:

- To help alleviate the risk of traumatization or *retraumatization* (i.e., "the triggering or reactivation of trauma-related symptoms originating in earlier traumatic life events"; Carello & Butler, 2014a, p. 156).

- To prevent *vicarious traumatization,* a process wherein those "who work with victims (trauma survivors) may experience profound psychological effects, that can be disruptive and painful for the helper and can persist for months or years after work with traumatized persons (trauma survivors)" (Pearlman & Mac Ian, 1995 p. 588) or *secondary traumatic stress* (i.e., "the phenomenon wherein the sharing of traumatic experiences—particularly in circumstances where the listener is highly empathic or trying to be—stimulates trauma related symptoms in the listener that can parallel those in the survivor"; Butler et al., 2017a, p. 417) for students exposed to trauma material during training.

Evidence has shown that indirect exposure to trauma content is associated with a substantial likelihood of PTSD symptoms among clinicians (Bride, 2007). Indirect exposure to trauma during clinical training is also related to vicarious trauma in all (e.g., students, field supervisors, and clinical educators). However, it is noteworthy to emphasize that the phenomenon of vicarious trauma was more prevalent in those who had less trauma training (Knight, 2010). Furthermore, a previous study suggested that clinical students, such as social work students, with higher ACE scores were vulnerable for an increased likelihood of *training-related retraumatization* (i.e., "a reactivation of own feelings/memories from negative past experiences upon exposure to trauma-related material") and symptoms of secondary traumatic stress (Butler et al., 2017b, p. 4).

For these reasons, clinical educators are responsible for safely integrating trauma content into the program curriculum while teaching about the topic meaningfully. However, it is evident that striking a balance between meaningful clinical training in trauma and student safety warrants intentional preparation and delivery (Agllias, 2012). Additionally, clinical educators must develop trauma curricula in a culturally responsive way. Mattar (2011) describes *culturally responsive trauma curricula* as "integrated" and "interdisciplinary," reflecting "the cultural realities of the populations affected by trauma, the student's background and culture" (p. 259). Cultural factors such as a socioeconomic background or religious/spiritual background are influential in perceptions and experiences of trauma (Mattar, 2011). Consequently, the ways individuals and families perceive and express trauma and their desired healing are undoubtedly deeply impacted by culture (Mattar, 2011).

Examples of selective TI andragogies, pedagogies, and teaching methods include TI educational practice (TIEP; Carello & Butler, 2015) and TI teaching and learning (TITL; Carello, 2016, 2020). These frameworks were both created to specifically meet the needs of social work education. Due to limited space in this textbook, selective elements of these models will be delineated in the following sections.

TIEP

TIEP is an andragogical model involving a systemic approach and requires a cultural shift in an organization (e.g., higher education institutions). The goal of the model is "to remove possible barriers to learning, not to remove traumatic, sensitive, or difficult material from the curriculum" (Carello & Butler, 2015, p. 265). It is critical to note that in the model,

> to be trauma-informed in higher education settings means (a) to understand the ways in which violence, victimization, and other forms of trauma can impact all members of the campus community, and (b) to use that understanding to inform policy, practices, and curricula. (Carello & Butler, 2014b, p. 2)

Furthermore, the model is based on the following eight principles: (a) physical, emotional, and social safety; (b) trustworthiness and transparency; (c) support and connection; (d) inclusiveness and shared purpose; (e) collaboration and mutuality; (f) empowerment, voice, and choice; (g) cultural, historical, and gender issues; and (h) growth and change (Carello & Butler, 2015).

The model promotes organizational change at every level of the higher education setting, and thus, the meaningful facilitation of such a shift in the system warrants including everyone in both collective and individual efforts. Similarly, the application of the model to a clinical training program requires change agents (e.g., students in training, staff, faculty, administrators, state-level policy makers, etc.) to collaborate to facilitate change when possible (Carello & Butler, 2015).

TITL

In contrast, TITL (Carello, 2016, 2020) is an approach to operationalize the TIEP model into TI teaching practice in higher education, with focus given to the individual learning classroom as a setting. Given the relationship between the model and the operational approach, TITL adopts the TIEP principles in application (Carello, 2016, 2020). Additionally, TITL adds a new element of academic safety into TIEP's first principle (i.e., physical, emotional, and social safety). A practical vehicle for clinical educators to assess the application of TI approaches in their individual teaching and learning environment is Carello's "Self-Assessment Tools for Creating Trauma-Informed Learning and Work Environments" (2022).

Summary

As previously stated, alarming rates of trauma exposure early in life among individuals living in the United States are considered a public health issue. Healing professionals in the nation, particularly mental health professionals, do not seem to be an exception to this prevalence. Results from a study suggest that approximately 77.8% of 195 social work students reported having experienced one or more ACEs, while 30% of such individuals experienced four or more (Butler et al., 2017a). These findings may give mental health professionals the opportunity to reflect and consider how they may lead to meaningful implications in relation to their own mental health and wellness.

Despite the importance of appropriate and comprehensive trauma education and accordant clinical competencies to effectively work with those impacted by trauma, it is documented that many mental health professionals may not be sufficiently trained to meet the needs of the U.S. public (Webber et al., 2017; Kumar et al., 2019). This disheartening fact does not align with a view that most graduate clinical training programs consider trauma education an integral part of the core curriculum (Black, 2006; Moh & Sperandio, 2022). Similarly, to respond to the U.S. public health issue, it is necessary that entry-level graduate clinical training programs provide comprehensive trauma education and training (Moh & Sperandio, 2022). Therefore, as change agents, it is critical that clinical educators, such as social work educators, counselor educators, and psychology educators, safely integrate sensitive material such as trauma content into the program curriculum (Black, 2006; Carello & Butler, 2015; Newman, 2011). In addition, teaching such material requires considerations such as culturally responsive approaches to educational practices so that trauma can be understood in a cultural context (Agllias, 2012).

As particular examples of TI education practices, the TIEP (Carello & Butler, 2015) and TITL (Carello, 2016, 2020) frameworks are delineated selectively in this chapter. In part, these frameworks were developed in social work to help with alleviating the risk of traumatization or retraumatization in all parties, such as students in training or trainees, clinical educators, and administrators. Their intentional preparation and careful delivery are meant to help strike a balance between meaningful clinical training in trauma and the safety of students in education (Agllias, 2012).

Experiential Questions

1. How do you think trauma-informed educational practices are exercised in the school district or higher education institution nearby where you currently work?

2. If there is a lack or void of trauma-informed educational practices currently in the school district or higher education institution nearby where you work, what advocacy actions would you like to take?

VOICES BY EXPERTS

Clinical Training: An Interview with Dr. Christine Courtois, April 26, 2022

Yoon Suh Moh: How would you describe your professional identity and training background?

Christine Courtois: I'm a counseling psychologist. I graduated from the University of Maryland program in 1979. And counseling psychology is oriented towards developmental issues and wellness more than pathology but, despite that, my work has brought me very much into the clinical psychology arena, even though my background is very developmental, but the background has really helped me in good stead. I have stayed active up until recently with Division 17 at the American Psychological Association and have been heavily involved in the trauma world since 1971 and '72, which were my first years of graduate training. The reason for my involvement was I was a resident assistant, and then a resident director, in the residence halls, and we had a series of very bad crises, we had at Maryland, at the time, had a series of kidnappings and rapes, gang rapes, and then rapes on campus, so I got involved with a number of women to establish a Rape Crisis Center at that time. And then we also had a series of suicides and copycat suicides out of our buildings, we had high-rise buildings, and so I was immersed in crises in trauma through no fault of my own, but it made me interested in what happens to people after these kinds of events and how to take care of the survivors, you know, and also the bystanders. And then finally, while we're running the Rape Crisis Center way back then, we started to get calls from young women who were living at home and saying that they weren't being raped by strangers, they were being raped at home, and that's how I got involved in looking into and studying incest survivors. And my dissertation, which was published in '79, was on having done a special interview of incest survivors who volunteered to talk to me about their experiences, and I literally did public advertising to get those women to come in. I had an initial group of 30 and that was the basis of, so, in my early work study, in understanding what happens to adult survivors of incest. So those are some of my foundational experiences and I was, I was also I trained as a College Counseling Center clinician. I have moved away from that subsequently into private practice with adults, but that was my background and I love doing that, working with college students as well.

Yoon Suh Moh: Wow! It is such a pleasure to hear from you about your training background, and how you in the first place were immersed in the trauma work you described.

Christine Courtois: From 1971. In 1972, we founded the Rape Crisis Center, and the public understanding was nothing. The women's movement was going on and Vietnam was going on, so there was beginning to be some awareness, but it was a very, very hidden problem, and in fact we were so in there, a group of about 10 women, and were so angry about what was going on on campus, and not blaming the campus per se, but it's just that people came in and were victimized.

Students and campus members, we live leafletted at the football game, one of the football games, to announce to parents that the school wasn't safe for their daughters on campus and, of course, that made us very unpopular, to say the least. Some parents paid attention to that, but that was the atmosphere back then. And I'm sorry to say that you know, even today, with all the efforts that have been made, rape on campus is still a major problem.

And you know it still has some of the same issues that it had back then, and then incest was just beginning to be talked about. There were two books that came out right before I did my study, and that was very helpful to me, that those came out. They were lay books, and Judith Herman had written her book *Father-Daughter Incest*, not the recovery book with her original book. So I had something to go on and what was really nice for me is my faculty—this was a very nontraditional topic and a very nontraditional way of going about doing the research.

And my faculty was very, very supportive of my doing this, but they made me research every single question that I asked, they had to be tied into the available literature at the time, so it took me quite a while, but what I did is, I got very immersed. I thought there would be no literature and it turned out, just like the war literature at the time, it was out there, but it was ignored.

There had been an effort to identify at least physical abuse in the family and some sexual abuse. And I was surprised, there was a lot more literature than I had expected. So I got very immersed in that.

Yoon Suh Moh: That's mind blowing.

Christine Courtois: And that was before the *DSM*—1980, before PTSD was in the *DSM*, it was really—we were talking about Rape Crisis Center, rape crisis syndrome or battered women's syndrome. But there was no place to put it diagnostically, so when PTSD was included, we were very happy, because there was finally a place to put it. But then Judith Herman's work came out, and I had also identified from my research that PTSD, as it was in the *DSM*, was not an exact fit for what we were seeing with adult survivors. So that's how the whole complex trauma initiative began, but we were really happy in those early days to have PTSD as an official diagnosis and a place that we could put things.

Yoon Suh Moh: Thank you. So many other questions that I'd like to ask, but for the limited time today, I am going to just hold them into myself, and move on to the next question, if I may.

Christine Courtois: Yes.

Yoon Suh Moh: Can you please tell me about your work in developing trauma-informed approaches to trauma education and clinical training and, particularly, trauma?

Christine Courtois: In the early 1970s, I started to be asked to provide training, because people began to realize that I had information to share that other people didn't have, so we began doing workshops and training efforts back then. And then, after I finished my doctoral work and took my first job, I couldn't believe it—my very first patient in my very first job was an incest survivor. A huge case, so it added even more information to the information I had. And I published my first book, *Healing the Incest Wound*, in 1988. And again during the '80s, when I was working various jobs, before I started my private practice, people were approaching me all the time because I had this set of information that nobody had. And then, when the book came out, I felt I was really naive and I felt like, I'm putting this out there, because I felt like I had a book in me, but I was terrified that it would go nowhere, and I was really a young naive therapist and nobody was more surprised than I was that the book really got embraced. And I still have people come up to me and say, you're the one that provided me with this initial information about this when I was so desperate to get information. So that was how, and after that, my work in training—I did most of the training in continuing education settings, I did not have an academic appointment, which in hindsight, I wish I had gotten one.

Because it would have given a little more credibility, I think. But this is hindsight, and one of the things I did not have at the time, which I really would recommend, because I did not have a good mentor who stayed with me, and because, I think, because we were so on the cutting edge in a way, and my peers, the same way, there was nobody to mentor us along, so we just did our thing. And then there were a series of us who started meeting at conferences and really cross-referenced each other's work. There was a group of people who were doing work with all kinds of trauma, but also working with adult survivors. It was peer mentoring at conferences.

And we were cross-referencing each other's work, and some of those folks were academics, but some of us were not, we're practitioners.

One thing that really propelled me at the time was, in 1990, I had the opportunity to establish an inpatient treatment program for adult survivors. Prior to that, it didn't happen very often, but when I had to hospitalize somebody, it was a horrible experience, typically. Because they would have been put on general units, and their symptoms weren't recognized, and they often experienced very out-of-control peers. It was very difficult, and in 1990, a hospital approached me to put together a specialized program, which had been my dream. We opened our program in 1990, and I was the training and clinical director there for 16 years. We sold the program to the hospital. The nice thing is the program has continued, and it closed after 29 years, so it was a very long-term program, and it has moved to another hospital, and it's one of the few programs like it in the country.

Prior to that, and with that is when I got really involved in trauma-informed—which wasn't called that at the time; I called it "trauma-referenced" instead of trauma-informed. But then, the people that started that movement, the professionals were in these conferences and in my peer group, and this was also a big consumer movement because consumers had identified how badly they were being mistreated. And how badly they had been mistreated and misunderstood by clinicians who didn't have a clue about their background or how to work with it, emerged. So, early on, we were talking about something like trauma-informed, then we began to use that terminology, but that was definitely what we were trying to do. And our hospital was to make it a friendly, non-threatening environment in which they came in, in very severe crises, life crises, or just the decompensation or suicidality, and it took time to really work with those crises and get them back on track.

When we started, we had a 28-day length of stay, which is unheard of today, and it decreased to about 12 to 14 days. The program was dismantled because we lost so much money, and managed care just, you know, crunch things, but I'm very proud to say that we treated thousands of women and some men in that program. We helped a lot of people, and I think they should see, you should be doing those programs across the country, but of course they are not. The ones that are still standing are pretty much being closed, so it's unfortunate.

Yoon Suh Moh: Definitely. I'm just wondering what played a role in closing some of those programs.

Christine Courtois: I would say, some of it was ongoing suspicion about the patients and ongoing stigma of the patients in our case. Our patients were very intelligent, and they didn't take a lot of baloney from anybody, especially as a group, so they didn't make themselves popular with the administration, and I'm sure that in other programs—but more than that, managed care came along, and really decimated patient care and the ability to have an extended, a relatively extended stay. And then, in 1992, the false memory controversy, or what I call the recovered memory controversy, began, and that had a huge impact on us also.

The other thing that we were doing was, we were to treat highly dissociative patients. Not all patients, but a number of them, were dissociated, and that controversy really stuck and really caused a lot of anguish for patients. And many clinicians left the field. A lot of damage was done, and so I think managed care was influenced by that as well. We immediately shifted to telling managed care that we were doing stabilization of the patients, that we were not specifically doing memory work, because they were very suspicious of memory work. In that, by talking about memories, you are going to make false memories and you're going to make patients worse, which, of course, was not our intention, but that's how they took it.

In terms of training, my group at that time ran an international conference that ran for seven years, and it was called the Eastern Regional Conference on Abuse and Dissociation. And that was seen as the premier conference on the topic. Over the years, we got a lot of mileage out of that, we did a lot of training, and obviously we brought conference participants and conference presenters in from all over the place, so that was a big training effort, but that's got interfered with by the false memory challenge. I was doing the inpatient work, and I had a private practice later on. I never gave up my private practice, because I was always afraid the hospital was going to close down. I was a half-time clinical director of the hospital and in private practice the whole time.

Yoon Suh Moh: How long have you been doing private practice?

Christine Courtois: I retired six years ago, and I did private practice for 35 years.

Yoon Suh Moh: You have done so much work that has influenced the mental health field.

Christine Courtois: The other thing I can mention is that, when I had been working on guidelines for therapists in terms of how to work with memory issues, I still am very ticked off that therapists came under major attack for creating false memories of sexual abuse, and it wasn't proven how they did that. Nonetheless, and I know the only therapist that made some really bad mistakes, I'm not naive about that, but I really wanted to set the record straight by my understanding and also provide some guidance, so my second book was called *Recollections of Sexual Abuse* and it came out in 1999, I think.

From there, I finished up working in the hospital around 2007. I had been nominated to take on a complex trauma task group, and that was somewhat easier than a previous task force, but it has not been friendly to complex trauma. And this is still not—in some quarters, the belief is PSTD, and this complex PTSD, you know, is bogus, and so all this time we've been sort of rolling a rock up a hill. And that task force was charged with doing a survey of expert clinicians about the treatment of complex trauma, so that we could write guidelines. Well, it just took forever to do it, and we finally did, and we put out a set of noncontroversial guidelines. But we also found what we thought complex trauma was, so that was, sort of, greatly received. We were glad that, at least, it was part of the International Society for Traumatic Stress Studies (ISTSS) policy statements. There were about 10 of us on that working group, and we decided that they needed to be a book, to compare with the treatment guidelines that ISTSS was putting out at the time, which were mostly on standard PTSD. And everybody on that task force was so busy. And I had just finished my job at that hospital, so I had time, and Julian Ford had time and interest, so that's how we got started writing what have now been four books on complex trauma, and we're revising our treatment book right now.

So, since 2000, and it was the first one, we've written this series of books, which have been well received. But just today, there are still people in the trauma field that are very skeptical about complex trauma. However, when I go to conferences, people are coming up to me and saying, thank you for talking about complex trauma, because we now understand that this is more than PTSD, and we now know more about what we're treating and how to treat it. It's not a finalized thing—we're going to be working on this forever, but it's made some inroads. We finally got the diagnosis in the *International Classification of Diseases* (11th ed.) ICD. A lot of that has occupied me in the last couple of decades.

Yoon Suh Moh: What are some of projects that you or your team your team are/ is working on currently? How would you envision the impact of those projects in the future?

Christine Courtois: Well, some of it has to do with complex trauma. A number of us have been working on treatment guidelines for complex trauma for a decade now. It's never ending.

And we were doing it through APA, as an APA Division 56 project, in conjunction with the International Society for the Study of Trauma and Dissociation. We're getting to the end of that project and hope that it will be adopted by APA. I was the chair of the clinical practice guidelines for the treatment of PTSD in adults (https://www.apa. org/ptsd-guideline/ptsd.pdf) at the APA. We published in 2017, and that also was a difficult experience in some ways, because the APA had decided to use the Institute of Medicine standards for doing clinical practice guidelines, which are only oriented towards the research and randomized control trials, and so it's very, very narrow and very restricted, and it's really following what medicine has done.

Our task force was the very first one that APA did, and so there was a huge learning curve about how to do this and how to manage it, how to teach the task force members, all of us, how to do this. And what came out was a very restricted set of treatment recommendations, based on the available research. But we could not get them, and it was only looking at PTSD, the effect of PTSD treatments on remission and on loss of diagnosis, and because of that, it just was restricted. Several of us clinicians on that task force said, there are other factors here and we're talking about this research that mostly is about standard PTSD. Does it apply to complex PTSD? How does it apply? There was a debate among the members, and we ended up not incorporating any of that into the guidelines. A lot of clinicians only incorporated the randomized control trial on evidence, and so when it went out for public comment, a lot of clinicians were really upset, because they said that this is just PTSD symptoms, and that's not all we see in our clients. That was another huge effort.

Well now, we're still working on these professional practice guidelines on complex PTSD, and those are not so research-based. It's describing the population, describing what's recommended, what's not recommended, and how to incorporate the research literature. So anyway, it will be a good statement when we finally get it out. Since then, I've coedited a book last year on sexual boundary violations in therapy with two colleagues—that's long been an interest of mine. And I've also been working with a group of individuals from Division 56 on trying to get a specialization of trauma psychology. We put in our first proposal at the end of last year, and we just got feedback that it's not being accepted as is, so this year is rewriting. The process is sort of like writing an article and getting feedback, that you know you need to revise and resubmit, so, we still feel hopeful about that.

Jefferson sets a good example of curriculum that includes a lot more attention to trauma. We may be contacting you because we're going to be having to look at programs. And there are very a few of them at this point.

Yoon Suh Moh: For the limited time, this is going to be my last question for you. **Is there anything else that you'd like to share that you have not had a chance yet during the interview that you think readers or the audience might find helpful?**

Christine Courtois: Yes, you're giving me my soapbox. I think that we've given a lot of attention to trauma in the mental health field across the board, and the public understands more than previously. However, I believe that there are a lot of therapists who are not adequately trained. And that they need much more in-depth training, which is why the specialization. So I really want to encourage anybody who's doing work with complex trauma or dissociative disorders to not rely on one weekend course. They need much more information and they also need to examine themselves, whether they can do this work. I think we have a huge ethical obligation to not do any more damage to these individuals who have been so touched by trauma, and so I have modified the Hippocratic oath from "do no harm" to "do no *more* harm." Because these clients have been so harmed, and we have an ethical obligation to them, but also to ourselves, in terms of not putting ourselves into situations we can't manage or that are emotionally too difficult, and of course that's been recognized as we talk about vicarious trauma and secondary traumatic stress. But I don't think people really understand or get it, so I want to argue for ongoing supervision, ongoing consultation, ongoing training and certification for anybody who would get in this field. The other thing I wrote about a couple of years ago, and it's related to my latest book on sexual boundary violations, is the issue of what I call "colleague betrayal." And that is—I personally have been affected tangentially and directly by a number of situations where colleagues or mentees or employees got sexually involved with patients. And the fallout from that has been the dark spot of my career. I ended up getting sued for one of my employees' misdeeds, and luckily the suit got settled, but not before we went through two and a half years of just agony.

And a number of years ago, I wrote an article called "Colleague Betrayal." There were so many different ways that I got impacted by other people's transgressions. So I'm paying attention also to what I call "collateral damage." When we're working, we owe it to our colleagues, to our patients, to the community, and to the profession to be very mindful of ethics and competencies, and things like that. That's where my big interest in training comes from. It doesn't get talked about, and when I wrote this article, it's really almost a confessional. I sent it to my peers and said, "Should I publish this? Because it feels like very much a major self-disclosure." They said yes, because nobody talks about this and we really need to begin. To do clinical work, you have to be mentally healthy, and you have to be willing to get support or get further education or to say, I don't have the competence to do this.

Yoon Suh Moh: I am immensely honored to hear from you about all the work you and your colleagues have done and are doing.

Christine Courtois: I'm glad that we've had this contact and, you know, we can continue it going forward.

Yoon Suh Moh: Absolutely, such an honor. Thank you so much for your time today.

Christine Courtois: Good luck with the rest of your work.

Clinical Education: An Interview with Dr. Janice Carello, May 11, 2022

Yoon Suh Moh: How would you describe your professional identity and training background?

Janice Carello (she/her): One and two blur in together for me. Really, who I am is very much a part of why I got into this work. I identify currently as a social worker and social work educator. My background, though, the path getting here, is what led me to the trauma-informed teaching to begin with. So I'm going to start a little ways back. Many people are surprised to find out that I was a high school dropout. I decided that was not the path for me. Luckily, a guidance counselor let me know that, should I wish to return to school, that I could go to my local community college, because I was not aware of that. I thought once I left school, I would never be able to access higher education. So in my 20s, I did that. When I was 24, I went to my local community college. I absolutely loved it. And I got my associate's degree, and then I went to a 4-year college, got my bachelor's degree in English, and then a master's degree in English. And I taught college-level writing for about 20 years.

What I noticed during my first semester as a writing teacher was that the students who were having the most difficulty adjusting to college and who were getting bad grades, who were failing, who were struggling, those were students who had encountered some type of crisis during their time in my class. I was also teaching a lot of college orientation classes and doing a lot of advising, so a lot of the tutoring and teaching I was doing was with students who came from underserved backgrounds already, and maybe were struggling. So I was working with students who were struggling, and I really wanted to be able to do something about that. I was also challenged because there were policies that I had inherited when I first started teaching, like really strict policies, such as, if a student misses more than three classes, they automatically fail. And so I found myself getting into conflict with my students, and I just started questioning, "Is this the right profession for me?" Because this doesn't feel like what I want to be doing. I don't feel like it's making a difference. And so I decided to enroll in a master of social work program.

And in the program that I chose, they had just integrated trauma and trauma-informed care into their curriculum. And the whole world made sense to me in a way it never did before, and what I found was that I started integrating what I was learning, those principles of trauma-informed care and that understanding of trauma, into the work that I was doing in my classroom, changing my policies, changing the interactions that I had with students. And it made a really big, positive difference. I had fewer students failing my courses, and I felt less often like I was failing my students. And my relationship with them improved, and what I realized was I didn't need to become a counselor in order to help students stay in school. And helping students stay in school is really important to me as a high school dropout. I wanted people to have access to higher education. It was important for me for students to be able to access that and to also not have to leave college with a lot of debt without a degree.

So then once I started applying it to different classrooms, I recognized other people might benefit from this kind of approach also, so that's when I decided to enroll in a doctoral program. And so then I got my doctorate degree and focused on trauma-informed teaching, and that's what I've been doing ever since. So that's a long answer to your question about training and background, but all of those things go together, and that's how this came about.

Yoon Suh Moh: Absolutely! I totally understand, and think that a part of your previous experience seems like very instrumental in the way that brought you where you are now and where you will be, moving forward.

Janice Carello (she/her): Yeah, very much. One of the things I focused on in my dissertation, as someone who was in a program that was trauma-informed and then someone who then taught, was students who started saying, "Okay you're telling us to be trauma-informed with our clients, but what about you all being trauma-informed with us?" So that was part of that discussion also, and that was the focus of my dissertation, because when we're talking about trauma-informed approaches, it's not just what we do with clients. Being trauma-informed means creating a trauma-informed organization, and changing the culture, changing policy and practice. So that was something that we needed to do as educators, for our students, but also that the system needed to do for us as well, and so that was a big part of this, too.

Yoon Suh Moh: So I think it's related to something that you might have already touched on. My next question for you is, **can you please tell me about the background and also a little bit of the process of developing trauma-informed educational practices?**

Janice Carello (she/her): I've touched on that a little bit. So part of it came out of my own work as an educator. And then, for me, there's a difference. There's the trauma-informed educational practice piece, but I often talk in terms of trauma-informed colleges and universities. That's the work that really needs to be done at the organizational level. We have an understanding of that from our background about trauma-informed care and the people who developed that, Harris and Fallot. And at the time when Harris and Fallot were developing trauma-informed care, we had Sandra Bloom, who was developing the sanctuary model. And what these folks were noticing was that standard operating procedures in behavioral health, particularly inpatient behavioral health, was sometimes causing more harm than good, and people weren't staying retained in services. And so, they needed to have a different approach, and that's how some of these principles and these new practices and trauma-informed approaches arrived. And so you need it at all levels of the organization. It's not just what I do as an individual practitioner; this is a system-level issue. That's what I think of with that trauma-informed educational practices piece.

And then trauma-informed teaching and learning is what we can do in the classroom as educators, and so it's trying to do both: on the one level you're trying to do things that are supportive of organizational change. And at the same time you're also working with educators on what we can do in classrooms. I started off more with the trauma-informed educational practices, the more organizational pieces of it. I'm still doing some of that. It's nice to see some people are organizing and trying to work on that together, because you have to organize to get at this level of policy. That's not something an individual does. You have to do that as a group. You can do trainings, but there's a lot more that needs to be done.

Since the start of the pandemic I've been getting a lot more requests for trainings around the trauma-informed teaching and learning piece, because educators are burned out. There was a big shift during the pandemic to online learning, and we're used to having students in crisis, that's always been part of higher education. But usually it's a few students in a class. All of a sudden, it became a lot of students in a class. And it became us impacted also, because we forget that crisis affects educators also, and administrators also, and staff also. And so some of that needs teasing out and figuring out, because again, with just one person there's only so much time and energy. Where do you channel that energy? And so a lot of it, then, has been trying to find ways to develop a community.

This is a budding field as far as adapting and bring the trauma-informed approaches to higher education. We've seen it in behavioral health; we've seen it in child welfare; we've seen in K–12 schools. Since the start of the pandemic people become more interested in higher education, which is fantastic, and we're starting to see some resources, more research on it, and some funding we're hoping that will become available to help with that. But yeah, it's been trying to figure out where to put that time and energy and really trying to build a sense of community, because we can't do this alone. This is work that has to be done together.

Yoon Suh Moh: Exactly! I cannot agree more. Building the community takes a lot and it is time consuming, too. It can be tough work, especially during this prolonged pandemic. And I'm glad that you touched on the burnout piece in higher education, including everyone, including clinical educators.

My next question for you is, **why do you think it is important for helping professionals to be knowledgeable of effects of trauma in childhood and its association with chronic health issues in adulthood?**

Janice Carello (she/her): Yeah, there's multiple reasons and levels to this. So obviously one of the first ones is the impact on clients. In order for us to be able to do effective assessment, we have to know what questions to ask, and if we're not asking about trauma, childhood adversity, we don't know the impacts of that. Then we can end up with a misdiagnosis. Sometimes symptoms won't rise to the level of a diagnosis, but they may still be a result of trauma, so we're starting to see things like depression, anxiety, or even things like substance abuse and other problems, such as relationship problems, in response to childhood adversity and childhood trauma. And so, then, if we don't know that, we can't assess effectively, and then we can't develop appropriate interventions. So that's one of the pieces. In order to actually be able to help reduce suffering of the individuals with whom we're working, we need to have the right tools, and we have to ask the right questions, and we have to be able to develop appropriate interventions. So that's one piece of it.

There's also the impact on the helping professionals, and I think of educators as helping professionals. We work with people who are highly traumatized. And we don't have a lot of research on that yet. We're starting to see some in K–12 around secondary traumatic stress, vicarious trauma, burnout, things like that. We do know from the literature with folks who have clinical experience that those things happen when we are working in relation to people who have trauma histories, and we hear a lot of trauma narratives. Burnout is about occupational stress and occupational functioning and gets back to the culture of the organization. We know that piece matters, too. So another piece of this is thinking in terms of, how do we support helping professionals? How do we take care of ourselves? How do we create agencies and communities that help support the well-being of educators? Of mental health professionals?

Then being able to understand the benefits that come with this work, also. Some of the research that I've been involved in, we looked at self-care and trauma exposure among social work students, and what we found too is that there may be a higher incidence of secondary traumatic stress, particularly for people who have a trauma history themselves, but there's also a higher incidence of compassion satisfaction, which is the satisfaction that we get from doing this kind of work. So there are benefits that we want to be able to pay attention to also, because that's why most people get into the helping professions to begin with.

There's also thinking about how these types of experiences impact communities. So one of the things that we know that came out from the Adverse Childhood Experiences Study findings is, that started to help us pay attention to trauma and to these types of experiences as a public health issue. So that we're not just paying attention to the impact on individuals, but again we're going back to looking at interventions at the micro level, the mezzo level—the family level at the community level—and at the macro or policy level, because one of the things we realized is that some of the reasons students struggle, such as poverty, racism, ableism, these are structural barriers, and all of the therapy in the world does not eradicate those. So we need to have interventions at other levels also. So these, to me, are some of the main reasons why this is really important.

Yoon Suh Moh: Absolutely! I totally agree with you, and I am glad that you focus emphasis on many different levels of determinants that are impactful on health and wellness, mental illness.

What are recommendations you might have for clinical training programs, and/or clinical educators that might help increase trauma competencies in their clinical students or trainees?

Janice Carello (she/her): Christine Courtois, back in 2008, issued a call to integrate trauma into the clinical training curriculum for all helping professionals. So part of my recommendation would be getting it into the explicit curriculum, for sure. And making sure that people understand trauma, especially the different types. And there are challenges to this, because we are often using a medical model or a model that is based on the *Diagnostic and Statistical Manual of Mental Disorders*. Cristine Courtois has been trying to get complex trauma as a diagnosis and looking at developmental trauma. Those are not diagnoses, and so there's more research that needs to be done around that, but being able to then, in the explicit curriculum, talk about trauma, talk about different types of trauma, including not only what we think of as acute traumas, but also looking at other types of symptoms, looking at complex trauma and developmental trauma, looking at systemic trauma, because we haven't been considering that. We've been a little better about doing that in the last, you know, in recent years. So making sure that those different types of trauma and the impact and the prevalence, that is included in the curriculum.

And another recommendation is also integrating trauma and trauma-informed care into the implicit curriculum so that, as I was talking about before, it's not just what we're teaching our students to do for their clients. We're modeling for them what an agency looks like by doing it in our classrooms and in our programs and in our schools. So how are we modeling for them what that looks like? And how are we integrating those principles and applying them to our own practice? So thinking about it in those terms, for me, is a huge part of all of this.

Also making sure that self-care is an explicit and implicit part of the curriculum. I think of self-care from a trauma-informed and human rights perspective: that self-care is something that is absolutely a professional duty—and that's typically how it's taught, and I'm on board with that. It is absolutely my responsibility as an individual helping professional to make sure that I am paying attention to taking care of my own well-being, so that I am able to work ethically and professionally with clients and make sure that I'm in good health—but to me that it's also a right, a responsibility of agencies and institutions and organizations to provide means for self-care, so if there's not paid time off, if there's not access to health insurance, if there are not policies, there's a problem.

I'm thinking of things that we do in classrooms to make space for self-care. I taught a winter session course recently and students are burned out, and it's in a master's program, it's a four-week course between fall and spring semesters, and that's rough. And it was a course on substance use disorders, so it's heavy content, so I was thinking, how do I build in self-care? In general, I build things like late days, where it's no questions asked, students do not need to provide me with any type of personal health information in order to get some extra time, which I do in all my classes. But how do I build in for a discussion board? There are always choices as to which prompts they want to answer, and I added one around self-care that I built in as a weekly assignment option. I told them, I want you to take off one hour to engage in self-care, and then I want you to reflect on some questions, and here's why it's important for you. So it wasn't just something I'm telling them to go do, here's what you need to do, and it's your duty as a professional, but here's how we're going to build it into the system. And how do you think you're going to keep moving forward with this? And what was the impact on you and on the work that you're doing with your clients? So it's again thinking about how we build these things into our system, and then also we're back to thinking about building community, and one of the principles of trauma-informed care is support, and I think sometimes we don't pay a lot of attention to that, but, that being able to connect with others, and developing those internal and external resources is a big part of the self-care piece, too. It's not just boundaries, but it's also thinking about how we access those different resources, so that community building piece of it, too. So those would be some of my main recommendations for programs.

Yoon Suh Moh: It's amazing, I'm learning so much from you through this interview. Although I have more I would like to ask you, for the time being, let me move on to ask you my next question. **What are some of projects you and/or or your team are working on that you may share?**

Janice Carello (she/her): The umbrella that I put a lot of this under is really awareness building and community building, because as I've been talking about, I can't do this by myself, and being trauma-informed is not about me saying, here's how to be trauma-informed. It's something that we create as a community, and it's something that we do as a community together. It's not something that gets passed down from on high, where somebody says, you need to do this. That doesn't help with mental well-being. This is something that we do together. I think of the quote from Judith Herman around psychological trauma and its impact on control, connection, and meaning. That works at the individual level—trauma disrupts our own sense of control, connection, and meaning—but it works for institutions as well. We've seen that during the pandemic. So how do we help restore that sense of control, connection, and meaning? A lot of the work I'm doing is around that awareness and community building, because trauma and trauma-informed is a newer field in higher education, so I've been doing a lot of training and consultation. I do lots of trainings for not just individual programs but also for schools. Deans contact me, accrediting bodies, so getting the word out that way and providing some basics to help people have an understanding of trauma and its impact and what trauma-informed care is, building some awareness around that so that people can take those tools and think about how to move forward within their organizations. What are the next steps? What training do they need? Do they want to start a committee to try to become more trauma-informed in their community? So there's some of that.

Some of my work is publications. I recently worked with Phyllis Thompson from East Tennessee State University on two books. And what was great about those books again was not that Phyllis and I wrote a book and said, "Here's what it means to be trauma-informed." We did a call for proposals to find people who may not even be using the term trauma-informed, but they're working on improving mental health and well-being. For people in higher education: staff, faculty and students, so it's looking at everybody and so gathering information and insights and sharing those best practices and those experiences in publication form.

I've been on a lot of dissertation and thesis committees recently. And that feels like very important work because, as you know, as a new field there's not a lot of people doing research, and we need more research in order for things to keep going. I can't do all of that research myself, so though the plate is full, when I get invitations to serve on a research committee or for research consultation, I'm always saying yes, so that we can get more people out there and build this community and more people to do this work.

I'm trying to get back to doing my own research, also. I've got some projects that are started. It's hard to find a time for that with all of the rest that's going on now. One of the conversations that you and I have had previously is the importance of looking at some tools. That would be helpful. And then really being able to look at again the tools, not just in terms of measuring what's wrong with people, focusing on the trauma, but also focusing on the resilience and growth and well-being part, so tools that take those into account as well, looking at the literature that exists to help support that as well.

And then a lot of networking, because community building, it takes time, but to me that's a really important piece of this, that to get anywhere we're going to have to do it collectively, and so it's trying to be part of those conversations, being able to collaborate with folks like you who are doing wonderful work and thinking about how do we continue to help support each other.

Yoon Suh Moh: That's great that you are invested in networking, and community building and awareness building at many different levels while you are trying to find time to do your own research. Also, I hope that you get enough time for your own self-care because oftentimes I have a hard time taking time for my own wellness.

Janice Carello (she/her): Yeah, and I think one of the things that I pay attention to is, the work itself is restorative. As we talked about, it's a lot of work, but it gives me a sense of meaning and purpose, it helps me with my own recovery. So again I think back to, there were times when teaching was really painful for me. But when I'm using this approach, and I'm maintaining these boundaries, I'm doing work that gives me meaning and purpose, and I'm able to collaborate with others, that is restorative. And then the boundaries piece is still really important, how do I have work-life balance and make sure I'm not working too much, because then I'm not good to anybody.

Yoon Suh Moh: Thank you for the wisdom! **I'm wondering if there is anything else that you'd like to share that you haven't had a chance yet during this interview that the audience might find helpful.**

Janice Carello (she/her): I can't really think of anything. I was trying to think of something, but I think we've covered a lot. Your questions were very thought-provoking, and I enjoyed reflecting on them. I think, maybe the only thing I always remind people, just it can be so challenging in the face of such adversity, when you hear about things that people have gone through, to remind ourselves that, even though we can't fix everything, what we do makes a difference. These large world problems still exist, but knowing that even those small things that we're doing really does have an impact on individuals. They do have an impact when we are able to group together, and helping people to keep their eye on that, so that they understand the importance of what they're doing and their contributions.

Yoon Suh Moh: Absolutely! Thank you for the last piece of that wisdom, and I think this sums up all the interview questions that I had on the agenda.

References

Agllias, K. (2012). Keeping safe: Teaching undergraduate social work students about interpersonal violence. *Journal of Social Work Practice, 26*, 259–274.

Black, T. (2006). Teaching trauma without traumatizing: Principles of trauma treatment in the training of graduate counselors. *Traumatology, 12*(4), 266–271. https://doi.org/10.1177/1534765606297816

Bride, B. E. (2007). Prevalence of secondary traumatic stress among social workers. *Social Work, 52*(1), 63–70. https://doi.org/10.1093/sw/52.1.63

Butler, L. D., Carello, J., & Maguin, E. (2017a). Trauma, stress, and self-care in clinical training: Predictors of burnout, decline in health status, secondary traumatic stress symptoms, and compassion satisfaction. *Psychological Trauma: Theory, Research, Practice, and Policy, 9*(4), 416–424. https://doi.org/10.1037/tra0000187

Bulter, L. D., Maguin, E., & Carello, J. (2017b). Retraumatization mediates the effect of adverse childhood experiences on clinical training-related secondary traumatic stress symptoms. *Journal of Trauma & Dissociation, 19*(2), 1–14. http://dx.doi.org/10.1080/15299732.2017.1304488

Carello, J. (2016). *Practicing what we teach: An overview of trauma-informed teaching and learning for social work educators.* https://socialwork.buffalo.edu/content/dam/socialwork/home/teaching-resources/3-5-TITL-Overview-Carello-2016-presentation.pdf

Carello, J. (2020). *Trauma-informed teaching and learning principles.* https://traumainformedteaching-blog.files.wordpress.com/2020/04/titl-general-principles-3.20.pdf

Carello, J., & Butler, L. D. (2014a). Potentially perilous pedagogies: Teaching trauma is not the same as trauma-informed teaching. *Journal of Trauma & Dissociation, 15*(2), 153–168. https://doi.org/10.1080/15299732.2014.867571

Carello, J., & Butler, L. D. (2014b). Some principles and practices to enhance classroom emotional safety. University of Buffalo, School of Social Work. https://socialwork.buffalo.edu/content/dam/socialwork/home/teaching-resources/3-2-TI-Principles-Practices-Table-Carello-Butler-2015.pdf

Carello, J., & Butler, L. D. (2015). Practicing what we teach: Trauma-informed educational practice. *Journal of Teaching in Social Work, 36*, 262–278. https://doi.org/10.1080/08841233.2015.1030059

Carello, J. (2022). Self-assessment tools for creating trauma-informed learning and work environments. In P. Thompson & J. Carello (Eds.), *Trauma-informed pedagogies: A guide for responding to crisis and inequality in higher education.* Palgrave Macmillan.

Giano, Z., Wheeler, D. L., & Hubach, R. D. (2020). The frequencies and disparities of adverse childhood experiences in the U.S. *BMC Public Health, 20*, 1327. https://doi.org/10.1186/s12889-020-09411-z

Knight, C. (2010). Indirect trauma in the field practicum: Secondary traumatic stress, vicarious trauma, and compassion fatigue among social work students and their field instructors. *Journal of Baccalaureate Social Work, 15*, 31–52. https://doi.org/10.18084/basw.15.1.l568283x21397357

Kumar, S. A., Brand, B. L., & Courtois, C. A. (2019). The need for trauma training: Clinicians' reactions to training on complex trauma. *Psychological Trauma: Theory, Research, Practice, and Policy.* Advance online publication. https://doi.org/10.1037/tra0000515

Mattar, S. (2011). Educating and training the next generations of traumatologists: Development of cultural competencies. *Psychological Trauma: Theory, Research, Practice, and Policy, 3*(3), 258–265. https://doi.org/10.1037/a0024477

Moh, Y., & Sperandio, K. R. (2022). The need to consider requiring trauma training in entry-level academic training programs in clinical mental health counseling. *Journal of Mental Health Counseling, 44*(1), 18–31. https://doi.org/10.17744/mehc.44.1.03

Newman, E. (2011). Teaching clinical psychology graduate students about traumatic stress studies. *Psychological Trauma: Theory, Research, Practice, and Policy, 3*(3), 235–242. https://doi.org/10.1037/a0024476

Pearlman, L. A., & Mac Ian, P. S. (1995). Vicarious traumatization: An empirical study of the effects of trauma work on trauma therapists. *Professional Psychology: Research and Practice, 26*(6), 558–565. https://doi.org/10.1037/0735-7028.26.6.558

Webber, J. M., Kitzinger, R., Runte, J. K., Smith, C. M., & Mascari, J. B. (2017). Traumatology trends: A content analysis of three counseling journals from 1994 to 2014. *Journal of Counseling and Development, 95*(3), 249–259. https://doi.org/10.1002/jcad.12139

Glossary

Adverse childhood experiences (ACEs): a term used to refer to experiences in early childhood that can result in immediate and long-lasting disruptions in human development and that are known to be associated with chronic adult health conditions

The Adverse Childhood Experiences (ACE) Study: a landmark public health study that involved 17,337 adults responding to a questionnaire designed to examine adverse childhood experiences (i.e., childhood abuse, neglect, and home dysfunction) prior to the age of 18

Alexithymia: concerned with a condition characterized as "difficulty in identifying, interpreting, and describing emotions" (Lloyd et al., 2021, p. 2)

Allostasis: refers to "the adaptive processes that maintain homeostasis through the production of mediators such as adrenalin, cortisol, and other chemical messengers" (McEwen, 2005, p. 315)

Allostatic load: adaptive processes to cope with stressors and return to homeostasis in the body of functioning

Autobiographical memory construction: refers to "a process of forming early memory where contextual and semantic information set a stage for a particular memory to be recalled and then brought to make a mental representation" (Lanius et al., 2020, p. 4)

Autonomic imbalance: "a hyperactive sympathetic system and a hypoactive parasympathetic system" (Thayer et al., 2010, p. 122)

Biology: a study of discipline that concerns genetic predispositions pertaining to human development

Bottom-up communication: refers to feedback loops in the BGM network that transmit information from the gut and its microbiome to the brain (Mayer, 2021)

The brain-gut-microbiome (BGM) network: part of the larger network in the body, and is responsible for dynamic, complex, and circular communication, as opposed to a simple or linear fashion (Mayer, 2021)

Burnout: a gradual process of negative effects as a result of working with those who are exposed to traumatic events

The central executive network (CEN): a network involving key hubs of the dorsolateral prefrontal cortex (dlPFC) and posterior parietal cortex (PPC)

Chronic health condition: a health condition (e.g., heart disease, metabolic disease, or mental disorders such as depression) that persists over time, leading to negative consequences

Collective trauma: a term used to address the psychological or emotional responses to a trauma event experienced and shared by a social group of individuals that becomes persistent in the group's collective traumatic memories

Commensal microorganisms: refer to small organisms that reside on and in host bodies that help with varying functions and promote neurodiversity

Compassion fatigue: a term used to describe an emotional experience in helping professionals who work with those who are exposed to traumatic events in which their stress reactions parallel those of the trauma survivors

Complex trauma: refers to "the experience of multiple, chronic and prolonged, developmental adverse traumatic events, most often of an interpersonal nature and early-life onset" (van der Kolk, 2005, p. 2)

Complicated grief: a term, also known as prolonged grief, that is characterized as "debilitating recurrent pangs of painful emotions, with intense yearning, longing and searching for the deceased, and preoccupation with thoughts for the loved one" (O'Connor et al., 2008, p. 969)

Culturally responsive trauma curricula: involves "integrated, interdisciplinary" practices and reflects "the cultural realities of the populations affected by trauma, the student's background and culture" (Mattar, 2011, p. 259)

Cultural trauma: defined as "an overwhelming and often ongoing physical or psychological assault or stressor perpetuated by an oppressive dominant group on the culture of a group of people sharing a specific shared identity or affiliation (e.g., race, ethnicity, nationality, religion)" (Subica & Link, 2021, p. 2)

The default mode interference hypothesis/the default network interference hypothesis: a framework to address altered neural patterns of the default mode network compared to the normal transitioning between states of task positive and task passive (Sonuga-Barke & Castellanos, 2007)

The default mode network (DMN): consists of the ventromedial prefrontal cortex (vmPFC), posterior cingulate cortex (PCC), and the precuneus

Developmental trauma: refers to "the impact of early, repeated trauma and loss which happens within the child's important relationships, and usually early in life" (Lyons et al., 2020, p. 5)

Developmental trauma disorder (DTD): a disorder that was proposed as "an integrative framework for assessing and treating children's emotional, biological, cognitive, behavioral, interpersonal, and self/identity dysregulation in the wake of traumatic victimization and disrupted attachment" (Spinazzola et al., 2018, p. 631)

Dysbiosis: refers to "any change to the composition of resident commensal communities relative to the community found in healthy individuals" (Petersen, & Round, 2014, p. 1024)

The ecobiodevelopmental (EBD) framework: a framework developed to promote the importance of healthy human development (Shonkoff et al., 2012)

Ecology: refers to a social and physical environment

Embodiment: a term to refer to "how an individual's perception of the world can shape how the body meaningfully interacts with their environment" (Harricharan et al., 2021, p. 13)

Empathy-based stress: a term used to refer to "a process of trauma exposure combined with the experience of empathy that results in empathy-based strain, adverse occupational health reactions, and other work-related outcomes" (Rauvola et al., 2019, p. 298)

Energy homeostasis: a biological process that involves the orchestrated homeostatic regulation in balance between energy inflow and energy outflow

Epigenetics: a field of study that examines "the molecular biological mechanisms (e.g., DNA methylation, histone acetylation) that affect gene expression without altering DNA sequence" (Shonkoff et al., 2012, p. e234)

Episodic memory: concerned with "the ability to encode and retrieve stored information" (Fair et al., 2008, p. 4028)

Exteroception: "the perception of the body from the outside" (Harricharan, 2021, p. 3)

The Global Burden of Diseases, Injuries, and Risk Factors (GBD) Study: a systematic process of conducting a scientific assessment of data on incidence, prevalence, and mortality for a mutually exclusive and collectively exhaustive list of diseases, injuries, and risk factors globally

The gut ecosystem: a complex system in the gut in which diverse and abundant microorganisms exist

Gut microbiota: a term used to refer to collectively small organisms that reside on and in host bodies

Healing-centered: a term used to refer to an approach that is "holistic involving culture, spirituality, civic action, and collective healing" (Ginwright, 2018, para. 10)

Healing-centered engagement (HCE): a practical, holistic approach to promote collective well-being and collective healing from human suffering (Ginwright, 2018)

Healing justice: concerned with a perspective to promote and sustain social change by "shifting how individuals, organizations, and communities relate to one another as they envision a new way of creating collective hope" (Ginwright, 2016, p. 28)

Heart rate variability: the amount of time between the oscillation of heartbeats

Helping professionals: individuals who work in a human service field and who collaborate with individuals, families, and groups in need

Historical trauma: defined as the psychological, emotional, and social responses to a traumatic event inflicted on a group of people who share a social identity or affiliation that has been experienced collectively and taken down from one generation to another over time

Human health: refers to "the absence of disease or disability" also describes "a state of fitness and ability" (WHO, 2004, p. 16)

Human well-being: an incorporation of subjective satisfaction with life and positive affect or mood, and meaningful functioning and human development

The hypothalamic-pituitary-adrenocortical (HPA): a system that releases steroid hormones (Gunnar & Quevedo, 2007)

The innate alarm system (IAS): an interconnected network consisting of thalamic, midbrain, and brainstem regions

Intergenerational trauma: defined as "exposure to extremely adverse events that have the ability to impact individuals to a high degree so that their children find themselves dealing with their parents' post-traumatic state" (Yehuda & Lehrner, 2018, p. 243)

Interoception: "the perception of the body from the inside" (Harricharan, 2021, p. 3)

The intestinal barrier: the most outlining layer of the gut that is responsible for varying functions, including homeostasis in the gut and educating the immune system

Intestinal epithelial cells: refer to human cells lining the surface of the intestinal epithelium in the human body

Leaky gut: a condition in which an increase in intestinal permeability can result in low-grade activation of the gut immune system (Ghosh et al., 2020)

Lipopolysaccharide (LPS): a gut-bacteria component and endotoxin (Ghosh et al., 2020)

Local field potentials: concerned with "signals coming from the integrated electrical activity in pre- and post-synaptic terminals of the brain" (Raichle, 2011)

Macronutrients: nutrient components consisting of carbohydrates, free sugars, and saturated fats

Mental disorders: "disturbances of thought, emotion, behavior, and relationships with others that lead to substantial suffering and functional impairment in one or more life activities" (Patel et al., 2018, p. 1562)

Mental health: "a state of well-being in which the individual realizes his or her own abilities, can cope with the normal stresses of life, can work productively and fruitfully, and is able to make a contribution to his or her community" (WHO, 2004, p. 12)

Metabolic health: a health state of the body that is able to respond to the food taken and alleviate the risk of health conditions such as obesity, cancers, autoimmune disorders, and metabolic diseases (Nobs et al., 2020)

Metabolic syndrome or cardiometabolic disease: a group of disorders including obesity, glucose intolerance, adult-onset diabetes mellitus, hypercholesterolemia, non-alcoholic fatty liver disease, and hypertension

Microbiome science: a discipline that addresses microorganisms and their genetic information

Microbiota: a term used to refer collectively to all microorganisms

Microorganisms: a variety of small organisms that vary in type and composition; selected examples include bacteria, archaea, fungi, and viruses

Network science: a discipline that accounts for "the interplay among individual elements in complex networks using such methods as graph theory, statistical mechanics, and data mining to create predictive models" (Mayer, 2021, p. 18)

Neurobiology of stress-informed counseling (NSIC): concerned with a developmental approach to counseling that specifically addresses immediate and long-lasting effects of stress on human development, functioning, and behavior from a neurobiological perspective in a multicultural frame

Neurofeedback: a non-invasive, therapeutic or clinical application of providing live feedback through a computer-based program

The neuroimmune network hypothesis: a framework describing that under normal physiological conditions, brain circuits involved in emotion regulation engage in bidirectional interplay with peripheral immune cells that mediate inflammation (Nusslock & Miller, 2016)

The neurovisceral integration model: proposes that cardiac vagal tone is associated with the integrity of prefrontal and subcortical circuits (Thayer & Lane, 2000)

Non-communicable diseases (NCDs): diseases that are not directly transmissible from one organism to another

Parental socialization of emotion: a term defined as "parent behaviors that either support or discourage child emotion expressions via implicit or explicit means" (Morgan et al., 2022, p. 4)

The periaqueductal gray: a region located in the midbrain and is responsible for defensive responses (e.g., fight, flight, or faint) in response to impending threat

Precision nutrition: an area of research supported by the National Institutes of Health that is concerned with the personalized dietary intake as a way of preventing from or treating a disease

Resilience: a multifactorial concept characterized as "a dynamic process wherein an organism displays a positive and functional adaptation in the face of stress events and adversity, while preserving its stability" (Perna et al., 2020, p. 754)

Retraumatization: "the triggering or reactivation of trauma-related symptoms originating in earlier traumatic life events" (Carello & Butler, 2014a, p. 156)

The salience network (SN): involves the ventrolateral prefrontal cortex (vlPFC) and anterior insula, and the anterior cingulate cortex (ACC)

Secondary traumatic stress: an acute emotional reaction or feeling driven by fear and trauma elicited from work

Self-care: defined as "the deliberate and self-initiated attempt to take care of oneself" (Rokach & Boulazreg, 2020, p. 1)

Serious chronic illness: a serious illness (e.g., cardiovascular diseases, diabetes, cancers, neurodevelopmental disorders, neurodegenerative disorders, etc.) or a health condition that persists over time

The Social-Ecological Model for Prevention—Modified (SEMP-M): a modified model adapted from the CDC's social-ecological model for violence prevention that accounts for the complex interconnection between factors such as individuals, relationship, community, societal, and microbial factors

Social engagement system: the primary defense in the hierarchical mechanism of human survival in the context of distress

Stress: a term that refers to "experiences that are challenging emotionally and physiologically" (McEwen, 2007, p. 874)

Stress reactivity: a response to varying stressors, including a combination of genetic variability, experiences early in life, social environment, relationships, and physical environment (Boyce, 2019)

Stress sensitivity: one's special susceptibility to life stressors

Stress susceptibility: a state or likelihood to be influenced by stress

Subliminal threat conditions: a condition in which the memory of individuals with symptoms of traumatic stress is triggered related to the trauma and (re)experienced outside of conscious awareness

Suffering: a variety of human experiences resulting from psychological, emotional, spiritual harming due to oppression and discrimination

The sympathetic-adrenomedullary (SAM) system: a sympathetic branch of the autonomic nervous system and releases stress mediators (Gunnar & Quevedo, 2007)

Systems biology: concerned with the study that accounts for the interconnectedness of bodily systems

Three distinct types of stress responses: a positive stress response resulting from an experience that leads to activation of stress response systems and is a physiological state that is brief, and mild to moderate in magnitude; a tolerable stress response resulting from an unusual experience (e.g., the death of a family member); a toxic stress response resulting from the greatest magnitude of activation of stress response systems either or both frequently or in a chronic manner in the absence of the counterbalancing protection of a supportive adult

Top-down communication: feedback loops in the BGM network that transmit information from the brain to the gut and microbiome (Mayer, 2021)

Toxic stress: a form of stress that can "result from strong, frequent, or prolonged activation of the body's stress response systems in the absence of the buffering protection of a supportive, adult relationship" (Shonkoff et al., 2013, p. e236)

Training-related retraumatization: refers to "a reactivation of own feelings/memories from negative past experiences upon exposure to trauma-related material" and symptoms of secondary traumatic stress (Butler et al., 2017b, p. 4)

Trauma: refers to "individual trauma results from an event, series of events, or set of circumstances that is experienced by an individual as physically or emotionally harmful or life threatening and that has lasting adverse effects on the individual's functioning and mental, physical, social, emotional, or spiritual well-being" (SAMHSA, 2014, p. 7)

The trauma-informed educational practice: an andragogical model involving a systemic approach that requires a cultural shift in an organization (e.g., higher education institutions) (TIEP; Carello & Butler, 2015)

Trauma-informed teaching and learning: an approach to operationalize TIEP into trauma-informed teaching practice in higher education with focus given to the individual learning classroom as a setting (TITL; Carello, 2016, 2020)

Ultra-processed food: "industrially manufactured, ready-to-eat/heat formulations that are made with multiple additives and largely devoid of whole foods" (Juul et al., 2021, p. 1)

Vagal break: responsible for a mediating role in cardiac output by decreasing or increasing the inhibitory vagal control of the heart to influence heart rate

Vicarious traumatization: refers to "the transformation that occurs within the therapist or other trauma worker as a result of empathic engagement with clients' trauma experiences and their sequelae" (Pearlman & Mac Ian, 1995, p. 558)

Weathering: concerned in the proposed weathering hypothesis with "the result of chronic exposure to social and economic disadvantage that leads to the acceleration of normal aging and earlier onset of unfavorable physical health conditions among disadvantaged persons of similar age" (Forde et al., 2019, p. 1)

Index

A

Advancement of Clinical Practice Committee, 5
Adverse Childhood Experiences (ACE), 5, 44
  prevalence rate, 145–146
Adverse Childhood Experiences (ACE) study, 44
alexithymia, 83
allostasis, 36
allostatic load, 36
Alzheimer's Association, 124
Alzheimer's disease, 95
American Counseling Association (ACA), 17
American Mental Health Counselors Association (AMHCA), 5
anterior cingulate cortex (ACC), 72
apolipoprotein e4 gene, 124–178
attachment adversity, 51
attachment ruptures, 48–49
  borderline symptoms, 48
  experience of severe verbal abuse, 48
  infant's attachment cues of emotional communication, 49
  maternal withdrawal in infancy, 48
  quality of caregiver-child interaction, 48–49
autism spectrum disorder, 95
autobiographical memory construction, 76–77
autonomic imbalance, 92

B

Baekdudaegan National Arboretum Seed Vault Center, South Korea, 14
behavior competencies, biological basis of, 5–6
bereavement, mental and physical health consequences of, 120–121
Bifidobacterium infantis, 68
biofeedback, 112
biomarkers
  of complicated grief, 123
  of early life adversity and mental health risk, 117–119

bottom-up communication, 97
Boyce, W. Thomas, 38–39
brain development and function, 71–85
  early caregiving, role of, 73
  sense of self, 73–74
brain-gut-microbiome (BGM) network, 97–99
brain plasticity, 112
burnout, 59–63

C

cardiometabolic disease, 33
cardiovascular disease, among adults with mental disorders, 93
central executive network (CEN), 72, 84
childhood abandonment and neglect, 49–50
children's mental health, factors influencing
  gut microbiota, 119–120
  maternal social support, 117–119
  parental socialization of emotion, 120
  TEETH (Teeth Encoding Experiences and Transforming Health) model, 117–118
chronic grieving, 121
chronic grieving trajectory, 121
chronic health conditions, 5
climate change, impact on mental health, 14–15
clinical mental health counseling, 5
collective trauma, 46
commensal microorganisms, 20, 68
Commission on Accreditation of Allied Health Education Programs (CAAHEP), 5
compassion fatigue, 60–61
complex trauma, 50
Complex Trauma Taskforce of the National Child Traumatic Stress Network, 50–51
complicated grief, definition, 122
complicated grief prevention, 120–124
  biomarkers of complicated grief, 123
  grief-informed, principles of, 123–124
  treatment, 123–124

Council for Accreditation of Counseling and Related Educational Programs (CACREP), 5
  standards for counselor preparation, 17
Courtois, Christine, 149–163
  approaches to trauma education and clinical training, 151–163
  developing trauma competencies, 151, 158
  effects of trauma in childhood and health issues in adulthood, 159–160
  Rape Crisis Center, 150–151
COVID-19 pandemic, impacts of, 15–16, 31–32, 43, 124
C-reactive protein (CRP), 99
culturally responsive trauma curricula, 147
cultural trauma, 46

D

death among Blacks and Whites, 53
default mode interference hypothesis/ the default network interference hypothesis, 77
default mode network (DMN), 72, 75
  altered functional connectivity in, 78–79
  anatomy, 76–77
  atypical patterns of, 77
  development and maturation, 77
  functional connectivity of, 78
  functions, 75–76
  in children, 77
  in individuals with PTSD, 78–79
  medial prefrontal subsystem, 77
  role in sense of self, 77–79
depression screening, in women during perinatal period, 113–114
depressive symptoms of grieving individuals, 121–122
developmental trauma, 40, 46–50
developmental trauma disorder (DTD), 50–52
  diagnostic criteria, 51–52
dietary inflammation, 99–101

dorsolateral prefrontal cortex (dlPFC), 72
dysbiosis, 67

E

early childhood development, 135
ecobiodevelopmental (EBD) framework, 17–20
ecology, 18, 108
electroencephalogram (EEG) neurofeedback, 113
embodiment, 84
empathy
    cognitive components of, 61
    definition, 60
empathy-based stress, 60–62
energy homeostasis, 99, 109
environmental challenges on mental health, 13–14
    climate change impacts, 14–15
    COVID-19-related traumatic stress, 16
epigenetics, 18
episodic memory, 77
exteroception, 79–80

F

Felter, Jeanne, 134, 137–144
    clinical training programs, 140–144
    counseling competencies, 140–141
    developing counselor education program, 137–138
    frameworks, 138–139
    J-TEN project, 142
fronto-insular cortex (FIC), 72
functional networks of human brain, 73

G

gastrointestinal barrier, 35
gastrointestinal health screening, 114
Global Burden of Diseases, Injuries, and Risk Factors Study (GBD), 31–34, 52
    dietary risk factors, 33
    global attributable deaths, 33–34
    human health and, 33–34
    lifestyle factors, 33
    risks for attributable deaths, 33
    social determinants, 32
grief disorder, 122
gut ecosystem, 66
gut microbiota, 20, 65–69
    as helpers, 66–67

development of gastrointestinal (GI) distress or disorders, 69
development of microbiota during infancy, 119–120
diversity, 68–69
dysbiosis in, 67
effects of early childhood adversity or toxic stress on, 69
factors for development of, 68
microbiota-gut-brain axis, 67–68

H

healing and prevention strategies, 22–23, 62
    at community level, 132–134
    at microbial and individual levels, 108–116
    at relationship level, 116–126
    at society level, 134–136
    biopsychosocial and lifestyle approaches, 108–111
    dietary and nutritional practices, 108–111
    healing-centered engagement (HCE), 133–134
    in clinical education and training programs, 146–148
    neurofeedback, 112
    nutrition, 109–111
    physical activity, 111
    sensory-oriented therapeutic interventions, 112
    Social-Ecological Model (SEM), 23–25
    state-level trauma prevention initiatives, 134
    use of heart rate variability, 111–112
healing-centered engagement (HCE), 133–134
healing justice approaches, 21–22
health care spending, in United States (1996–2016), 22–23
heart rate variability (HRV), 92–93, 111–112
helping professionals, 59–60
    complicated grief prevention, 120–124
    depression screening in women during perinatal period, 113–114
    gastrointestinal health screening, 114
    healing-centered engagement (HCE), 133–134
    policy development, implementation, and evaluation, 135–136

race-based stress assessment, 115
social isolation and loneliness prevention, 124–125
state-level trauma prevention initiatives, 134
trauma or toxic stress screening, 114
women during perinatal pregnancy, 117–120
historical trauma, 46
Hope and Healing in Urban Education (Ginwright), 21
human development, conceptualization of, 16–20
    modified ecobiodevelopmental framework of, 17–20
human health, definition, 32
hypothalamic-pituitary-adrenocortical system (HPA), 4

I

immune system
    adaptive, 95
    human microbiome and, 97
    immune signaling between gut and brain, 96–97
    interplay between diet and, 108–110
    protective role for human development and health, 95
inflammation processes, 94–95
inflammatory biomarkers, 99
innate alarm system, 79
intergenerational trauma, 47
interleukin-6 (IL-6), 99
interleukin-8 (IL-8), 99
interoception, 79–80
intestinal barrier, 96, 99, 101
intestinal epithelial cells, 20, 66
intestinal microbiota colonization in infants, 97
introspection, 40
irritable bowel syndrome (IBS), 114

L

Lactobacillus, 98
The Lancet commission, 32
leaky gut, 98
life expectancy, 32
lipopolysaccharide (LPS), 96
local field potentials (LFPs), 112–113

M

macronutrients, 110
maternal positive-emotion socialization, 120

maternal psychosocial stress, 119
McEwen, Bruce S., 4
mental disorders, definition, 32
mental health
    association between heart health
        and, 91–93
    definition, 32
metabolic health, 99, 109
metabolic syndrome, 33, 44, 54, 100,
    102
microbiome science, 18
microbiota, 20
mindfulness practices, 62
mood disorders, 93–94
mortality, 31

N

network science, 18
neurobiology of stress-informed
    counseling (NSIC), 6
    application of, 7–8
    case study, 9–10
neurofeedback, 112
neuroimmune network hypothesis,
    99
neurovisceral integration model, 93–94
non-communicable diseases (NCDs),
    33

O

orchestrate metabolic health and
    disease, 99

P

parental socialization of emotion, 120
pathological grief, 122
periaqueductal gray (PAG), 78
physiological stress, 4–5
posterior cingulate cortex (PCC), 72,
    78
posterior parietal cortex (PPC), 72
posttraumatic stress disorder (PTSD),
    50, 74, 79, 147
    dissociative subtype, 83
    sensory processing in individuals,
        83–84
precision nutrition, 111, 115
pre-existing chronic depression, 121
prevalence, 31
prevalence rate, 145–146
prolonged grief disorder, 122
prolonged grief disorder therapy
    (PGDT), 123

R

race-based stress assessment, 115
resilience, 111–112
resilient, 121
retraumatization, 147, 149
right fronto-insular cortex (rFIC), 72

S

salience network (SN), 72
Schore, Judith and Allan, 48
secondary traumatic stress, 61, 147
self-care, 62
sense of self, 73–74
    default mode network (DMN) role
        in, 77–79
    neurobiology of, 75
sensory-oriented therapeutic
    interventions, 112
sensory processing, 79–85
    impact of trauma, 83
Shear, M. Katherine, 122
Shonkoff, Jack P., 135
Social-Ecological Model for
    Prevention—Modified
    (SEMP-M), 23–25, 108, 132
    community factors, 25
    individual health behaviors, 24–25
    microbial factors, 24
    relationships, 25
    societal factors, 25
social engagement system, 73–74
social isolation and loneliness
    prevention, 124–125
state-level trauma prevention
    initiatives, 134
State of the World's Plants and Fungi
    Report, 14
State of the World's Plants and Fungi
    Report, 2020, 14
Stephen Porges's polyvagal system, 73
stress, 3–5
    brain-gut-microbiome (BGM)
        network and, 97–99
    children exposed to toxic, chronic,
        98–99
    COVID-19-related traumatic stress,
        16
    definition, 4
    effects of, 4
    empathy-based, 60–62
    environmental challenges, 13–14
    epigenetic influences of, 38
    in behavioral health, 4
    in brain development and function,
        71–85

    in clinical training, 60
    induced structural remodeling, 4
    in human gut and gut microbiota,
        65–69
    in immune system, 94–101
    patterns of emotionality and, 4
    reactivity and susceptibility, 38–40
    secondary traumatic, 61
    sensitivity, 38
    susceptibility, 38
stress reactivity, 35
stress responses
    differences in temperature, 39
    individual differences in stress
        reactivity, 39
    physiological responses to, 35–36
    positive, 36
    responsiveness, 4
    taxonomy of, 36–37
    tolerable, 36
stress taxonomy, 35–40
subliminal threat conditions, 78–79
suffering, 14–15, 21, 32, 61, 108, 115,
    136
sympathetic-adrenomedullary system
    (SAM), 4
systemic racism and discrimination,
    52–54

T

TEETH (Teeth Encoding Experiences
    and Transforming Health)
    conceptual model, 117–118
temporal parietal junction (TPJ), 83
top-down communication, 97
toxic stress, 46–50, 69, 114
training-related retraumatization,
    147
transformative organizing, 21–22
translocator protein (TSPO), 112
trauma, 43–44, 74
    collective, 46
    conceptualization of, 44–45
    cultural, 46
    developmental, 46–50
    historical, 46
    intergenerational, 47
    interpersonal, 51
    sensory processing post, 83–84
    sensory transmission post, 85
    toxic stress experienced in
        childhood and, 46–50
Trauma-Informed Educational
    Practices (TIEP), 146–148
Trauma-Informed PA plan, 134

Trauma-Informed teaching and learning (TITL), 148
trauma or toxic stress screening, 114
tumor necrosis factor-a, 99

U
ultra-processed foods, 110
unhealthy coping strategies, 47

United States Preventive Services Task Force, 113
U.S. Global Change Research Program, 15

V
vagal activity, 92–94
vagal brake, 93
ventrolateral prefrontal cortex (vlPFC), 72

ventromedial prefrontal cortex (vmPFC), 72
vicarious traumatization, 61, 147

W
weathering hypothesis, 54
well-being, definition, 32
wellness, 17
Western diets, 100
Wolf, Tom, 134

CPSIA information can be obtained
at www.ICGtesting.com
Printed in the USA
BVHW021509140323
660407BV00005B/591